Y0-EEA-328

MECHANICAL RESOLUTION
of
LINGUISTIC PROBLEMS

Mechanical Resolution of Linguistic Problems

ANDREW D. BOOTH, D.Sc.

L. BRANDWOOD, B.A.

J. P. CLEAVE, Ph.D., B.Sc.

NEW YORK

ACADEMIC PRESS INC., PUBLISHERS

LONDON

BUTTERWORTHS SCIENTIFIC PUBLICATIONS

1958

BUTTERWORTHS PUBLICATIONS LTD.
88 KINGSWAY, LONDON, W.C.2

U.S.A. Edition published by
ACADEMIC PRESS INC., PUBLISHERS
111 FIFTH AVENUE,
NEW YORK 3, NEW YORK

Made and printed in Great Britain by
William Clowes and Sons, Limited, London and Beccles

PREFACE

THE present book contains an account of some of the results which have been obtained at Birkbeck College Computational Laboratory on the application of digital calculators to linguistic problems. Almost all of the material which has been published in the field is of a very general, not to say nebulous, character and it seemed worth recording the actual details of the techniques which we have used. There is one obvious exception to this—the detailed programmes for machine translation on APEXC—these are deliberately omitted for two reasons: firstly because many readers will not be professional mathematicians and would therefore not find them interesting, and secondly because the more important ones appear in the book *Programming for an Automatic Digital Calculator* by Kathleen H. V. Booth (Butterworths Scientific Publications, 1958).

Although the idea of machine translation originated at Birkbeck College in 1947, it was not until 1955 that extensive effort could be devoted to it, and this became possible because of the generosity of the Nuffield Foundation whose support the authors most gratefully acknowledge.

Thanks are also due to Miss Jill Metherell for performing so well the onerous task of preparing the typescript for the press.

The senior author wishes to add a note of personal thanks to Dr. J. F. Lockwood, Master of Birkbeck College, for his unfailing encouragement and help in solving the problems which confront a scientist when he ventures, like Daniel, into the den of his colleagues in the Faculty of Arts.

Birkbeck College,
October 1957.

A. D. B.
L. B.
J.P.C.

CONTENTS

1

HISTORICAL INTRODUCTION

IT is impossible to trace the date, from the point of view of history, when man first considered whether machines could be applied to the resolution of various problems of language. From the time of the ancient Greeks various schemes[1] have been debated for setting up ideal languages to replace those which have grown through the history of intelligent man, and many of these imply, in their structure, the possibility that a mechanical means might be found for the treatment of all problems of linguistic analysis.

Much of the most important work on statistical analysis of language[2] resulted from the desire of telegraph engineers to utilize in the best possible manner the various transmitting media available. In particular, the problem of band width restriction for the transmission of spoken sounds over telegraph lines and cables formed an invaluable spur which culminated in the invention by Shannon of what is now called Information Theory[3]. Whilst these applications were directed primarily to the improvement of technological systems involving the transmission of information, nevertheless, the results obtained were also important for more literary spheres of linguistic endeavour.

The use of a machine to translate one language to another was first suggested by Booth in the course of conversations with Warren Weaver, in New York in 1946. At that time the problem was simply an intellectual exercise directed at finding yet another use for the new high-speed digital calculators[4], which were just coming into existence. Little support was given to machine translation and this, coupled with the lack of calculating machines themselves, limited progress in the field of translation to the development of ideas instead of the actual production of a translating machine or to the practical demonstration of translation. In 1947 Booth and Britten, working at the Institute for Advanced Studies, Princeton, produced a programme[5] enabling an automatic digital calculator to make use of a dictionary stored in its memory-organ to facilitate the looking-up of words presented to the machine on a standard teletype input. At a later point in this book the functions of dictionaries by themselves will be considered in some detail, but it is appropriate to mention here that a dictionary of the ordinary sort implies the knowledge by a user of certain basic syntactical features of the language with which the dictionary is concerned. For this reason the early dictionary programmes would have been of little use in real language translation, even had they been put on a computing machine, supposing such to have been then available. In 1948 Booth and Richens considered further how a dictionary might be constructed in a form more suitable than ordinary dictionaries for the unintelligent processes available on a computing machine. This collaboration resulted in a pioneer paper[6] which suggested that the appropriate method for translation was to construct dictionaries involving not whole words, as is normally the case, but stems and endings. The validity of these ideas was tested very extensively on ten languages, ranging from the Romance to languages of the Near and Far East as well as to Russian and Arabic.

Although no machine was available at this time, the ideas of Booth and Richens were extensively tested by the construction of limited dictionaries of the type envisaged. These were used by a human untutored in the languages concerned, who applied only those rules which could eventually be performed by a machine. The results of these early 'translations' were extremely odd, a typical example being:

'De ziekte treedt dus zeer hevig op en heeft in vele gevallen een totale misoogst ten gevolge.'

'disease come thus very rapidly up and has in many case a (one) total amiss crop then follow (P).'

where the symbols in brackets give grammatical information derived by the machine from a consideration of the endings. Two things were realized: firstly, that when they became available calculating machines would be rather limited in the scope of their linguistic comprehension, and secondly, because of the great expense of storage organs, the vocabularies which could be held in the machine would be rather limited. This in turn led to the realization that it would be necessary to store in the machine, not a dictionary of the normal size, but one consisting of two parts: the first, a microglossary of those words peculiar to the subject being translated, and the second, a set of words of general utility. Some very rough examinations of scientific texts suggested that in each case about one thousand words would be adequate, this number to include both stems and endings. It was proposed that when a foreign language word was not to be found in the dictionary, the machine should produce it in unmodified form at the output, so that it could receive the detailed attention of the human translator.

In July 1949 a historic paper entitled 'Translation'[7] was circulated by Warren Weaver to various potentially-interested workers in the United States, and this led to an upsurge of interest in the subject in that country. Despite the unfavourable reception of this paper by a number of distinguished linguists, a nucleus of younger and more energetic workers was immediately forthcoming to take up the development of the new subject, and in 1950 Reifler produced the first of his 'Studies in M.T.'[8], a fundamental paper in which was postulated the pre- and the post-editor. The pre-editor was to remove known ambiguities and difficulties from foreign language texts for which function he needed to know nothing of the language into which translation was to be effected. The post-editor, on the other hand, would render the output of the machine into a respectable grammatical form. Reifler has himself abandoned the idea of a pre-editor, and it is perhaps not unfair to say that at the present time there is a general agreement that neither of these two posts will be necessary for the translating machine of the future.

In 1951 a second fundamental paper appeared, written by Oswald and Fletcher[9], which discussed the analysis of German syntax in a form suitable for use on a computing machine.

In 1952 the general interest in the subject led to the sponsorship by the Rockefeller Foundation of a conference devoted entirely to machine translation and held at the Massachusetts Institute of Technology. At this conference all the workers currently interested in M.T. were able to meet together and hold discussions over a period of about a week. In the course of these several members seemed to reveal a fixed opinion that the subject was too difficult for any practical experiments. Others, however, were less sceptical, and agreed with the British view that experiments were the only way in which the subject would progress at all. Although it was not the business of the conference to reach any formal conclusions, there was a general feeling at the end that two major lines of attack should be pursued. The first of these was for analyses of word frequency and word meaning to be conducted on a large scale, both for a number of subjects and for all the languages for which workers could be found, and the second was that operational analysis and syntax should be developed, so that, even supposing machines were not already in a state to receive them, these rules would be available as and when required.

After the conference work proceeded on a considerable scale both in England and in the United States. Harper[10] and Oettinger[11], for example, were occupied with various aspects of the Russian language, Oswald and Lawson[12] made word frequency analyses of the literature of neurosurgery, Yngve worked on the utility of partial translations[13], and Booth[14] devoted a considerable amount of attention to means whereby the time required for the examination of the contents of a dictionary could be reduced. Aspects of dictionary search will be considered in detail in Chapter 6, but it may be mentioned here that up to this time the only proposals for searching a dictionary were that each word should be stored in a storage location, whose code number was simply that of the letters of the word taken in aggregate. This it may be said had been simply demonstrated to be so inefficient as to be outside the range of any conceivable machine either at the time or in the foreseeable future. Alternatively, the foreign language word could be compared with the dictionary entries, starting at the beginning. This of course means that, on the average, half of the dictionary must be examined to determine the sense of any word.

In 1954 an experiment in the machine translation of a language was conducted at Georgetown University with the assistance of the I.B.M. Corporation[15]. In this, a computing machine was programmed to translate selected sentences from Russian using a restricted vocabulary of about 250 words. Also of historic importance in 1954 was the first appearance of a periodical devoted entirely to the machine translation of language. This was called 'M.T.' and is produced by the M.I.T. under the editorship of Yngve and Locke.

Work on translation in England had, however, been severely limited by the fact that the active workers could devote only a very small part of their time to this subject. But in 1955, the Nuffield Foundation made an extremely generous grant to Birkbeck College, University of London, for the furtherance of the work on machine translation. This grant could not have been better timed. The machine APEXC[16] was now working in a satisfactory manner. The enormous interest which had accompanied the inception of these machines, to see to what extent they affected the problems of numerical analysis, mathematics, physics and engineering, had largely been satisfied, so that a certain amount of machine-time was available. The art of programming, too, had risen to heights which enabled the problems of linguistic analysis to be contemplated without undue trepidation.

With the coming of the Nuffield grant, the group at Birkbeck College expanded, so that not only were programming aspects considered, but also the detailed analysis of languages themselves. It was in 1955 that Booth suggested the first practical logarithmic method for dictionary search. This will not be discussed further here, except to say that for a dictionary of one million words, which under the second of the schemes mentioned above would take about half a million examinations to locate any given word, it was now possible by the logarithmic technique to define the position of the word in about twenty look-up operations.

At the same time Cleave commenced work on an examination of the possibilities for transcribing standard English into Braille. This at first seemed to be a project of little interest from the linguistic point of view, but soon showed itself to contain many of those elements peculiar to real language, for example, the existence of context[17]. Brandwood was similarly examining the French language in considerable detail, so that a realistic programme for the translation of French into English could be constructed[18]. All of this work proceeded with great rapidity, so that, by the middle of 1955, machine programmes had been devised and applied to the machine to translate from the French language on the basis of restricted dictionaries. A further highlight of 1955 was the appearance of the first book on machine translation[19] of language, edited by Booth and Locke, and containing essays by all the active workers in the field.

The following year saw continued activity in the field both in England and in the United States, and particularly from a newcomer in Moscow. Work in England and in the United States was devoted not only to the general problems outlined above, but also to the examination of the possibilities of a meta-language, which might facilitate the problems of translation between various languages of a group. The work in Moscow was chiefly concerned with translation from English into Russian, and led to a paper by Mukhin[20], first read at the April, 1956 conference of the I.E.E. in London. A number of examples which are claimed to be actual translations are given in this paper, and some of these will be considered later in this book.

To sum up the situation at this time, it is perhaps fair to say that the group at Birkbeck College had produced valid methods of translation, and tested these on an actual computing machine, that the group in the Soviet Union had done the same thing, but that apart from the I.B.M. Georgetown experiment of 1954, the United States had been particularly backward in the testing of translation routines on any actual machine. On the other hand it should be noted that the American workers had started on the construction of a dictionary machine specially designed for translation, and this, when it is available, will be of the greatest help to the work which is going on.

So much, then, for the problems of translation as such. In

parallel with these problems are various others, sometimes of a higher, sometimes of a lower degree of sophistry. There is, for example, the problem of the analysis of the frequency of occurrence of words in a given text. Workers such as Shannon had made use of pencil and paper methods of analysis which were laborious and could result in accurate estimates only when applied to short segments of text. The availability of machines had suggested that the machines themselves might be used to construct the frequency analyses required in machine translation, and considerable work in this field was carried out by the Nuffield research group at Birkbeck College. Another problem of the same generic type is that of constructing concordances for given texts, that is, lists, usually in alphabetic order, of the words in those texts, each word being accompanied by a set of page and line references to the place of its occurrence. Such concordances are of course familiar to linguists, having been available for many years for such classics as the Bible and Shakespeare. The interest at Birkbeck College in this field was chiefly engendered by some earlier research work[21] on the Dialogues of Plato, which had been considerably hampered in the past by the absence of such concordances. Parallel work in this field has been carried out by the I.B.M. Corporation, and it appears that some of this work is now being put to practical use in the preparation of a concordance for the works of Thomas Aquinas.

A more involved application of the same sort is to the stylistic analysis of a work by purely mechanical means. Here again there is a considerable literature, but previous workers have considered the subject, not within the framework of a machine, but for analysis by a human linguist acting in a mechanical way. Roughly speaking, a problem of this type is the following:

Given a set of books, for example the Dialogues of Plato, and given also that the actual dates of production of some of these are known. Find, by an analysis of word frequencies, structure and so on, the position of unknown works in chronological order within the date framework known unequivocally.

This problem will be discussed at a later point in the book, and it will be shown that problems of this sort are indeed quite amenable to purely mechanical resolution on a computing machine.

The examples of linguistic analysis just mentioned are only a few of those which are now coming into the ambit of computing machines. Problems of the same sort, although not so conspicuous for their linguistic content, concern the cross-referencing of libraries, the indexing of scientific and other information, telephone directories, and certain problems of mathematical logic. Not all of these problems will be examined in this book, but it is hoped that in the following chapters sufficient information is given to enable people interested in the fringe applications of the subjects to work out methods for using an automatic computing machine to resolve their problems in the way already used for language.

REFERENCES

[1] Elliot, W. V., 'Isaac Newton's "Of an Universall Language"' *Mod. Lang. Rev.*, LII (1), (1957), 1–18

[2] Shannon, C. and Weaver, W., 'The Mathematical Theory of Communication', Illinois Univ. Press, Urbana, (1949)

[3] Brillouin, L., 'Science and Information Theory', Academic Books, London, (1956)

[4] Booth, A. D. and Booth, K. H. V., 'Automatic Digital Calculators', (2nd Ed.) Butterworths, London, (1956)

[5] Booth, A. D. and Britten, K. H. V., 'Coding for A.R.C.', (2nd Ed.) Inst. Adv. Study, Princeton, (1947)

[6] Booth, A. D. and Richens, R. H., 'Machine Translation of Languages', Wiley, New York, (1955), 24–26

[7] Weaver, W., 'Translation', Mimeographed, New York, July, (1949)

[8] Reifler, E., 'Studies in Mechanical Translation, No. 1, M.T.', Mimeographed, Washington, (1950)

[9] Oswald, V. A. and Fletcher, S. L., 'Proposals for the Mechanical Resolution of German Syntax Patterns', Mod. Language Forum, 36, (1951), 1–24

[10] Harper, K. E., 'The Mechanical Translation of Russian: Preliminary Report', Mod. Language Forum, 38, (1953), 12–29

[11] Oettinger, A. G., 'A Study for the Design of an Automatic Dictionary', Mimeographed, Harvard, (1953)

[12] Oswald, V. A. and Lawson, R. H., 'An Ideoglossary for Mechanical Translation', Mod. Language Forum, 38, (1953), 1–11

[13] Yngve, V., 'Mechanical Translation of Languages', Wiley, New York, (1955), 208–226

[14] Booth, A. D., *Nature,* 176, (1955), 565

[15] Dostert, L., 'Mechanical Translation of Languages, Wiley, New York, (1955), 124–135

[16] Booth, A. D., M.T.A.C. VIII, (1954), 98

[17] Cleave, J., 'Information Theory', (Ed. C. Cherry) Butterworths, London, (1956), 184–194

[18] Brandwood, L., 'The Translation of a Foreign Language by Machine', *Babel,* 11 (No. 3), (1956), 111–118

[19] Booth, A. D. and Locke, W. N., (Ed.) 'Machine Translation of Languages', Wiley, New York, (1955)

[20] Mukhin, I. S., 'An Experiment on the Machine Translation of Languages', *Acad. Sci. U.S.S.R., Moscow,* (1956)

[21] Brandwood, L., 'Analysing Plato's style with an Electronic Computer', Inst. Classical Studies, (Univ. London) Bulletin No. 3, (1956), 45–54

2

THE NATURE OF CALCULATING AND DATA PROCESSING MACHINES

BEFORE the actual application of a machine to problems of linguistics can be considered, it is first necessary to see how language data can be presented to a machine, and this involves a study of the way in which data can be recorded in permanent form. Language no doubt arose in the first instance merely as vocal or other form of sonic expression. The spoken word can be made permanent in many ways, for example, it can be recorded upon a gramophone record, upon a magnetic tape in a tape recorder, it can be recorded on the sound track of film or, and more fundamentally, it can be committed to paper in the form of handwriting, typewriting or print.

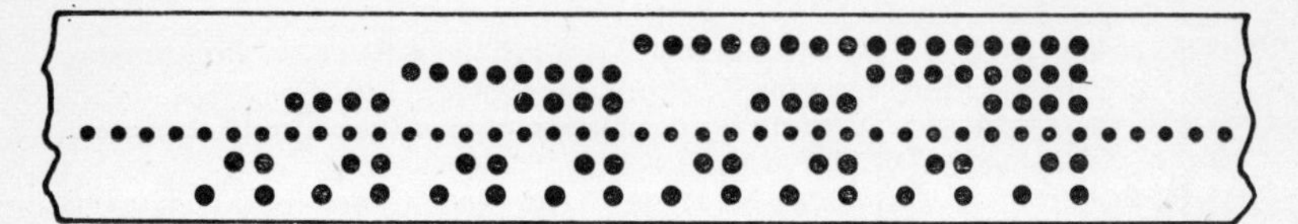

Figure 2.1. Teletype tape showing binary punching 0–31

From the point of view of machine handling, none of these forms is at present acceptable, and it turns out that, to feed data into a machine, it is first necessary to represent it in some form of numerical code. The encoding of letters has been studied very extensively in connection with the transmission of data over telephone and telegraph lines, as was mentioned in Chapter 1. Historically, one of the oldest forms of recording and encoding is in the form of a five-hole punching on what is known as teletype tape. In *Figure 2.1* is shown a small section of tape, and in Table 2.1 there is indicated the numerical code which is nowadays accepted by international convention for the encoding of alphabetic characters for transmission over telegraph lines. A cursory examination of the encoding system shown in the table will reveal that there is no particular logic behind the code symbol associated with each alphabetic character. The reader who has a knowledge of mathematics will see that the numerical symbols constitute numbers in the so-called binary scale of notation, but it does not happen, for example, that A corresponds to the number 1, B to 2, C to 3, and so on. In fact, for mechanical

Table 2.1

	Optional Characters	○*Start* *Code elements* ●*Stop* 1 2 3 4 5			○*Start* *Code elements* ●*Stop* 1 2 3 4 5
A		● ● ○ ○ ○	P	0	○ ● ● ○ ●
B	?	● ○ ○ ● ●	Q	1	● ● ● ○ ●
C	:	○ ● ● ● ○	R	4	○ ● ○ ● ○
D	Who are you?	● ○ ○ ● ○	S	′	● ○ ● ○ ○
E	3	● ○ ○ ○ ○	T	5	○ ○ ○ ○ ●
F		● ○ ● ● ○	U	7	● ● ● ○ ○
G		○ ● ○ ● ●	V	=	○ ● ● ● ●
H		○ ○ ● ○ ●	W	2	● ● ○ ○ ●
I	8	○ ● ● ○ ○	X	/	● ○ ● ● ●
J	Bell	● ● ○ ● ○	Y	6	● ○ ● ○ ●
K	(	● ● ● ● ○	Z	+	● ○ ○ ○ ●
L	)	○ ● ○ ○ ●	Carriage return		○ ○ ○ ● ○
M	.	○ ○ ● ● ●	Figures		● ● ○ ● ●
N	,	○ ○ ● ● ○	Letters		● ● ● ● ●
O	9	○ ○ ○ ● ●	Line feed		○ ● ○ ○ ○
			Space		○ ○ ● ○ ○

Elements which cause the setting of teleprinter combination discs or perforation of reperforator tape are shown thus ●. They are often referred to as marking elements, whilst those of the opposite kind are known as spacing elements.

Each group of code elements is preceded by a start signal and succeeded by a stop signal. The latter may be of 1 or $1\frac{1}{2}$ units duration.

handling, there is considerable reason to revise the alphabetic coding system to one more in accord with the needs of the subject.

Another example of a coding of alphabetic data into numerical form is the Morse code. Here, however, very much more thought has been given to the detailed form of the encodement. This will be seen by an examination of Table 2.2. In brief, the Morse coding system is such that the number of numeric symbols required to encode an alphabetic character has the property that the more frequent characters have the simpler numerical code, whereas the less frequent characters are coded in a manner which required the transmission of more digits.

The other principal form of numerical coding for data in use at the present time is on punched cards. A typical example of one of these is shown in *Figure 2.2*, p. 17; punched cards were first devised by Herman Hollerith for application, in a purely numerical context,

Table 2.2

Letter	*Probability*	*Morse symbol*	*Binary code*	*Letter*	*Probability*	*Morse symbol*	*Binary code*
Space	0·2			F	0·022	··—·	0010
E	0·105	·	0	U	0·022	··—	001
T	0·072	—	1	M	0·021	——	11
O	0·065	———	111	P	0·018	·——·	0110
A	0·063	·—	01	Y	0·012	—·——	1011
N	0·059	—·	10	W	0·012	·——	011
I	0·055	··	00	G	0·011	——·	110
R	0·054	·—·	010	B	0·010	—···	1000
S	0·052	···	000	V	0·008	···—	0001
H	0·047	····	0000	K	0·003	—·—	101
D	0·035	—··	100	X	0·002	—··—	1001
L	0·029	·—··	0100	J	0·001	·———	0111
C	0·023	—·—·	1010	Q	0·001	——·—	1101
				Z	0·001	——··	1100

to the problem of the analysis of census data. A typical card has eighty columns, each of which is capable of receiving a punching in any one of twelve positions. It follows that, since there are more than twelve letters to be encoded, it is either necessary to use more than one column to represent in numerical form a single letter, or alternatively that several punchings must be placed in a single column when alphabetic data is to be recorded on the card. Business machine manufacturers have, in fact, adopted the second of these alternatives. The normal method of designating the various positions on a card is shown in *Figure 2.2*, and when desired to represent alphabetic characters, a punching in the X or Y positions accompanies a second punching in one of the normal numerical positions. An alternative to this alphabetic code is given in *Figure 2.3*, p. 18.

The third means of data representation acceptable to a calculating machine is of far more recent origin, and is a development of the magnetic tape recorder used for speech. In this case, however, magnetic tape is used in such a way that data is recorded on its surface in pulse form, that is, the number is first represented in a binary code. This binary code is then recorded on the tape surface, using a positive pulse of electrical current through the recording coil to represent 'one', and a negative pulse to represent 'zero'. It may be argued that, if a virgin tape were taken, it would be sufficient to record only ones *or* zeroes, the other being represented by the absence of any signal. The use of this system, however, is open to a number of objections. The first of these is that it is always dangerous to represent information—and zero is just as much information as one—by the absence of information, since this absence can in fact be only relative. All electrical apparatus produces a certain amount of what is known as 'noise', and it may only be said that the absence of information means noise less that some completely definite and non-zero upper limit. The second objection to presenting digits of one sort by electrical impulses and of the other by the absence of an electrical impulse lies in the details of the means used to recover the data at a later date. To recover data in which only ones are recorded on a virgin surface requires the use of a clock track, that is, a set of pre-recorded markers on some part of the tape, these markers indicating that certain time intervals have elapsed during which no electrical signal has been generated, when, in fact, it could have been generated. The alternative to the use of such time markers is very accurate synchronization of the recording medium with some external source of time measurement. It is certainly true that modern tape-recording machinery is capable of a high degree of synchronization, but it is nevertheless still extremely undesirable to assume such constancy of reproduction when the need for this accuracy can be eliminated by the simple device of using two forms of electro-magnetic impulse to represent the two types of binary digit concerned.

At the present time magnetic tape is just coming into use with computing machines, but up to now it has not been much used with programmes of linguistic interest. The principles which accompany its use are identical to those which would be used with paper tape, and it will not be necessary to consider it further in this book.

PUNCHED CARD MACHINES

Since it is only intended to relate the discussion of linguistic data to calculating machines, it is not necessary here to enter into a detailed description of telegraph systems for handling data, because, at present, these systems are capable only of transmitting and reassembling data at two places, and not, in general, of making any transformation of the data during the course of its progress. The first machines which could absorb numerical data from a record were the punched card business machines. These machines are still of great importance, not only in office accounting, but also in certain aspects of linguistic work. They have the considerable advantage that a number of operators can be used to prepare cards either from different texts or from the same text, and that these cards can be brought together as a whole at the end of the operation and then presented to the computing machine. It was in fact on just such punched card accounting machines that the first Birkbeck College experiments in language translation by means of a simple dictionary were carried out.

Today the range of punched card machines is very great, but, from the linguistic point of view, it is necessary only to mention a few of these. The first machine to be considered is the card punch. This can take various forms from the extremely simple hand-operated type, shown in *Figure 2.4*, p. 19, to a complicated electrical system with storaged facilities for data and automatic handling for cards, shown in *Figure 2.5*, p. 19. The storage affords means for remembering data which has been punched on a single card, so that it may be repunched on successive cards.

After data has been processed through one of these punching machines, it is generally necessary to check it in some way. The checking operation is conveniently performed by means of a verifier shown in *Figure 2.6*, p. 20. Here a card, previously punched, is placed into the checking device and a different operator from the operator who prepared the card in the first place goes through the motions of preparing the card again. As the various keys are depressed, the electrical sensing mechanism examines them to see whether the depressed keys correspond with those keys which would have been depressed to produce the holes in the given position on the card. If, however, an error occurs, the device gives a signal in the form of a red light and refuses to feed the card. In this case the operator knows either that she has committed an error in operating the checking punch, or that there is an error in the card itself. This method of checking by reiterating the operation previously performed is open to certain well-known objections, but generally it enables a satisfactory check to be made, and is common in many forms of business accounting.

When the cards have been prepared and checked, various forms of analysis can be performed upon them by means of the punched card calculating machinery. A frequent operation is that of sorting and this is performed in the device shown in *Figure 2.7*, p. 20. Here a stack of cards is passed through sensing apparatus, and cards bearing various pre-assigned combinations of punchings are distributed into one of twelve hoppers shown in the figure. In this way it is easy to take a pack of cards, for example, and to sort them into groups which have, say, zero in column one, one in column one, two in column one, and so on. It can also be shown that by a sequence of these operations it is possible to take a pack of cards arranged in random order and to reassemble it into numerical order, alphabetical order, etc. No actual operation of calculation is involved, although types of sorting apparatus exist in which the cards distributed between the various hoppers actuate counters, so that the number of cards in each hopper is available after the cards have passed through the mechanism. This type of device is very useful when it is desired, for example, to ascertain the number of words starting with A, B, C, D, and so on, in any given pack.

The principal calculating device in the punched card range is the tabulator, shown in *Figure 2.8*, p. 21. With this it is possible to take the data, in this case of course numerical, stored on a card and to combine it with the data which has been stored on other cards, usually by the processes of addition and subtraction. The tabulator is also provided with printing facilities whereby totals and sub-totals of data can be printed and in addition alphabetic information which is held on a card can be output at the same time. Thus the tabulator can, in principle, perform the functions of printing out dictionaries and statistical data.

Another extremely useful machine is the collator, which has various applications not only in linguistics, but also in the handling of accumulations of data in general. A typical collator is shown in *Figure 2.9*, p. 21. The apparatus is provided with two feeds, into which can be placed stacks of cards. The action of the collator is to take the cards from each of the stacks, examine two from one stack and one from the other to see if certain conditions of ordering are satisfied, and then to distribute them to one of four output hoppers according to various pre-assigned criteria, which are set up on the plug-board shown in the front of the machine. One use of the collating machine will be described in Chapter 5, and it was this which enabled a mechanical dictionary to be synthesized in the early stages of machine translation.

Finally there is the reproducer or gang-punch. This device simply prepares a new card in accord with data supplied to it. This data can either be taken from cards which it feeds from its own hopper or alternatively from the output of a tabulating machine or collator. The use of the gang-punch will be described later, when we come to consider the realization of actual dictionary experiment.

At the present time electronics is extending the range of punched card machinery, and not only are more rapid devices available, but also such things as electronic multiplying punches are becoming commonplace. So far none of these more highly specialized arithmetical machines have found an application in linguistics, and, since it appears unlikely that they will find application, we shall not discuss them further here. Before we leave the subject of punched card machines, it is appropriate to give a short summary of the speeds of the operations of which these machines are capable. These are given in Table 2.3.

Table 2.3

Machine	*Speed, cards/min.*
Hand punch	2–3
Keystor punch	4–10
Verifier	2–3
Sorter	450–660
Tabulator	100–150
Collator	240
Reproducer	100

ALL-PURPOSE DIGITAL CALCULATORS

The revolution in arithmetical technique which made possible a detailed consideration of linguistic problems from the machine point of view was the invention of the all-purpose digital calculator. It is not our purpose here to enter into the history of these devices, except to say that the first conception of an all-purpose machine was that of Charles Babbage in 1833. In fact, no machine of a type which would be readily applicable to linguistic problems was produced until the early 1950s. For this reason it is not considered necessary to describe the various attempts, starting in the mid-1930s, which led to the eventual realization of such a machine. Nowadays numerous machines of the required type are available both in university laboratories and from manufacturers of business calculating equipment. The description which follows can be taken as typical of the facilities which are available on any of the better types of these machines.

Essentially, an all-purpose digital calculator consists of a control which orders the operations of the machine in accord with some previously decided programme, an input which enables the machine to absorb data from punched tape or magnetic tape, or punched cards, a store which enables the machine to hold such data as dictionaries, grammars, rules of procedure and so on, and also the actual instructions required by the machine to carry out the programmes, an arithmetical unit which is capable, generally speaking, of addition, subtraction, shifting, multiplication, sometimes division and always of transferring numbers to and from the storage organ. In addition to these units there is what may be described as a discriminator. This is usually taken by computer experts to be a part of the general control mechanism of the machine, but in view of its great importance to linguistic analysis it is worth particular mention here. The discriminator often takes the form of a unit capable of executing an instruction of the following type:

If the result of a certain calculation is positive or zero, take for the next instruction (*a*); if however the result of the calculation is negative take for the next instruction (*b*).

This is typical of what is known as a 'jump' or 'conditional transfer order'. More complicated instructions of the same sort are sometimes provided, one of which is 'collate'. In this, two numbers are taken and, remembering that they are represented in binary form, a result is generated in such a way that wherever each of the two numbers has corresponding digits identical a one is written, but wherever corresponding digits of the two numbers are different a zero is written. This instruction has considerable use in comparing input data with dictionary entries. Towards the end of this book it will become clear than an ideal linguistic machine should have certain instructions which are of a more sophisticated type than those just mentioned. Since, however, these instructions are not available on any given machine at the present time, we will leave discussion of them until Chapter 12.

Finally a computing machine, whether used for operations on numbers or not, must have some form of output. Some early machines took their output from a set of electric lamps. Today, however, all machines produce outputs either on punched cards, punched tape, or magnetic tape. Some of them have the additional facility that a directly typed output can be produced, but this is not considered generally satisfactory since the typing apparatus which is available for connection to a computing machine is usually considerably slower than the devices capable of producing either magnetic tape, punched paper tape, or punched cards.

Certain other output devices which can produce a directly printed record, are becoming available, among which must be mentioned the line-at-a-time printer. This can often print as many as a hundred letters simultaneously, and can repeat this printing operation, which effectively produces a 'line at a time', at a rate of about nine hundred lines per minute. Unfortunately these devices are extremely expensive and require very considerable ancillary equipment, so that to date no calculating machine available in Great Britian has a device of this sort attached to its output. Even when devices of this type do become generally available, it is doubtful whether a computing machine of the type available at present would be suitable for feeding it, since the programme for assembling data in the form of a complete line is quite complicated. Two examples of automatic digital calculators are shown in *Figures 2.10* and *2.11*, *see* p. 22 and 23. The first of these is the APEXC installed at Birkbeck College. This machine is the one which has been used in linguistic experiments. It will be seen that it is of small size and that the construction is of the sort normally encountered in laboratories. The second machine is a typical business electronic machine, the HEC General Purpose Electronic Computer, produced by the British Tabulating Machine Co. In principle, it is identical with the APEXC, but because of the superior engineering and the additional instructions specially designed for business use it is considerably more versatile.

COMPUTER DEVELOPMENTS

In the last chapter of this book some thought will be given to the form which a machine specially designed for linguistic operations should take. It is worth mentioning here, however, certain developments which will undoubtedly be made in the next two or three years, and which will be available on commercial calculating machines.

The first of these developments is concerned with the direct recognition of printed or possibly hand-written characters. Considerable work has been done in this field, and laboratory versions of devices for character recognition have been developed and operated on a small scale. A character-recognizing device can absorb data presented to it in the form of a typescript or printed document at a rate far faster than is possible with any other medium, with the exception of magnetic tape. The great importance of character recognition from the linguistic standpoint lies of course in the fact that the records for which analysis is required do not have to

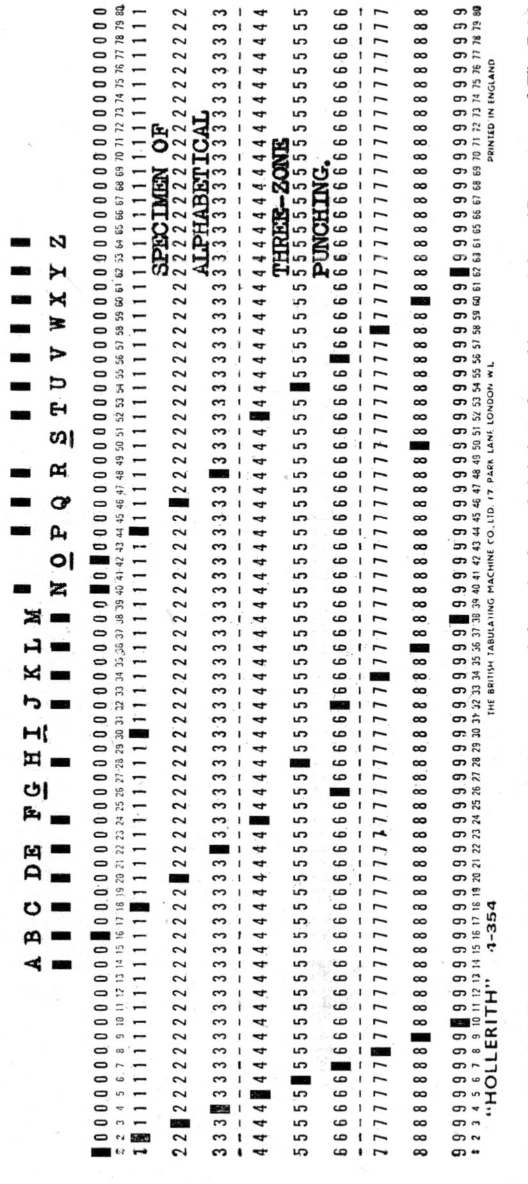

Figure 2.2. *'Hollerith' card, showing numerical punching on left, and a form of alphabetical punching on right.* (*By courtesy of The British Tabulating Machine Co., Ltd.*)

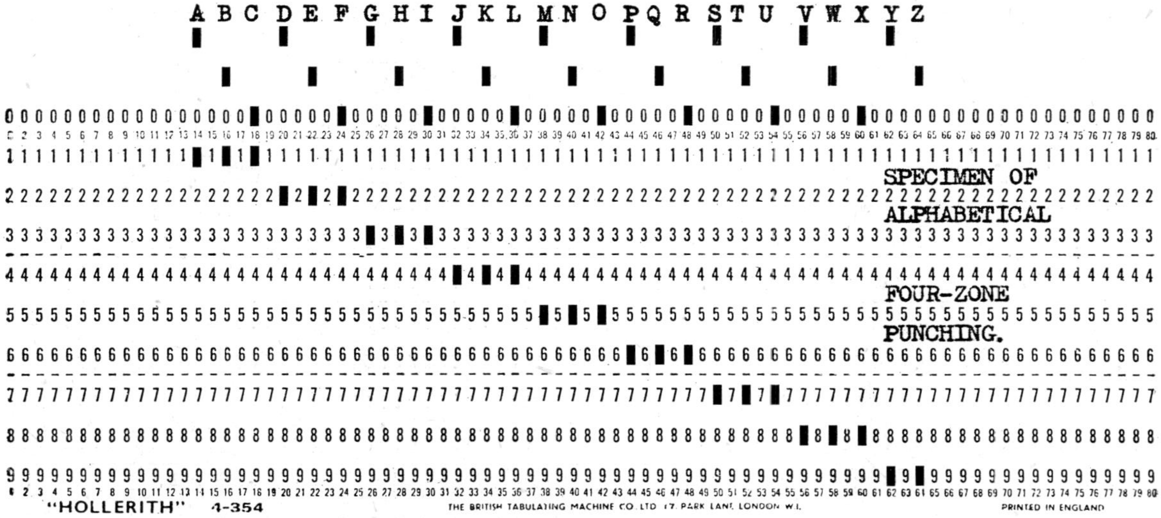

A B C D E F G H I J K L M N O P Q R S T U V W X Y Z

00000000000000000█00000█00000█00000█00000█00000█00000█00000█00000000000000000000

1 2 3 4 5 6 7 8 9 10 11 12 13 14 15 16 17 18 19 20 21 22 23 24 25 26 27 28 29 30 31 32 33 34 35 36 37 38 39 40 41 42 43 44 45 46 47 48 49 50 51 52 53 54 55 56 57 58 59 60 61 62 63 64 65 66 67 68 69 70 71 72 73 74 75 76 77 78 79 80

1111111111111█1█1█11111111111111111111111111111111111111111111111111111111111111

SPECIMEN OF

2222222222222222222█2█2█22222222222222222222222222222222222222222222222222222222

ALPHABETICAL

3333333333333333333333333█3█3█33333333333333333333333333333333333333333333333333

4444444444444444444444444444444█4█4█44444444444444444444444444444444444444444444

FOUR-ZONE

5555555555555555555555555555555555555█5█5█55555555555555555555555555555555555555

PUNCHING.

6666666666666666666666666666666666666666666█6█6█66666666666666666666666666666666

7777777777777777777777777777777777777777777777777█7█7█77777777777777777777777777

8888888888888888888888888888888888888888888888888888888█8█8█88888888888888888888

9999999999999999999999999999999999999999999999999999999999999█9█9999999999999999

1 2 3 4 5 6 7 8 9 10 11 12 13 14 15 16 17 18 19 20 21 22 23 24 25 26 27 28 29 30 31 32 33 34 35 36 37 38 39 40 41 42 43 44 45 46 47 48 49 50 51 52 53 54 55 56 57 58 59 60 61 62 63 64 65 66 67 68 69 70 71 72 73 74 75 76 77 78 79 80

"HOLLERITH" 4-354

THE BRITISH TABULATING MACHINE CO. LTD. 17, PARK LANE, LONDON W.1.

PRINTED IN ENGLAND

Figure 2.3. An alternative form of alphabetical punching. (By courtesy of The British Tabulating Machine Co., Ltd.)

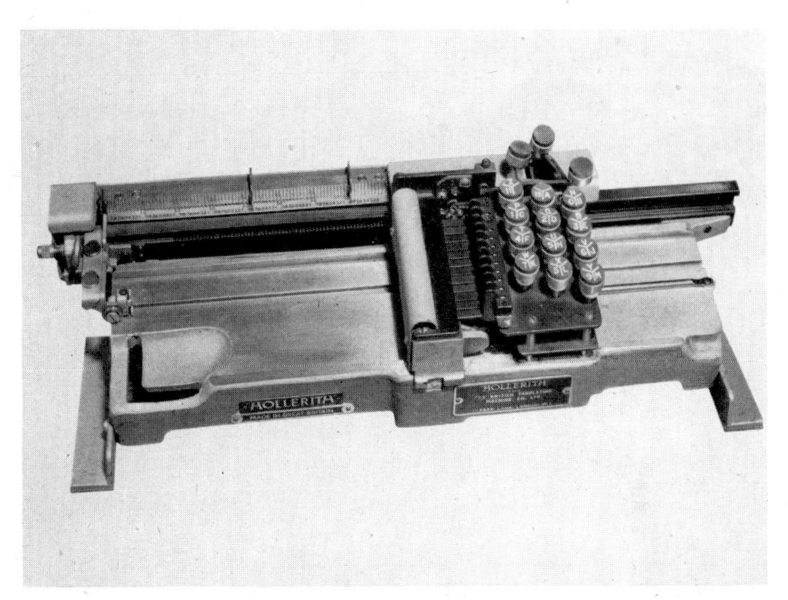

Figure 2.4. '*Hollerith' hand punch.* (*By courtesy of The British Tabulating Machine Co., Ltd.*)

Figure 2.5. '*Hollerith' automatic punch.* (*By courtesy of The British Tabulating Machine Co., Ltd.*)

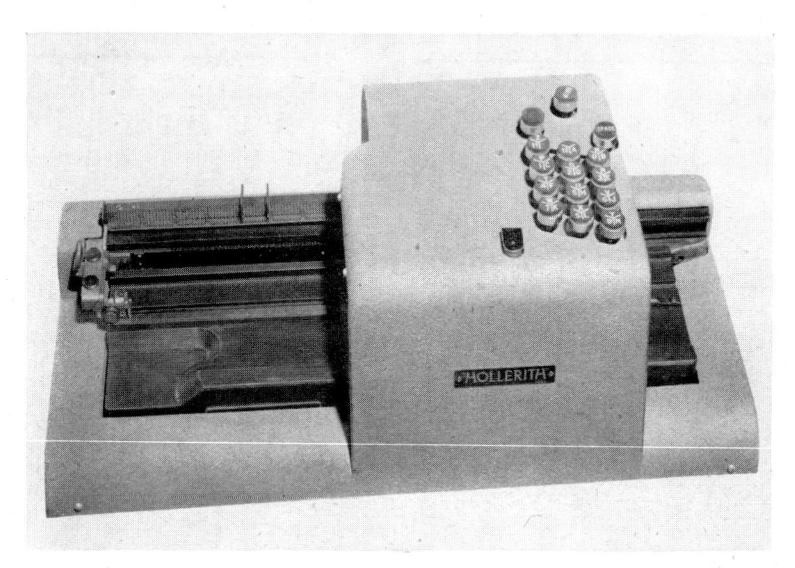

Figure 2.6. '*Hollerith*' *verifier.* (*By courtesy of The British Tabulating Machine Co., Ltd.*)

Figure 2.7. '*Hollerith*' *sorter.* (*By courtesy of The British Tabulating Machine Co., Ltd.*)

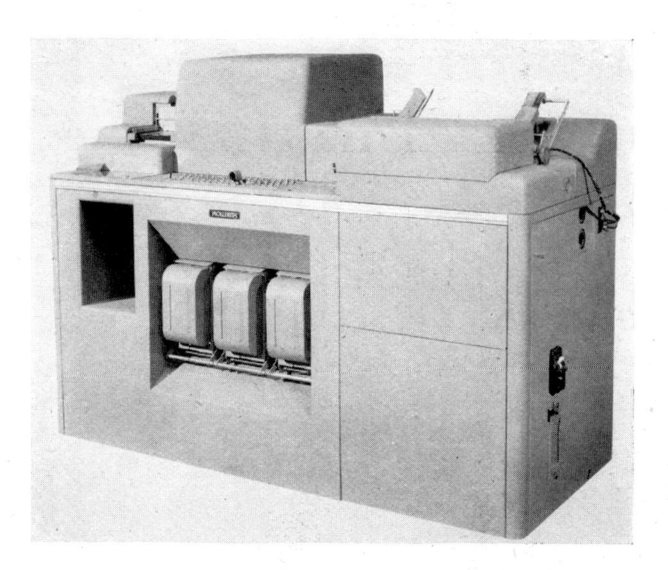

Figure 2.8. Senior tabulator. (By courtesy of The British Tabulating Machine Co., Ltd.)

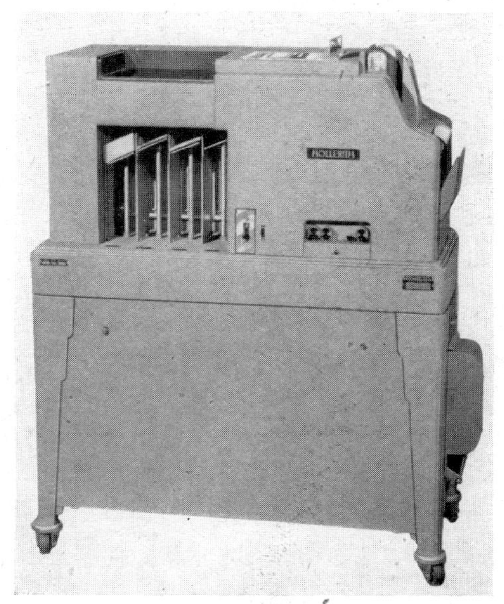

Figure 2.9. 'Hollerith' collator. (By courtesy of The British Tabulating Machine Co., Ltd.)

Figure 2.10. The APEXC all-purpose electronic computer

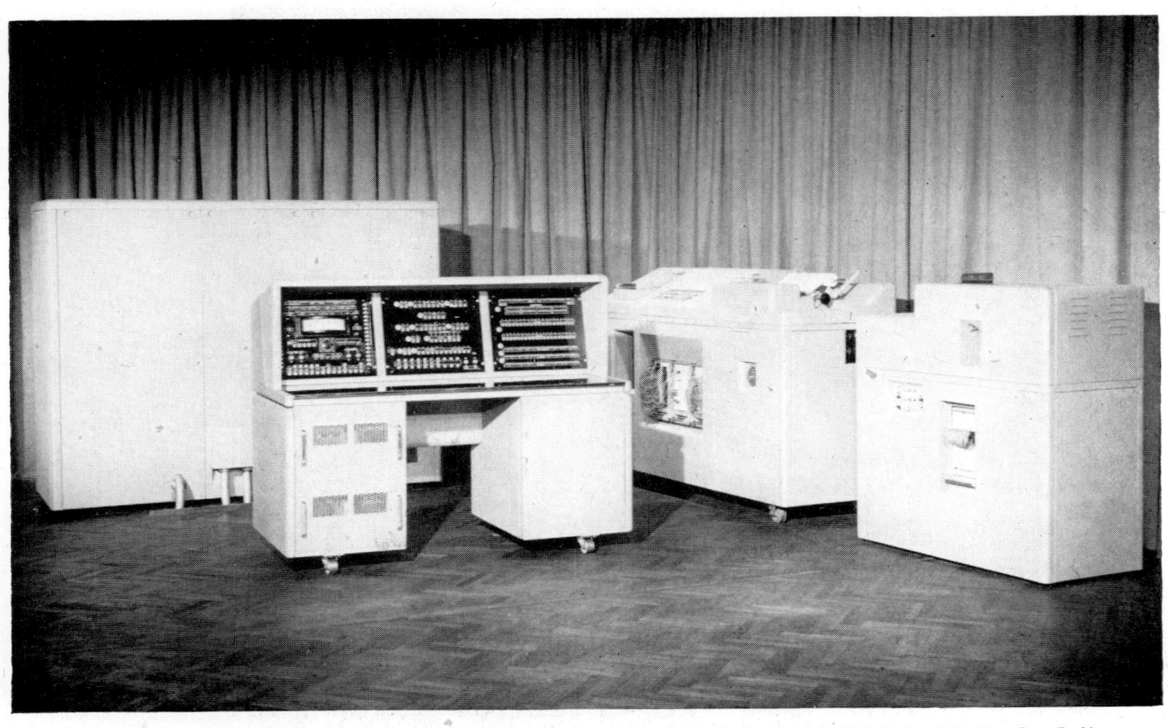

Figure 2.11. H.E.C. General Purpose Electronic Computer. (*By courtesy of The British Tabulating Machine Co., Ltd.*)

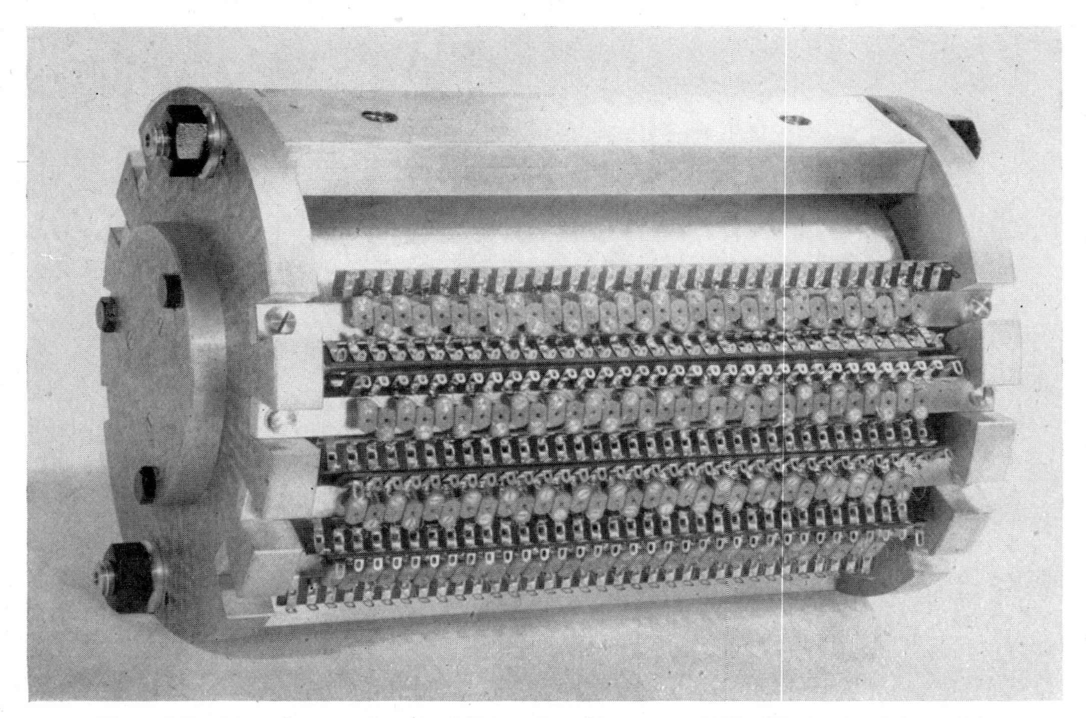

Figure 2.12. Magnetic storage drum for 8,192 words. (*By courtesy of Wharf Engineering Laboratories*)

be specially transcribed into a form acceptable to the machine, and when these character-recognizing devices become available, the scope of mechanical language handling will be vastly increased. An idea of the speed which may be expected is one second for an input of between 1,000 and 10,000 letters. At the present time, however, the laboratory models of the devices are capable only of much slower speeds, about fifty letters per second.

The second, which may be of linguistic application, is capable of recognizing directly the spoken word. Two lines of approach have been current in the development of these machines. In telegraphy, where band width compression is required, a special machine has been built which makes use of the acoustic content of the sound. By recognizing the proportions of various frequencies known as 'formants' in the spoken word the machine attempts to convert these into some numerical code. The devices of this sort so far demonstrated appear to be somewhat unreliable, and it is unlikely that in the very near future they will be suitable for linguistic work. The second development makes direct use of a computing machine for spoken word recognition. In this work care is taken to generate standard records from the person who is to use the machine, and a fair accuracy has been attained in experimental work using these techniques. Since the equipment required is relatively simple, it seems likely that some form of spoken word recognition-device may eventually form a valuable adjunct to either a calculating machine used for linguistics or to special linguistic machines. Here again, however, some years will probably elapse before these devices become available.

Mention has already been made in the discussion, of the storage organ in all-purpose digital calculators. Storage has been the problem besetting designers of computing machines over the last decade. It is still true that no completely satisfactory storage medium has been found. For linguistic use the magnetic drum has certain advantages, but also the disadvantage that a minimum waiting period is required before any particular piece of information may be examined at random. Developments going on at present suggest that large stores may soon become available in which the time required to locate particular data is independent both of the time when location is requested and of the particular positions of the data in the store. Whether these will be sufficiently inexpensive for storing the large quantity of data required in linguistic applications is a matter of some speculation, but certainly an ideal linguistic machine should possess at least a basic minimum of such storage.

Finally it is not impossible that a linguistic machine may, in the relatively near future, be provided with some form of output which will give rise to the spoken word. Experiments of this sort have been carried on over the past twenty years with an idea of providing some form of communication equipment for dumb people. Since it is trivial to cause a computing machine to emit musical sounds, there seems to be no real difficulty in causing one to produce spoken words.

DETAILS OF A TYPICAL COMPUTING MACHINE

To conclude this chapter, and to form a basis for the detailed considerations which will be given in the next chapter, the following data for the APEXC machine will be taken for the rest of this book as standard procedures available on a computing machine. Other machines may differ in detail but, generally, the operations involved are to be found in some form on all machines available at the present time. The input on the APEXC machine takes the form of punched paper tape, which is read by a medium-speed tape-reader capable of absorbing up to 50 alphabetic characters per second. For convenience, the alphabetic code used in the linguistic applications is the international teletype code which has been described previously. This produces certain undesirable effects in complicating linguistic coding, but has the advantage that, in principle, any teletype equipment can be connected to the machine.

The machine itself is known as the two-address type, that is, each instruction which is stored, say, in storage position Y_1, contains a reference to a datum stored, say, in position X, and also to the position of the next instruction stored in position Y_2. The actual instructions available on the machine are given in Table 2.4. It will be seen that, among other provisions, are those for multiplication. This instruction has not so far found any application in linguistics and can be ignored for the present purpose. The instruction P or punch makes reference to the output organ of the machine, which takes the form of a medium-speed punching device capable of producing up to 25 alphabetic symbols per second on a paper tape. This tape can be read by conventional teletype apparatus and its contents typed out on a teleprinter. It may be mentioned that existing teleprinters are capable of producing only capital letters *or* lower case, so that the beginning of sentences and so on are in fact indicated, not by a capital letter, but by their coming either at the beginning of a text or after a full stop. The storage of APEXC takes the form of a magnetic drum, shown in *Figure 2.12*, p. 24. The capacity of this drum is 8,192 words, each composed of 32

Table 2.4
APEXC Order Code

Function	*Number*	C_6	*Space*	*Explanation*
Stop	0	—	—	—
Input	2	—	—	Read 5 digits from tape into first 5 places of Register. These places must be clear initially.
P	4	—	—	Punch first five digits of Register.
$B<(X)\geqslant(Y)$	6	—	None	If contents of $A<0$ go to (X) for text order, if $\geqslant 0$ go to (Y).
$l(n)$	8	n	1 loc $n\geqslant 32$ 2 locs $n<32$	Shift contents of A and R n places left. Most significant end of A transfers to least significant end of R and vice-versa.
$r(n)$	10	$64-n$	1 loc $n\leqslant 32$ 2 locs $n>32$	Shift contents of A and R n places right. Least significant end of A transfers to most significant end of R. Least significant end of R lost. Sign of A propagates.
$\times(n)$	14	$33-n$	max. $32+12$ min. $2+12$	Multiply by last n digits of R. Normally $n=32$ and C_6 is set to 1.
$+c$	16	—	None	Send contents of memory to cleared accumulator.
$-c$	18	—	None	Send $-M$ to cleared A.
$+$	20	—	None	Add to A.
$-$	22	—	None	Subtract from A.
T	24	—	None	Transfer from M to R.
$R(1-n)$	26	$32+n$	1 loc	Record first n digits of R in M.
$R(n-32)$	26	$n-1$	1 loc	Record digits n to 32 of R in M. R afterwards filled with sign digit of number.
$A(1-n)$	28	$32+n$	1 loc	Record first n digits of A in M.
$A(n-32)$	28	$n-1$	1 loc	Record digits n to 32 of A M.

Allow 6 locations for each track switch.
DIGITS. 1–10X, 11–20Y, 21–25 Function, 26–31 C_6, 31 Vector.

If the vector digit is 1, the order is repeated at each location on the track. Thus $A_v(31I16)$ will record the contents of A in every location of track 31.

binary digits. This means, in effect, that in each of the storage locations on the drum up to six alphabetic characters can be stored, and this implies that in operations on real language, where many words have more than six letters, several storage locations must be associated together to give an adequate representation of a given word. These and other points will receive more detailed attention in Chapter 3.

To clarify the way in which the instructions are used, the following notes deal with their precise functions in the machine and also show some typical applications.

The instruction word consists of 32 binary digits and has the following structure:

Digit	1------10	11------20	21------25	26------31	32
	x Address	y Address	Order code instruction	Counter	

The instruction word thus specifies two addresses, the first ten digits specify the position on the operand, that is the set of digits on which operations are performed, whilst the second ten specify the location of the next order. The instruction digits determine the precise instruction to be performed, and the counter digits pre-set the counter controls the number of shifts in the shift orders or the number of digits recorded in the partial record order.

Numerical data, on the other hand, are stored in pure binary form. Since the actual storage medium is the same for instructions and numbers, the numerical word is also composed of 32 binary digits, the first of which represents the sign, $0 = +$, $1 = -$. For the mathematical reader it may be mentioned that negative numbers are stored as complements modulo 2.

A 32-bit number may be staticized on the 'register' or the 'accumulator', each of which consists of 32 'flip-flops' to store the individual digits.

The following functions may be performed on APEXC:

1. *Left-shift*

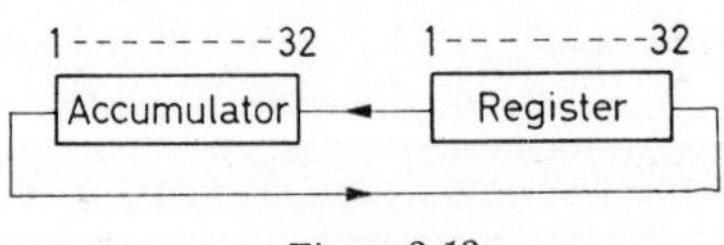

Figure 2.13

By means of this order the contents of the register and accumulator are shifted a certain number of places left, so that the n most significant digits of the accumulator become the n least significant digits of the register, and the first n digits of the register become the last n digits of the accumulator. In particular, the $n+1th$ digit of the accumulator appears in the first position, i.e. becomes the 'sign digit'. Thus no information is lost by this operation.

In constructing the programme this order is represented by '$l\,(n)(y)$', which is read as 'left-shift n places and go to address y for the next instruction'. The number of positions n shifted by the order is determined by the pre-set counter. If $n=63$, a right shift occurs without loss of information (*Figure 2.13*).

2. *Right shift*

Contents of the register and accumulator can be subjected to a right shift order. But here information is lost from the least

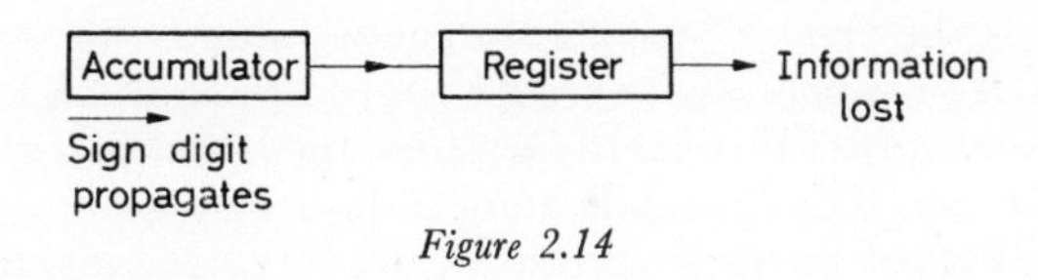

Figure 2.14

significant end of the register. The sign digit of the accumulator propagates, meaning that if the accumulator contains a negative number, then after the operation of a right-shift n places order, the first n digits of the accumulator are all ones. This instruction is symbolized by '$r(n)(y)$' (*Figure 2.14*).

3. *Transfer*

The function of a transfer order, symbolized by '$T(x)(y)$', is to transfer the contents of location x unaltered to the register (*Figure 2.15*).

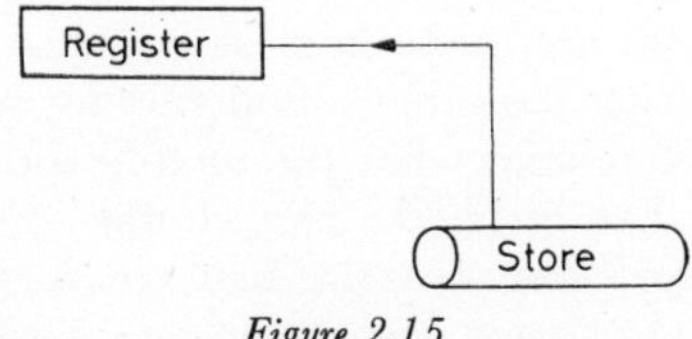

Figure 2.15

4. *Clear add, add, clear subtract, subtract*

The contents of any storage location may be added to or subtracted from the accumulator, which may first be cleared if desired. These instructions are symbolized by

$$+c(x)(y), \quad +(x)(y), \quad -c(x)(y), \quad -(x)(y).$$

The contents of location x remain unaltered after these operations (*Figure 2.16*)

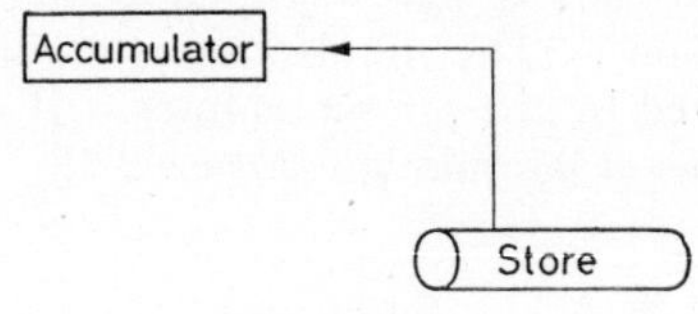

Figure 2.16

5. *Record from register or from accumulator*

The first n digits of either the register or the accumulator may be recorded in the first n digits of a storage location. These orders are represented symbolically by $R(1-n)(x)(y)$ and $A(1-n)(x)(y)$, respectively. After the record operation the remaining $32-n$ digits of x remain unchanged, and the state of the accumulator is unaltered. After the record operation from the register, the register is filled with 0s or 1s, according to whether the number in it was positive or negative.

Likewise, recording may be made from the least significant ends of the register or accumulator, and here we write $R(n-32)(x)(y)$, $A(n-32)(x)(y)$ to denote these operations (*Figure 2.17*).

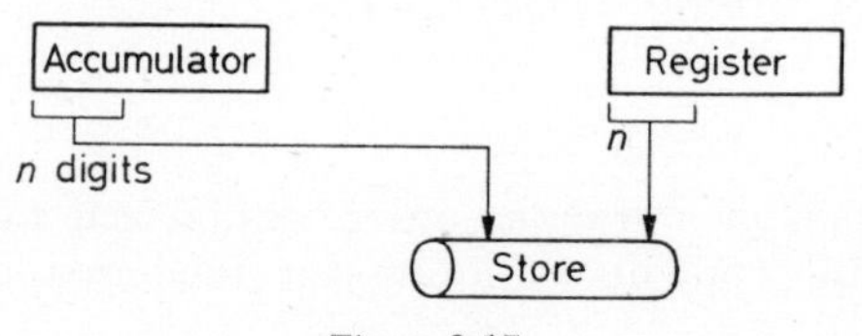

Figure 2.17

These instructions are useful in a programme where orders have to be modified during the course of operations, but where it cannot be determined beforehand what the modifications are to be. For instance, suppose that during the programme a number is generated in the accumulator, and that the first ten digits of this number specify the location of some corresponding information. Then the following instructions, beginning with the order in track t position 1 (i.e. $(t/1)$), place this information in the register

$$t/1: A(1-10)(t/2)(t/2)$$
$$t/2: T(\quad)(t/3)$$
$$t/3:$$

The first ten digits of A are thus substituted in the first ten digits positions of location $t/2$ to form the operand address of the order $T(\quad)(t/3)$.

6. *Branch*

This order is symbolized by '$B(x)(y)$', and means 'for the next instruction go to location x if the sign digit of the accumulator is a "1", and go to location y if it is a "0"'.

A branch order of some sort is a facility built into every automatic digital computor, and distinguishes it from a mere calculator. It enables a computor to perform a series of repetitive operations a predetermined number of times, or an indefinite number of times according to some programmed criterion, where the number of repetitions cannot be decided beforehand by the programmer. An example will illustrate a typical procedure. Suppose an operation J, the programme of which occupies locations $j/0 \ldots j/n$, is to be repeated 140 times. Let the last order of the operation be $R(j/x)(t/3)$. The programme starts by placing 139×2^{-31} in the accumulator. After each performance of J, 2^{-31} is subtracted, so that on the completion of the 140th operation the accumulator is negative, which by means of the branch order, effects a new sequence of orders, viz.:

$t/0$:	$+c(t/1)(t/2)$	Start: place 140×2^{-31} in $(t/4)$
$t/1$:	140×2^{-31}	
$t/2$:	$A(t/4)(j/0)$	
$j/0$:	....	Sequence of operations defining J.
j/n:	$R(j/x)(t/3)$	
$t/3$:	$+c(t/4)(t/5)$	
$t/4$:	Storage for count index.	
$t/5$:	$-(t/6)(t/7)$	
$t/6$:	2^{-31}	
$t/7$:	$B(p/0)(t/8)$	
$t/8$:	$A(t/4)(j/0)$	
$p/0$:	Start next part of programme.	

7. *Input*

The input to APEXC is by means of a punched tape. Each character on the tape has five digits and can thus represent in binary form any of the numbers 0 to 31. The five digits read from the tape are set up on the first five stages of the register, which has to be cleared before each new input.

8. *Print*

The print instruction actuates a mechanism which transforms the digits contained in the first five stages of the register into some kind of material representation. After this instruction has been performed, the digits in the register remain unchanged. There are two printing devices (*Figures 2.18 and 2.19*):

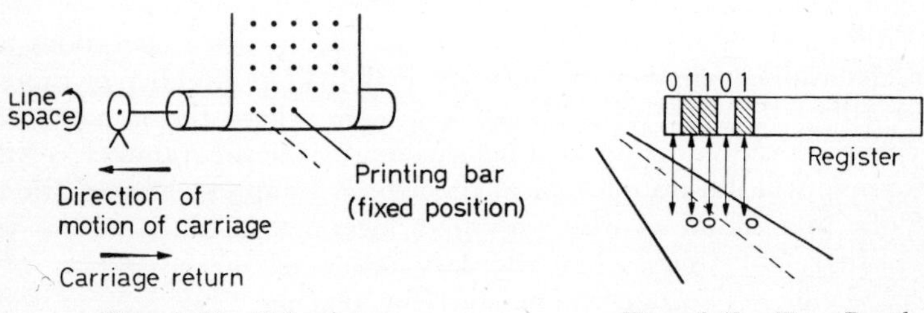

Figure 2.18. Teleprinter

Figure 2.19. Tape Punch

(i) *Tape-punch output*—The number in the first five register stages is here represented digit-wise by holes in a tape in the same manner as in the input tape.
(ii) *Teleprinter output*—For each of the 32 possible five-digit numbers in the five most significant stages of the register there is one distinct operation of the teleprinter. Two of the numbers pre-set the teleprinter so that it subsequently prints either numbers or letters. Another number returns the carriage to its initial position, while yet another moves the roller round one position, so that a new line is available for printing. Thus the teleprinter is able to print out, in any kind of array that may be desired, the numbers 0, 1, . . . 9, or the letters of the alphabet, as well as a few other symbols.

3

THE ANALYSIS OF CONTENT AND STRUCTURE

THE PROBLEM DEFINED

THE subjects covered in this chapter form a convenient way of introducing the idea of using machines for linguistic analysis. In principle the solution of any of these problems on a machine is extremely simple, but since the problems themselves are almost essential to the eventual discussion of machine translation of language, it is worth discussing the way in which a machine is used to solve them. In doing this it will be possible to illustrate various advantages and disadvantages of available machinery, and also to show how operations which have previously occupied considerable human time and effort are now brought within the field of completely mechanical activities.

The most elementary application of a machine is to the production of word counts. As an example, the analysis, by Handley and his associates, of James Joyce's 'Ulysses' may be mentioned. In this analysis, the 260,430 words contained in the text were analysed and shown to consist of 29,899 different words, whose number of occurrences was tabulated. A similar survey was conducted by Eldridge for United States newspapers. In this 43,989 words of texts were shown to be comprised of 6,002 different words.

In case it should be wondered what purpose is served by such an analysis, it may be mentioned that the two investigations just mentioned result in a vindication of the law of frequency first propounded by J. B. Estoup in 1916, but nowadays more usually known as Zipf's law, which is of fundamental importance when the detailed construction of machine dictionaries is considered. The Estoup–Zipf law may be stated simply as follows:

If in a large segment of text the different words are enumerated, and if after each different word the number of times which it occurs is recorded, then, supposing that these different words are arranged in order of occurrence starting from the most frequent word and proceeding to the least frequent, if the order of occurrence is called the rank R, then it has been shown that the product of the rank and the number of times of occurrence is very nearly constant.

For example, in the case of 'Ulysses', the product $R \times F$ is approximately equal to 26,000. The remarkable thing about this particular law is that it holds not only for 'Ulysses', which will be considered by many a highly non-typical work, but equally for the analysis of United States newspapers just mentioned and also for an analysis of Homer's 'Iliad'. This justifies the suggestion that the relationship be dignified by the name 'law'. It will be seen later that the technical means of making word counts of this sort are extremely simple.

The next analytic operation in order of complexity is the construction of a concordance. Concordances are of great antiquity, and everyone is probably familiar with Cruden's Concordance to the Bible and to various concordances to the works of Shakespeare. Essentially a concordance consists of one of two things: in its simpler form it is merely a list of the words contained in the text in alphabetical order, each word being accompanied by the page and line numbers for its occurrence. In the more complex form the words are reduced to basic types, so that, for example, all of the forms of the verb 'to have' would be entered under the same heading. Apart from this there is no difference. Naturally, for reasons of space, common structural words, such as 'have', 'be', 'run', 'to' and so on, are not entered in the corcordance, which merely consists of a list of those words which either have especial meaning in the text under consideration or, alternatively, are nouns and other special types of word. Concordances are of wide utility in various forms of basic linguistic study, as well as in the more sophisticated attempts at stylistic analysis which appear from time to time. In the past the construction of these works has been a lifetime occupation of the scholars making them. Nowadays, with the use of a machine it would be a relatively simple task to construct a concordance for a work the size of the Bible in a month or two.

The third machine application in order of complexity is that of constructing a dictionary of sentence structures. This has never been done on a large scale up to the present time, probably because of the extreme labour of carrying out the work manually. The importance of such analyses of structure is now becoming apparent when the programming of a machine for actual translation is considered. The amount of data which is available is pitifully limited, and it seems that only by turning machines to production of data for their own eventual consumption can any rapid progress be hoped for in the field of machine translation.

WORD COUNTING

The easiest method of counting the different words in a text is by means of a punched card installation. The method is as follows. A team of operators take the work to be analysed and punch each of the words contained in the text on a card. For reasons of economy, since most of the words have a length less than twenty letters, the eighty columns available on the card can be used for the storage of four text words. When cards containing all the text words have been prepared, they are taken to a sorting machine of the type described in the last chapter, and thus arranged in alphabetical order. The first stage is to examine the twentieth letter of each word, after a passage through the sorter, the packs of cards, each of which contains only cards having words ending in the same twentieth letter (if this exists), are arranged in order A, B, C, . . . Z, followed by cards having no twentieth letter. The process is now repeated on the nineteenth, and earlier letters until, at the last stage, when the first letter is considered, the final merging operation will produce a set of cards in which all of the words appear in alphabetic order in just the same way as they would be encountered in an ordinary dictionary. A simple example of this process is given in Table 3.1.

It is then only necessary for a human operator to count the number of cards containing the same word and to record words and numbers for the analysis to be complete. On the other hand, if it is desired to proceed in a purely mechanical way, the cards can be passed to a tabulating machine which is so plugged that it will accumulate the total number of cards for each word and print both words and totals in a list. Alternatively, one of the more complex sorters, which is capable of counting as well as sorting, can be put to use.

It was mentioned that to economize in cards more than one word might be recorded on each card. If this is done, it is necessary to complete the analysis of all first words on the cards and then to proceed to analyse the second, third and fourth. The results of all these analyses must then be merged into order by a later operation. It is apparent that the system in which one card is used for one word is more efficient if it is desired to conduct the whole of the analysis mechanically.

The disadvantage of using a punched card installation is threefold. In the first place the multiple punching which is required when alphabetic information is recorded on a card is a relatively slow operation; in the second place, the installations themselves are very expensive; and in the third place, the punched cards have a far from negligible cost. All of this is a consequence of using a machine

Table 3.1

An example of sorting by means of punched card machines

machines	punched	punched	punched	punched	example
an	machines	example	machines	card	means
example	example	machines	sorting	machines	machines
of	sorting	sorting	example	example	punched
sorting	an	an	means	means	card
by	of	of	an	sorting	sorting
means	by	by	of	an	an
of	means	means	by	of	of
punched	of	of	of	by	by
card	card	card	card	of	of
8th letter	7th letter	6th letter	5th letter	4th letter	3rd letter

machines	an	an	1
card	by	by	1
means	card	card	1
of	example	example	1
of	machines	machines	1
an	means	means	1
sorting	of	of	2
punched	of	punched	1
example	punched	sorting	1
by	sorting		
2nd letter	1st letter	Final frequency list	

designed essentially for non-alphabetic operations for the analysis of purely linguistic data.

The second method of word counting makes use of an automatic digital computing machine. It will be assumed for the purposes of the discussion, that the machine concerned is the APEXC, whose code was described in Chapter 2. For the first illustration the storage capacity which is available inside the machine is taken as infinite. It has already been stated that this is not true of any existing machine, but, since the availability of very large storage makes a direct solution of the word-count problem rather simple, this will be assumed. Available teletype equipment which would be used to produce a real punched tape of the text concerned has a code which is unsuitable for linguistic applications. There is no real difficulty in adapting the machine to deal with standard teletype code, but since this involves another step of translation in the process and this in turn would cloud the essential details which it is desired to illustrate, it will be assumed here that the teletype machine encodes letters in the simple form shown in Table 3.2. From the machine point of view each of these letters is encoded into a group of five binary digits, and this is particularly convenient when the

Table 3.2

Letter	*Fig.*	*Decimal*	*Binary*	*Letter*	*Fig.*	*Decimal*	*Binary*
Space		0	00000	P	0	16	10000
A	,	1	00001	Q	1	17	10001
B	;	2	00010	R	2	18	10010
C	:	3	00011	S	3	19	10011
D	.	4	00100	T	4	20	10100
E	?	5	00101	U	5	21	10101
F	!	6	00110	V	6	22	10110
G		7	00111	W	7	23	10111
H		8	01000	X	8	24	11000
I		9	01001	Y	9	25	11001
J		10	01010	Z		26	11010
K		11	01011	Line change		27	11011
L		12	01100	Page change		28	11100
M		13	01101			29	11101
N		14	01110	Letter shift		30	11110
O		15	01111	Figure shift		31	11111

numerical value of a word comes to be considered. If the ordinary decimal digits are used for the encoding, the difficulty arises that, when the letter J is reached, the decimal representation changes from a single digit, namely 9 for I, to two digits, 10 for J, 11 for K, and so on, and this would be rather inconvenient inside the machine. Using the five-binary digit representation, however, this change in digital representation of numbers does not occur, at least when there are less than 32 symbols. The text is typed onto a teletype tape in the same way as in producing an ordinary typescript. Letters are encoded by the depression of a normal typewriter key, full stops, commas, spaces and other punctuation marks are inserted in the usual way, but line space or carriage return symbols are omitted from the tape. It is not necessary in the simple counting application to insert page or line numbers.

When the tape has been prepared, it is presented to the reading device of the computing machine. It will be assumed from now on that some of the tape has already been processed by the machine and what happens when a new word is read to the machine will be examined. The machine, after reading each input character, has first to see if it indicates that the current word has ended. This it does by recognizing the occurrence of a punctuation mark or a space symbol. Any of these informs the machine that the word concerned has ended. How are these symbols to be recognized? It will be seen from Table 3.2 that they correspond to the binary numbers: space = 00000, , = 00001, ; = 00010, : = 00011, . = 00100, ? = 00101, ! = 00110. After each letter has been read at the input, the machine first tests for the space symbol. This is done by using the branch instruction to see if the code number is greater than or equal to zero. If so, 00001 is subtracted, whereupon the result becomes negative if the code number is actually zero, but not otherwise.

If the test for the space symbol is not satisfied, the machine next tests for one of the other punctuation symbols. This is done by observing that each is preceded by a Figure shift symbol (11111). The test for this is simple, since it is the only code number, the subtraction of (11111) from which will leave a positive or zero number. In the present application no interest attaches to the exact nature of the punctuation symbol, so the machine, after analysing the word just received, skips the next two characters (i.e. the punctuation mark and the Letter shift symbol which must follow it) and proceeds to the analysis of the next word. The actual programme for performing these operations is:

Assume that the characters just input are in the accumulator with the last character received occupying the five most significant binary digits.

(0)	$B \geqslant 0(1) < 0(6)$	
(1)	$-(2)(3)$	
(2)	(00001)	
(3)	$B \geqslant 0(4) < 0(10)$	
(4)	$+(2)(5)$	Restores the character to its original form since it was not (00000)
(5)	Start of feed operation for next character	

(6)	$-(7)(8)$	
(7)	(11111)	
(8)	$B \geqslant 0(11) < 0(9)$	
(9)	$+(7)(5)$	Restores the character to its original form since it was not (11111)
(10)	Character was (00000), i.e. space. Programme to deal with word starts here	
(11)	Character was (11111), i.e. Figure shift. Programme to deal with word starts here	

When all of the digits of a word have been assembled, they are assumed to be recorded in one of the storage locations of the machine.

The store of the machine which, as it was explained above, is considered for this purpose to be of effectively infinite extent, is at the present stage of the programme partially filled with the different words which have arisen in the text which has already been processed. Each computing machine word contains, first of all, the number representing in coded form the letters of the text word, followed by a second number which is a count of the number of times which the word has occurred up to date, as shown, for example, in Table 3.1. The numbers representing the words are assumed to be arranged in ascending order of magnitude starting from the first letter and working the end of the word. In this way the words stored will resemble an ordinary dictionary, starting with A, and finishing with Z.

When the new word has been received by the machine, it is subtracted from the first of the words already stored in the dictionary. Suppose, for example, that the word 'by' = 00010 11001 00000 . . . has been received, and that the words already stored in the dictionary are as follows:

	Code	*Count*
an	00001 01110 00000	00001
example	00101 11000 00001	00001
of	01111 00110 00000	00001
sorting	10011 01111 10010	00001

Subtraction of the unknown word will give a negative result for the first word in the dictionary. When subtracted from the second word, however, the result of the subtraction will become positive, so that the machine knows that the word just received has not previously occurred. The next operation is to start at the last word which has already been stored, in this case 'sorting', and to displace this by one place in the dictionary. This process will leave a spare space where 'sorting' originally occurred and this is now filled with the word 'of'. This displacement downward continues until space is made for the new word 'by' immediately following the word 'an'. When the word 'by' has been stored, unity is placed among the count digits of the storage position to indicate that it has so far been recognized just once. The machine storage is now as follows:

	Code				*Count*
an	00001	01110	00000	....	00001
by	00010	11001	00000	....	00001
example	00101	11000	00001	....	00001
of	01111	00110	00000	....	00001
sorting	10011	01111	10010	....	00001

This, then, is the process which is involved when a word not previously encountered is to be placed in the dictionary. Had the word 'by' already occurred, then it would have been found that a word existed for which the difference between the unknown word and the dictionary word was zero. In this event one would be added to the contents of the count position, thereby changing them to the new count number. For the sentence previously analysed the final analysis is:

	Code				*Count*
an	00001	01110	00000	......	00001
by	00010	11001	00000	......	00001
card	00011	00001	10010	......	00001
example	00101	11000	00001	......	00001
machines	01101	00001	00011	......	00001
means	01101	00101	00001	......	00001
of	01111	00110	00000	......	00010
punched	10000	10101	01110	......	00001
sorting	10011	01111	10010	......	00001

When all of the words from the text have been examined, the final part of the programme consists merely in having the machine type out the contents of all of those storage positions occupied, and in each case following the word typed by the count number contained in the same position.

In practice, not only has this programme the fault that it assumes the storage available to be infinite in extent, but also the method of examining each of the words in the dictionary in sequence is highly inefficient. A real programme to perform this operation would make use of the 'bracketing' procedure which is discussed in Chapter 6, but, to avoid complicating the matter at this point, it will be assumed that the process just described has been used.

When only limited space is available, other means must be adopted for the construction of the dictionary. In practice these resolve themselves into various methods of using the output mechanism of the main computing machine. It has been explained earlier that the machine can produce a tape in accord with numbers presented to the punching device by the programme. This leads to the idea that the tape output of the machine can be used as an auxiliary storage device, and, since tape is cheap, it can be considered to form a storage device which is not limited as is the internal store. There are several methods by which tape can be used in the word count problem, but probably the easiest is as follows: The machine examines the input text in just the same way as indicated above. In the present case, however, since the internal storage is limited, say, to N words, the programme proceeds as described above until the internal storage has been filled by the first N different words which have occurred in the text. At this point a further branch of the programme is brought into play, by which the mode of examination of the input text word is changed. If it has already occurred, it is located among the N entries in the machine's high speed store and one is added to the appropriate count number; but if it has not already occurred, the word is immediately recorded on the output tape and followed by a space symbol punching.

It is clear that when the whole of the input tape has been processed, the result will be a count for each of the first N different words which have been encountered, and associated with this will be an output tape which contains all of those words from the original text which have not so far been dealt with. At this point the contents of the dictionary of words stored in the machine is punched on a second output tape and this is kept for future use.

The output tape for those words not already dealt with is now reprocessed by exactly the same method, and the next group of N

different words is extracted. After a number of cycles of this process all of the original text will have been resolved, and a number of output tapes will be available, each of which contains N different text words with their count numbers arranged in alphabetical order.

The reprocessing of these tapes to form a final continuous tape in which all of the words occur in alphabetical order can again be performed in a number of ways, which depend upon the type of input facility which is available on the computing machine. If the machine has several input reading stations, it is possible to process, say, four of the tapes simultaneously. The first word is read from each of the four tapes and a comparison is made to see which of these words has the least numerical magnitude. The second word from the tape which gave rise to the least first word is now read and the magnitudes of the first words from the other tapes are compared with it. If none of these magnitudes is less than that of the second word the latter is punched out and the third word from its tape is obtained. This process continues until a word is found on the tape which is numerically greater than one of the three first words held in suspense. At this point the least of the remaining words is punched out and the next word on its tape of origin is read. The process now continues in exactly the same way as that described for the tape containing the initially least word. It will be clear that this process requires the storage of at most four words at any given time.

This process is repeated with groups of four tapes until all of the first tapes have been processed. The result is a set of one quarter the number of output tapes than there were tapes to start with, and the process is repeated until a single tape remains containing all of the words in order.

If only one input station is available a different technique must be adopted. Possibly the simplest is to read from the first of the primary tapes sufficient different words to half-fill the available storage capacity of the machine. The position reached is marked and the tape is then replaced by the second of the input tapes and from this sufficient words are read either to fill the available internal storage completely or until a word is encountered which exceeds, in numerical magnitude, the last word obtained from the first tape. The count numbers of these words are either amalgamated with those of words from the first tape, or alternatively, positioned so as to make the entries in the store occur in alphabetic order in the way described previously. When this operation is complete, a new output tape is produced containing these words. A repetition of the process will result eventually in the production of a single tape containing all of the input information arranged in alphabetic order.

THE CONCORDANCE

The next linguistic operation in order of sophistication, which can be performed either by punched card accounting machinery or by means of an all-purpose digital computer, is the construction of various forms of concordance. Just as was the case with word counts, from the conceptual point of view it is easier to see how punched card machinery can be used to produce the desired concordance. The basic data is exactly that for the word-count problem, except that in preparing the text it is necessary not merely to record the words but also the page and line of occurrence of each word. There is ample space available on a card for this data, although it is probable that only three words could be punched on each card instead of the four which were possible when words only had to be recorded. The basic operation of concordance making is again the arrangement of the text into alphabetical order so that each time a given word occurs all of the cards bearing that word find themselves associated together in a group in the finally arranged pack. Furthermore by continuing the sorting operation, which was described in the discussion of word counting, to include the ordering not only into alphabetical order but also into order of page and line numbers within that alphabetic configuration, exactly the same output printing routine as was used to give the word count will give the concordance. Various technical points may be mentioned. For example, if the tabulator is used to produce the eventual list of words, it will be desirable, not only for speed and economy but also for general intelligibility of the output, to type the word only at the start of each group of page and line references, and not to have the word accompanying each of these references. This can be achieved quite simply on an ordinary tabulator by arranging for what is known as a 'change of control' to take place only when the word changes from one card to the next and in this event, but not otherwise, for the alphabetic contents of the next card to be printed.

It will be realized that if a concordance is made containing all of the words in any given text, a very large proportion of these will be such uninteresting words as 'a', 'as', 'be', 'to', 'have', 'saw', and so on, that is, words of ordinary usage which are, generally speaking, of no interest whatever to the scholar, who perhaps in a Shakespeare text wishes to know who said 'A plague o' these pickle-herring!'. For this reason concordances list not all of the words in the given text but only those words not included in, say, the first hundred most frequent words. An application of the Estoup–Zipf law shows that the use of such a criterion will greatly lessen the number of references which are required following each word. To take the example which was given in the opening section of this chapter, it can be seen that in Joyce's 'Ulysses', the most frequent word would occur some 26,000 times whereas the thousandth most frequent word would only occur twenty-six times, and, whilst the typing-out of 26 entries following a given word is eminently practical, the typing-out of 26,000 entries is quite beyond the realms either of possibility or of interest. For this reason, if a concordance is being made by the punched card technique, and if it is known in advance that the data will never be required for the construction of word counts, at least for the more frequent words, then an overall instruction could be given to the people preparing the punched cards that they are to ignore any words occurring in a selected list.

When the preparation of a concordance on a digital computer is considered, the programme required for word counting needs little alteration. Supposing that infinite storage facilities are available, the whole operation can be performed within the computer in one run of the input tape. In this case, however, a slight difference occurs in the actual constitution of the input tape itself. The machine must have a knowledge of the page and line numbers of the words as they arise. This can be done in a number of ways, for example, it is possible to punch on the tape, following each word, the page and line number of its occurrence. This would involve a vast amount of extra work, as can be seen if 'Ulysses' were being prepared, with over 250,000 words, 500,000 extra words defining page and line numbers would be required. A more satisfactory technique is to arrange that a symbol is typed at the start of each page, and similarly at the end of each line, to indicate that a change of page has occurred. From these symbols, which are identical for all pages and lines, the machine calculates by a simple process of addition the position which the tape has reached, e.g. if 100 page-change symbols have occurred, the word under examination would be found on page 101. Similarly, if the current line symbol which, incidentally, is reset to unity each time a page change occurs, is now 26, it is known that the given word is on line 26. The use of this technique means that with a work such as 'Ulysses' (assuming that a normal page contains about 250 words, so that the book is 1,000 pages long) only 1,000 page-change symbols would be written and about 30,000 line-change symbols. This is an enormous decrease over the 500,000 which would be required if the other method was used.

A schematic idea of the way in which the programme works is as follows:

1. Machine examines current symbol. If this is an alphabetic character, it reads in the next character from the tape.

2. When a non-alphabetic symbol is reached, if it is a space, the complete word is compared with the words already in the store, its position is located, and it is found either that it has occurred already or that it is a new word. In the former event, the page- and line-count numbers, which are held elsewhere in the storage organ, are inserted into a vacant space in the location which is already holding that particular word. If this is the first occurrence of the word, it is inserted in the appropriate memory space, all following words being displaced by one position. After the word has been placed, the page and line reference are inserted after it.

3. When a line end symbol is detected unity is added to the line number count held in the store.

4. When a page end symbol is detected the line count number is reset to unity and the page number count is augmented by unity.

It will be noticed that, since the word length in most computing machines is between 30 and 40 binary digits, that is, between six and eight alphabetic symbols, more than one computer word will usually have to be taken to represent a text word and its associated concordance data. This is not difficult to arrange and between four and eight computer words will usually suffice.

When the whole of the text has been processed, it is merely necessary to produce an output tape which contains the contents of the machine's store. This will give, in alphabetical order, the words of the text followed by the page and line references of their place of occurrence. When the machine is used in this way, it is easy to delete the most frequent words in the text, if this is desired. Several methods may be adopted. In the first a word-count is kept as the input tape is processed. When the whole of the text has been analysed, the word-count numbers are examined, and the most frequent words are detected and rejected. An alternative method of achieving the same result is to allocate a definite number of storage locations for the word and for its page and line references, and to arrange for the machine to detect when the number of these references exceeds the available storage space allocated to given word. This would mean that any word which occurs more than a certain number of times would only be accompanied by the first few references to its occurrence. Or again, any set of locations, known to be full, might be deleted before the final record is produced. An added sophistication would be to output, say, the first dozen occurrences of a frequent word and also the total number of its occurrences in the whole text. This would serve the two-fold purpose of giving a word count and making the output of the machine small enough in volume to be comprehensible to a human being.

One point should be mentioned in connection with this programme, that is, the way by which a machine can detect the various symbols. In discussing the problem of word counting, a simple programme was given which applied when only three classes of symbol were involved. This method demands the use of a number of computer instructions for each examination of the input character. A easier way, which is not only quicker and saving in storage space, but also is better applicable when large numbers of different characters have to be detected individually, is by means of what is termed the 'partial substitution facility' of the machine. Instructions number 13 and 14 of the typical instruction set of APEXC given in the previous chapter were shown to imply the possibility of replacing part of a computing machine word by part of a word held in the machine's accumulator or register. A normal machine instruction for APEXC takes the form:

Perform operation (0) on the word in position (x) and proceed to the word in position (y) for the next instruction.
The branch instruction is of the form:

Proceed to the position (x), if the number in the accumulator is negative, but to the position (y), if it is zero or positive.

To detect the presence of one of a selected group of characters, the unknown character can be substituted in the digits of the (x) location of a conditional transfer instruction by means of the partial record order $A(1\text{–}5)$. Remembering the binary equivalents for page and line, given in Table 3.2, those storage locations bearing the numbers of any of the 26 characters which are not page, line, punctuation or space symbols, contain instructions which lead directly back to the programme. In any position, however, there is recorded the first instruction of the sequence of operations required by that symbol. For example, suppose that the symbol $(11100) = 28$ occurs, the programme followed is then:

(0) $A(1\text{–}5)(1)(2)$
(1) $B \geqslant (y) < (28 = 11100$ substituted by $(0))$
(2) $+c(3)(1)$ (sets accumulator to negative value)
(3) 1000 ......
(28) Starting order of programme resetting line count to unity and augmenting page number by one.

It is clear that there is no particular difficulty or complexity about operations of this sort.

It was mentioned that there are two forms of concordance. That just described is the simple one, in which words are treated as different, even though they are derived from the same stem. The more comprehensive form of concordance treats variants of any word as one for the purpose of referencing and counting. Here again, once the rules have been formulated, there is no particular difficulty in carrying out the operation, although, since a special dictionary will be required for the more exotic words, it may be ncccssary to carry out a preliminary analysis of the text.

ANALYSIS OF SENTENCE STRUCTURE

The most difficult operation which the machine may be called upon to perform is the production of a dictionary of the sentence structures involved in a given text. This problem is one of greater difficulty than either of the ones just described. The problem may be stated as follows. Given any sentence or any portion of a sentence, defined by its inclusion between specific words or specific punctuation or space marks, it is required either to decide whether the grammatical structure within that sentence falls into one of a given set of groups or, alternatively, to list those different sentence structures which occur within a given text. Effectively, this means that the machine must be capable of passing the entire content of a book, considered in small units, and then of making an analysis of the different part of speech orders which occur in that text. The first problem which occurs here is that of identifying the part of speech of the word concerned. Two methods are available; in the first, each word is accompanied on the input tape by an indication of its part of speech. This, of course, implies that the person producing the tape is not only a competent typist but also a master of the language and of the particular grammar concerned: it is not, quite clearly, an operation for an unschooled typist. The second method implies that some form of dictionary is available which contains all of the words which are going to occur in the text under analysis. The dictionary entries bear alongside them an indication of the part of speech each usually represents. Since the use of dictionaries is properly a function of machine translation of language and will be dealt with in Chapter 6, this method of performing the operation will be ignored for the present. We shall indicate how the dictionary may be incorporated into the scheme of things, but we shall not consider in any detail at all the actual means of its operation.

Suppose that a text has been prepared in which, apart from page and line numbers, which are generated in the same way as for a concordance, there are available, following each word, indications of the function of that word in the sentence. It is required to make an analysis of sentence structures as the tape is processed through the machine assuming that the whole of the analysis can be conducted within the high-speed storage organ of the machine. The method of operation is this: The machine reads in the words one at a time, using the same technique as that discussed previously. After each word it reads in the grammatical symbol accompanying that word. As the words appear, the grammatical symbols are assembled in order, and, since these consist of single letters, say, N, V, A, P, and so on, they may be considered to comprise a new word, which defines the sentence structure. The letters of these sentence-structure words are assembled so long as the words in the text are not separated by a punctuation symbol. When a full stop symbol occurs, it indicates that the particular structural group is at an end and that the structure word is now complete. This structure word is now compared with those structure words already held in the dictionary of structures which is being assembled. The programme for doing this is identical with that discussed under word-counting and concordance making, and the result is, that if the particular structure has been previously encountered, one is added to the count number under that structure and possibly a page and line reference is given if the structure analysis is of the concordance type. If the structure word has not been previously encountered, succeeding words are displaced by one position and the new word is written in the dictionary. This process is continued until the end of the text, at which point the structure words with their concordance or frequency data are output in the usual way.

This is the most elementary form of sentence structure analysis which can be performed on a machine. It is sometimes of more use to the linguist if the machine can produce a list of all of those sentences which have given structure in the text. Since whole sentences are involved, and the text may contain many such sentences, it will often happen that the whole of the output cannot be contained within the machine's high-speed store at a given time. In this event it is possible to make use of the output tape-producing mechanism to facilitate the operation of this particular type of analysis.

This is the method which is adopted*: The input tape is fed to the

* *Note:* A preliminary account of work on these lines, carried out on the American machine *SEAC,* has appeared in *Computers & Automation,* 6 (1957), 15.

machine. As the words between a pair of punctuation or other marks are received, they are immediately punched on an output tape in the order in which they arise. At the same time as they are being punched out the structure word is being assembled in the machine. When the group of words is complete, this structure word is compared with the structure word of the desired sentence form, and, if these prove to be identical, a double punctuation mark is inserted on the output tape. If, on the other hand, the sentence is not of the required structure, only a single punctuation mark is output. This process continues until all of the input text tape has been so treated. It is evident that the result of this operation is to produce a tape which is identical with the input tape with the exception that each sentence whose structure of the type desired is followed by a double punctuation mark.

When this second tape has been prepared, it is now fed to the machine again, but this time in the reverse direction, that is starting from the last letter of the last word of the text and proceeding to the beginning. As this occurs, it is evident that a double punctuation mark now precedes each sentence structure of the type required. The machine reads the tape and sees if any punctuation mark is doubled. If so, the succeeding words are punched out with their letters in reverse order, on the output tape, until the next punctuation mark is reached. This process is continued until the end of the input tape, and it is clear that an output tape is produced which contains only structures of the given type, but in reverse order. Fortunately, it is possible to insert a tape into a teletype reader for reproduction, either forwards or backwards, and the tape which has just been prepared in reverse order is now inserted, again in reverse, into a normal teletype reading and printing apparatus. The effect is thus to type out the given sentence structures in their normal letter and word order.

An exactly similar type of analysis can be applied to the detection of specific words or specific word forms, if an analysis of this type is required, but enough has been said to show the way in which a programme of this sort works.

4

STYLISTIC ANALYSIS

INTRODUCTION

THE applications of stylistic analysis are fairly numerous. There are, to mention but a few, the analysis designed to determine the authenticity of a work or by whom a work was written in a case of disputed authorship, that for tracing the development of a particular style (e.g. the historical, the philosophical, the scientific etc.) over a certain period of time, that which by referring to the results of an analysis of the preceding type assigns an approximate date of composition to works that are anonymous or whose author is otherwise unknown, and that which examines the styles of several contemporary authors and determines the extent of their influence on one another.

All investigations of this type are devoted to the literary styles of the famous or at least well-known authors of the past. Nowadays, however, it is not so much the styles of individual authors that need to be investigated as the styles employed in different circles; for example, the style—now almost traditional—of scientific literature (which can again be divided into the various forms recognized by the different departments), of the journalistic world, the parliamentary, and even UNESCO, which though founded comparatively recently has already begun to betray a style of its own in publications. Each, in short, has developed its style to suit its own needs, and if mechanical translation is to fulfil its function of making international communication quicker and surer, it must necessarily be able to deal adequately with the idiosyncrasies of these various styles.

PLATONIC CHRONOLOGY

With the present-day side of the subject, however, we do not intend to concern ourselves here, but having acknowledged its existence return instead to the past, to Greece in the fourth century B.C. and the writings of the philosopher Plato. In this chapter Plato's style, or rather the investigations made in connection with it by modern scholars, will be discussed with the idea of showing that the same and much more extensive investigations can be carried out with increased speed and accuracy through the aid of an electronic computer.

As one of the greatest figures in the history of philosophy, whose influence in this sphere extends right up to the present day, interest in Plato and his doctrines needs no apology. But when we read Plato in order to discover the nature of his philosophy, we receive something of a surprise: the three dozen or so works attributed to him (generally known as 'dialogues' from the manner of presentation of the argument in the majority of them, this taking the form of a conversation between two or more persons) reveal a variety of doctrines that are far from homogeneous and in some instances definitely irreconcilable with one another. That this is due in the main to a continuous development and consequent alteration of Plato's beliefs during his long life (he lived to the age of 80 years, of which probably between 50 and 60 were devoted to philosophy) cannot be doubted; whether it is entirely so, however, is debatable; other causes could have played a part, but these need not trouble us here. In order to understand the nature of this development, it is clearly necessary to know in what order the dialogues were written—which are early and which late, which present his early philosophical beliefs and which his mature doctrines.

Determining the order in which Plato wrote his works is a problem which has faced scholars ever since interest in his philosophy was renewed after the Renaissance. To begin with they had very little to go on, hardly any indications of the chronological sequence having been handed down from antiquity, and practically the only reliable piece of information being a statement by Plato's pupil, the philosopher Aristotle, that the 'Laws' (the largest work) is later than the 'Republic' (the second largest work). This is confirmed by two later authorities, both of whom add the further tradition that the 'Laws' was published posthumously by one of Plato's disciples. The only other clue that can be trusted, an internal one in this case, is a fairly definite reference in one of the dialogues to an event which occurred when Plato was about forty, and the nature of the reference makes it likely that the event was still of recent occurrence when the work was published.

With so little known for certain and so much to be found out the scholars set about arranging the dialogues in order. Various methods were employed, various 'leading' principles postulated, but all investigations were based ultimately on a consideration of the doctrine expounded in each dialogue and the individual's opinion of the position this doctrine might have been expected to occupy in the progress of Plato's philosophical career. A discussion of the relative merits and demerits of these investigations is unnecessary; it is sufficient to observe that this method of deducing the chronological order of Plato's dialogues more or less condemned itself by the contradictory results it produced.

The problem did not finally begin to resolve itself until 1867, when a Scottish scholar named Lewis Campbell introduced what has since come to be known as the stylistic method*. Taking as given the fact that the 'Laws' was, if not the last, one of the last works written by Plato, Campbell compared the vocabulary of technical words (i.e. those characteristic of philosophical argument) in each dialogue with the vocabulary of the 'Laws', and by the degree of approximation of each—allowing for accidental influences, of course—succeeded in demonstrating the close affinity of five other works to the 'Laws'.

The significance of Campbell's investigation was never appreciated by English scholars, and did not become known on the Continent until 1896, by which time the stylistic method had been 'discovered' anew. Its author this time was a German scholar, W. Dittenberger†. Devoting his attention not to the technical vocabulary but to certain everyday words, particularly pairs of synonyms, he found that

(*a*) some words occurred in one group of the works but not in the other,

(*b*) one of a pair of synonyms was used in one group of works, the other in the other group,

(*c*) these two groups were clearly distinguished by several different criteria.

Dittenberger concluded that the group including the 'Laws' was the later, the other works the earlier in composition. This was not all, however; other criteria were present in some works in the later group, but not in others, indicating a chronological distinction here too. Thus there were three groups in all, early, middle, and late, and though Dittenberger did not know it, his late group of six dialogues including the 'Laws' was exactly the same as that arrived at by Campbell.

Though the works had been successfully divided into three

* In the introduction to his edition of the 'Sophistes and Politicus'.

† 'Sprachliche Kriterien für die Chronologie der Platonischen Dialoge', Hermes XVI, p. 321.

distinct chronological groups, however, the correct sequence of the works within each of these groups was not yet known, and it was with a view to ascertaining something about this that several other German scholars attacked the problem in what might be termed a period of comparative enthusiasm lasting from 1881 to 1914. The majority followed in Dittenberger's footsteps and devoted their attention to various words, usually the less significant parts of speech such as adverbs, conjunctions and particles, which appeared to them to change greatly in their frequency from one work or set of works to another. Others gave their research a broader basis and examined classes of adjectives, the prepositions used by Plato, the rhythm of his prose. In all some 20 stylistic investigations were carried out by nearly as many scholars, mostly German, during the latter part of the 19th and beginning of the 20th century. The state of affairs when World War I ended the activity was that the 35 dialogues had been divided quite irrefutably into three chronological groups—the members being for the most part, but not entirely, the same as those resulting from Dittenberger's original investigation—but as for the sequence within these groups, while that of the last was reasonably certain, those of the middle and earlier were by no means so, except perhaps for a few dialogues in the earlier group which were generally recognized as closer to the middle group than the rest.

After the war interest in the subject never really revived, probably because of the stylistic method's failure to produce further striking results after its great initial success, and because the general division into three periods seemed adequate for a correct interpretation of the development of Plato's doctrines. Whatever the cause, only three or four investigations were carried out after the war, the last in 1935*; and these did not succeed in making much progress, so that our knowledge of the order in which Plato's works were written is much the same today as it was 40 years ago.

The success of the stylistic as compared with other methods has been great, but not great enough. To discover the reason why this should be so, we need to consider the facts about Plato's style reflected by the statistics published with the accounts of the above investigations. These show that up to the age of about fifty Plato wrote in a style which, if it changed at all, did so in such a slight degree and so haphazardly that the inquiring scholars could detect no definite trends. After this time, however, there are certain changes—as yet slight, but nevertheless recognizable—in his style

* Constantin Ritter, 'Unterabteilungen innerhalb der zeitlich ersten Gruppe platonischen Schriften', Hermes LXX, pp. 1–30.

leading up to a strange phenomenon which we may guess occurred when he was about sixty. At this age his style altered suddenly, deliberately, and completely. It was this feature which enabled the investigators to distinguish at once six works from the rest, simply because the style in these six bore not the slightest resemblance to that of the earlier works—it might in fact have been mistaken for that of another man.

The style in which a person writes is a personal characteristic, and he can be identified by it just as surely as by his fingerprints, provided that he does not deliberately set out to disguise it. Generally speaking, being unconscious of his style, he naturally makes no attempt to alter it, though it may be altered for him by the spoken and written styles of other people. Such alterations, however, are slight, being detectable only by their cumulative effect over what is in most cases a longish period, and apply mainly to the choice of vocabulary. A complete change of style, on the other hand, means a deliberately conceived and systematically carried out plan to remove all previous characteristics and replace them with new ones. This was exactly what Plato did. For some reason he abandoned the style which has since come to be regarded as one of the very best models of Greek prose and fashioned an artificial and totally inferior one on the basis laid down by the teacher of rhetoric, Isocrates. It was this artificiality which made the determination of the chronological sequence with the last group of works easier, inasmuch as the works written immediately after the change-over did not conform to Isocrates' rhetorical rules of smooth balance and precision in sentence structure as closely as did those written some time after.

Although the progressive perfection of the artificial mode provided a criterion lacking in Plato's earlier, natural style, there is no reason for assuming that no changes occurred in the latter. That they have so far remained undetected in the majority of the works concerned may be adduced by the fact that almost all the investigations made have been directed towards discovering changes in vocabulary in one form or another, and in this they have erred in one of two ways: either they have taken as their material the technical vocabulary, which is unsatisfactory because of the danger of changes in it being due not to a change of style but one of subject-matter, or having taken the common vocabulary have examined only a limited number of words instead of the whole body.

Vocabulary changes are in any case major changes, and these, as we have already remarked, are hardly likely to occur quickly or markedly enough in the natural development of a person's literary style to distinguish one work from the next in order of composition. There are, however, other more subtle aspects of style in which changes may take place without any alteration in the vocabulary; for example, the structure of sentences and the order of words within clauses. An investigation into the nature of these would have the further advantage of producing statistics not only much larger, but also—because such an investigation would be applicable to all works alike—more universal than those obtained in the past. On the other hand these would certainly be so copious as to require an index system to maintain a steady rate of progress. It is in counteracting this difficulty that an electronic computer can be of use, as it can in other respects as well. For, whereas previously, when the method of recording information was to read through the works and jot down the occurrences of the various stylistic features under investigation on separate pieces of paper, there was a limit to the number of features that could be investigated at once, because if too many were chosen some occurrences would inevitably be missed on account of the mind's inability to remember all the features for which it was supposed to be looking, by using an electronic computer a complete analysis of as many features as are desired becomes possible, because the mind can concentrate on the analysis, leaving the recording routine to the machine.

The scheme visualized for an analysis of Plato's style with the help of an electronic computer would deal with three main aspects, namely lexicography, rhythm and syntax.

LEXICOGRAPHY

The first information which must be put on the tape for the machine to store is a verbatim reproduction of the entire Greek text. This would apparently at once permit vocabulary investigations of all types to be carried out, but before this is possible two difficulties have to be overcome. Firstly, the computer will be unable to recognize that inflected forms are merely different forms of one and the same word; secondly it will be unable to make any distinction between the different meanings which a word may have in different contexts. The solution to the first problem is either to calculate the frequency of each inflected form separately and have the human operator combine them under one lexical item at the end, or to include on the tape along with the inflected form actually occurring in the text the lexicon form of the word, where the former differs from this. The solution to the second is to see that any word which may have more than one meaning has its meaning in the context concerned indicated either indirectly by some symbol or directly by inclusion on the tape of its English translation.

Though from this information the computer will be able to supply the statistics of Plato's vocabulary, the actual interpretation of them must be left to the human operator, who can eliminate those where changes are likely to be due to influences other than stylistic (e.g. change of subject matter or the satirical mimicry of other authors' styles to which Plato was occasionally prone). For the purpose of enabling the investigator to locate, whenever necessary, the context of any word, the page numbers of whatever edition is being used can be fed to the machine along with the text.

Finally, before passing on to consider the next aspect of style, it may be noted that the information entered on the punched tape up to this stage is sufficient for producing an index or lexicon either of the works as a whole or individual dialogues. Obtaining the index would be an easy task, but the lexicon would pose quite a few problems of programming, involving as it does adequate indication of the contexts in which the various meanings of a word occur, syntactical constructions, and so on.

RHYTHM

For practical purposes rhythm in Attic Greek can be regarded as simply the collocation of long and short syllables in such a way as to form set patterns, the units of which—if there are distinct units—may or may not coincide with the word units. Past investigations of rhythm in Plato's prose* have been devoted to the clausula only, that is the four or five syllables at the end of each clause or sentence. These investigations have shown that, when Plato made the great alteration in his style, he altered the rhythm of his prose as well as its other aspects. In his last four works he accepted the rhythms recommended by the school of rhetoric and applied them with increasing strictness, with the result that, whereas previously no particular rhythms had predominated to any great extent in his style, and certainly not enough to justify regarding it as a favourite rhythm, in each of these four works four basic rhythms constituted between 70 and 80% of all clausula rhythms. It would seem from this that Plato was not rhythm conscious up till the change-over, since if an author is concerned with the rhythm of his sentences this concern betrays itself in the part of the sentence where rhythm makes the greatest impression—at the end. On the other hand there is

* e.g., L. Billig, 'Clausulae and Platonic Chronology', *Journal of Philology*, 1920, pp. 989 ff.

the possibility (one is tempted to say certainty) that his feelings for rhythm did change to some extent during the period from his twentieth to sixtieth year, and this being so, there is also the possibility that the changes could be brought to light by an investigation on a somewhat larger scale than those carried out hitherto. After all, the only reason for limiting those to the last five syllables of each clause was the investigator's opinion—an opinion with which the present author would from personal experience readily concur—that while classifying all the clausula rhythms in Plato into the 32 categories available by permutation of the five syllables was a reasonably manageable scheme for onc pcrson, morc (addition of one syllable doubling the number of categories) would have led to difficulties. Since, however, the classification can now comfortably be left to the computer, an investigation of rhythms at the beginning and within the body of the sentence or clause as well as at the end becomes practicable. All that is necessary is to ensure that the computer is supplied with correct information, which in this case means information about the value of each syllable—whether it is long or whether it is short. It is here that the difficulties arise.

If the usual rules of Greek verse are accepted as valid for prose too, every type of syllable can be defined as long (containing a long vowel or a short vowel followed by two consonants) or short (containing a short vowel not followed by two consonants) with the following exceptions:

(*a*) A vowel short by nature occurring at the beginning of or within a word and followed by two consonants, one mute, the other liquid.

(*b*) A vowel short by nature occurring at the end of a word and followed by two consonants, one mute, the other liquid at the beginning of the next word.

(*c*) A vowel short by nature occurring at the end of a word and followed either by two consonants other than mute and liquid or by the letter *rho* at the beginning of the next word.

(*d*) A vowel long by nature occurring at the end of a word and followed by a word beginning with a vowel.

In verse the first of these can be either long or short, its value in the particular context at hand being determined by the metre and the position in which it is used. The same is true of the second and third types, though the former would normally remain short and the latter be lengthened. The fourth would not be regular in Attic Greek (the dialect of Plato), but in the language of Homer, where it is, the long vowel is usually shortened before the succeeding one, and previous investigations have shown that this may be a feature of Plato's prose as well. Since, however, there is some doubt about this and about the other three types, the value of the syllable in all four cases must be regarded as an unknown quantity for the purpose of an investigation directed towards discovering whether there are any specially favoured metres in Plato's prose, and if so, what these are.

In addition to the values of the syllables a distinction in their position is also essential. It is not possible for the writer to alter the value of a syllable within a word, so that, if it does not suit the rhythm which he has in mind, he must choose a different word. Whether we can hope to detect where this has actually happened is doubtful, but if it should be possible, it will result from a comparison of the rhythmical and lexicographical statistics. The value of a syllable at the end of a word, on the other hand, can be altered in most instances simply by the choice of an appropriate succeeding word, and since for metrical purposes there are only three kinds of succeeding word (i.e. according to whether it begins with a vowel, with one consonant, or with two consonants), the requisite rhythm can almost always be obtained solely by rearrangement of the words which the writer already has in mind. This in itself makes the latter device easier to detect than that depending on the choice of words: it can be found in profusion in the 'Laws', for instance, where the author's desire to maintain a stereotyped set of rhythms often leads to excessive hyperbata.

Besides between a syllable at the beginning of or within a word and one at the end it may also be advisable to distinguish between a syllable at the end of a word within a sentence and a syllable at the end of the final word in the sentence. Considering that Plato avoided hiatus (the juxtaposition of a word ending in a vowel with one beginning with a vowel) in the latter position as much as anywhere else, such a distinction might seem superfluous. And indeed, if he felt that there was no break in speech between the end of one sentence and the beginning of another for the purposes of hiatus, it would be inconsistent to assume that he did not have the same attitude for metrical purposes. At the same time, however, it should not be forgotten that Plato's prose rhythm was subjected to the same drastic change as the rest of his style, and the avoidance of hiatus together with other features of Isocrates belongs only to the period after this change. It is quite likely, moreover, that not only his actual rhythms changed under Isocrates' influence, but also his principles of rhythm. For this reason it would be as well to make the distinction mentioned.

Lastly, several other characteristics of rhythm must be taken into consideration, such as the gratuitous insertion of *nu ephelkystikon*, *elision*, and perhaps *prodelision* and *crasis**.

All these devices may be used for the purposes of creating specific rhythms, so that by comparing the various instances, which in the case of the first two are very frequent, certain conclusions may be drawn about the writer's rhythmical preferences and dislikes.

For a mechanical analysis of prose–rhythm, then, we require about 30 different symbols for representing the following items on the tape to be fed into the computer:

A. Syllable at beginning of or within word:

1. vowel naturally short – short
2. vowel naturally long or lengthened by position – long
3. vowel naturally short before mute + liquid – doubtful

B. Syllable at end of word within sentence:

1. ending in short vowel, vowel opening next word – short
2. ending in short vowel, single consonant opening next word – short
3. ending in short vowel, double consonant (mute + liquid) – dubious
4. ending in short vowel, double consonant (not mute + liquid) – dubious
5. ending in short vowel + consonant, vowel opening next word – short
6. ending in short vowel + consonant, consonant opening next word – long
7. ending in long vowel, vowel opening next word – dubious
8. ending in long vowel, consonant opening next word – long
9. ending in long vowel + consonant, opening of next word irrelevant – long

* NOTE: *Nu ephelkystikon* is the use of the consonant *nu* to prevent a hiatus, the *nu* being attached to the end of the word ending in a vowel. This is a regular feature of the language. Its use becomes gratuitous when there is no hiatus to be avoided, that is, when the following word does not begin with a vowel, in which case it can only be used to lengthen the short vowel by placing two consonants after it instead of one. *Elision* is the opposite method to the preceding for avoiding a hiatus; instead of having a consonant suffixed, the vowel at the end is omitted. *Prodelision* is similar, but in this case it is the vowel at the beginning of the following word that is omitted. *Crasis* is the fusion of certain pairs of vowels, thus combining two words into one.

C. Syllable at end of final word in sentence: repeat B. 1–9.

D. (*a*) *Elision* of (i) α, (ii) ϵ, (iii) ι, (iv) ο, (in addition possibly several symbols will be necessary to denote the *elision* of long vowels or diphthongs, e.g. Philebus 38b *γίγνεθ' ἑκάστοτε* (the reading adopted by Burnet).

(*b*) Gratuitous insertion of *nu ephelkystikon* (i) at end of a word within the sentence (ii) at end of the final word of the sentence.

(*c*) *Prodelision* of ϵ.

(*d*) Symbol indicating that a syllable is a *crasis*.

SYNTAX

The investigation of the last of these main aspects of literary style involves progressively more detailed analysis of the basic syntactical structure, the sentence, in which this is dissected into successively smaller units. First of all it is divided into clauses as follows:

(*a*) Main	– 1. statement	2. question	3. command
	– 4. wish	5. exclamation	
(*b*) Substantival	– 1. nominative	2. accusative	3. genitive
	4. dative		
(*c*) Adjectival	–		
(*d*) Adverbial	– 1. time	2. manner	3. place
	– 4. cause	5. comparison	6. condition
	7. purpose	8. result	9. concession

Experiment soon shows, however, that many clauses do not fit into one of these categories. Some are a combination of two different types of clause and consequently require a combination of categories to account for them satisfactorily, e.g.

ἦ ἀφῖκται τὸ πλοῖον οὗ δεῖ ἀφικομένου τεθνάναι με (Crito 43c)
= ē aphiktai to ploion hou dei aphikomenou tethnanai me?
= has arrived the ship which it is necessary having arrived to die me?
= Has the ship arrived on whose arrival I must die?

Here the second part of the sentence (*οὗ δεῖ ἀφικομένου τεθνάναι με*;) is primarily adjectival, inasmuch as it qualifies *τὸ πλοῖον* but also contains an adverbial clause of time in the genitive absolute *οὗ ἀφικομένομ* (when which has arrived). The only solution, therefore, is to classify such a clause as adjectival/adverbial of time.

With this kind of clause, in which the two component clauses are inherent in the Greek construction, may be compared others like

συνήθης ἤδη μοί ἐστιν διὰ τὸ πολλάκις δεῦρο φοιτᾶν (Crito 43a)
=synēthēs ēdē moi estin dia to pollakis deuro phoitan
=used by now to me he is through the often here visiting
=He is used to me by now through my often visiting here.

In this instance the Greek construction *τὸ πολλάκις δεῦρο φοιτᾶν* forms only one type of clause (i.e. substantival), but the fact that it is preceded by a preposition (*διά*) makes it in actual fact adverbial in sense. To indicate this difference in the analysis it seems advisable to classify all clauses as follows:

A. According to grammar and sense where these agree, according to grammar where they do not.
B. According to the sense, where this differs from the grammar.

Thus the instance above would be marked on the tape as A. substantival-accusative, B. adverbial-cause.

In connection with the classification of clauses the problem arises of whether or not participles and infinitives in Greek should be regarded as equivalent to finite verbs. If expediency be the primary consideration, since a clause with a finite verb can usually be substituted for an infinitive or participial construction, comparison between the two will be rendered easier if the latter too are reckoned as clauses. On the other hand perhaps some distinction between the various uses of the infinitive or participle should be made, though it is difficult deciding where to make it. Whereas few doubts are entertained about calling the article + infinitive alone (e.g. in *κακόν ἐστι τὸ τεθνάναι*) a noun, or the participle in an attributive position (e.g. *ἡ παρεστῶσα συμφορά*) an adjective, the addition of a subject to the former (e.g. *κακόν ἐστι τὸ τεθνάναι Σωκράτη*) or an adverb to the latter (e.g. *ἡ νῦν παρεστῶσα συμφορά*) leads at least to some uncertainty, an uncertainty which increases with the further addition of a direct and indirect object to the infinitive, a series of adverbs to the participle, and prepositional phrases to both.

However, where the distinguishing line is drawn between the infinitive and participle constructions which are to be reckoned as clauses and those which are not, is not important, provided one remembers that the distinction is only utilitarian, not inherent in the syntactical structure of Greek. The simplest line of demarcation is probably that between unqualified and qualified infinitive or participle. That is to say, if the article + infinitive or the participle in attributive position (when predicative, it should clearly always be reckoned as equivalent to a clause) stand alone, they are noun and adjective respectively, but when qualified become equivalent to a clause.

This division of the sentence into clauses permits various stylistic calculations to be made, of which the following will serve as examples:

1. Measurement of the complexity of an author's sentences on a basis of the constituent clauses.
2. Measurement of the relative length of the clauses themselves on a basis of the number of words in them.
3. Determination of the preference for a particular order among the types of clauses.
4. Determination of preference for expressing certain syntactical relations by means of certain constructions (e.g. cause by a participle, preposition + article and infinitive, or subordinating conjunction and finite verb).

At the next stage of analysis each clause is divided into syntactical blocks, as follows*:

(*a*) Subject, (*b*) Attribute of subject, (*c*) Direct object, (*d*) Attribute of direct object, (*e*) Indirect object, (*f*) Attribute of indirect object, (*g*) Vocative, (*h*) Attribute of vocative, (*i*) Adverb 1. manner, 2. time, 3. place, 4. cause/purpose, etc., (*j*) Attribute of adverb, (*k*) Verb, (*l*) Verb containing subject, (*m*) Verb in subordinate clause with subject (contained in verb) = object (direct or indirect) of main clause, (*n*) Complement of verb, (*o*) Attribute of complement.

The most important stylistic feature which can be examined through this level of analysis is the relation of the syntactical blocks to each other both as regards frequency and position, the latter being what is generally called word-order. Subject to the limitations of the author's knowledge the first suggestion recommending the use of this criterion for the investigation of Platonic chronology came from W. Lutoslawski (Origin and Growth of Plato's Logic, 1897). It is worthwhile to quote the relevant passage:

'One of the characteristics of arrangement is the numerical proportion between verbs, adjectives, substantives and other kinds of words, because in many cases the same word appears as adjective or verb or substantive; the repetition of a noun can be avoided by a pronoun, and this allows many possible variations. For example, "a wise man is unable to become unjust" and "wisdom forbids

*Note: These divisions are only provisional. Several more may in fact be necessary, especially in the case of the adverb; exactly how many only actual experience in the course of the investigation itself will show.

injustice" express substantially the same thought, while in the first we have thrice as many adjectives as substantives, and in the second no adjective at all. It is highly probable that Plato did not always preserve the same proportion in the use of various parts of speech*. More especially, the numerical relations between adjectives and substantives, between substantives and verbs, between these and adverbs, afford very characteristic properties of style which might enable us to notice similarities or differences between one composition and another. The knowledge of these quantitive relations of every kind of word is intermediate between the lexicographical statistics of the scarcity or frequency of each term and the study of the construction of phrases. Here the immediate object of study would be the relative position of subject and predicate, of nouns and determinatives, adverbs and verbs, which may all occupy the first or the second place. No author follows a uniform practice in this respect, and variation is the rule; but at each period of his life an author may show a certain predilection for one or another order in the phrase. Taking only the first 500 words of the "Laws" and comparing them with the first 500 in the "Protagoras", we may readily see how great are the differences between the two dialogues as to the use and order of the substantives and the adjectives:

Number of	*In 'Protagoras' words* 1–500	*In 'Laws' words* 1–500
Substantives	63	102
Adjectives	13	31
Verbs (incl. participles)	91	79
Adjectives preceding correlated substantive	7	9
Adjectives following the correlated substantive	0	13

If further calculations confirmed these, then it would appear that in his later style Plato used many more substantives and adjectives than in his earlier writings, and that he acquired in old age a predilection for putting the noun before its qualifying words. But in order to draw such conclusions the examination should be extended to all the works of Plato, and should include the position of adverbs before or after the verb, of genitives before or after the noun on which they depend, and of all kinds of words in their mutual interdependence.'

* Subsequently proved by Y. Vanachter, 'Un Aspect du Style de Platon', *L'Antiquité Classique XV*, 1946, pp. 183–195.

The 'parts of speech' mentioned by Lutoslawski result at the third stage of the analysis from a division of the syntactical blocks: they are

(1) definite article, (2) common noun, (3) proper noun, (4) personal pronoun, (5) reflexive pronoun, (6) reciprocal pronoun, (7) qualifying adj., (8) ordinal number, (9) possessive adj. (7*a*–9*a* are 7–9 used as pronouns with addition of definite article), (10) cardinal number, (11) demonstrative adj., (12) interrogative adj., (13) indefinite adj., (14) relative adj., (15) intensive adj. (*αὐτός*) (10*a*–14*a* are 10–14 used as pronouns with addition of definite article), (16) finite verb (*a*) personal (*b*) impersonal, (17) participle (*a*) personal (*b*) impersonal, (18) infinitive (*a*) personal (*b*) impersonal, (19) verbal adj. (*a*) personal (*b*) impersonal, (20) adverb (*a*) ordinary (*b*) relative (*c*) interrogative (*d*) demonstrative (*e*) indefinite, [(i) manner, (ii) time, (iii) place, (iv) degree, (v) cause/purpose, etc.] (21) preposition, (22) co-ordinating conjunction, (23) subordinating conjunction, (24) continuative (i.e. those adverbial co-ordinating conjunctions used to connect sentences both in Greek and English e.g. 'therefore', 'however', and the ordinary conjunctions, the similar use of which is peculiar to Greek, e.g. *καί*, *δέ*), (25) interjection, (26) particle, (27) simple negative, (28) reinforced negative (*οὐδαμῶς* etc.).

It is possible to recognize the different functions of a part of speech mechanically in many cases simply by combining the information resulting from this level of analysis with that from the preceding one. Participles and infinitives used substantivally, for example, will be marked at the former level as subject, object, etc., a participle used adjectivally as an attribute, an adjective used adverbially as an adverb, and so on. Likewise, association of the part of speech indication with the reproduction of the text on the input tape will enable different functions of a word to be distinguished. As an example may be quoted the distinction of the co-ordinating from the emphasizing use of *καί*, since *καί* in the former sense will be denoted as a co-ordinating conjunction, in the latter as a particle. Where, however, such methods are not enough to permit the mechanical recognition of differences in function, these must be indicated by some symbol or other on the input tape.

If as complete an analysis as possible is desired, the grammatical details can be added to the parts of speech—indication of case and number for nouns, pronouns, adjectives and participles, of degree for adjectives and adverbs, of mood, voice and tense for verbs, etc. In addition a simple classification of the less usual and idiomatic constructions may be obtained by using the chapter or section numbers of some elementary book on syntax as a reference code. Finally, some notation will be required to indicate interruptions in the syntactical structure, whether it be two halves of a clause separated by the insertion of another, an article separated from its noun by a dependent genitive or prepositional phrase, an antithetical or correlating *μὲν -δέ*, *ούτε -ούτε* etc., and so on.

This then is the scheme of a stylistic analysis for Greek. As it stands, of course, it is suitable only for Greek or—with some modifications—Latin; but there is no reason why the principle of using a computer as a means of recording and analysing texts should not be applied in other languages, once the appropriate syntactical categories have been set up. And if the latter are not yet fully known, as structural linguists would have us believe, then there is no better or quicker way of establishing them than by a computer analysis.

One question still remains to be answered in connection with our own analysis: the time required to carry it out. The answer of course would depend on how many people were engaged on it. If it were left to one person, it would undoubtedly require many years of full-time research; if, on the other hand, the work were divided among several persons, it would take proportionately less time but involve the danger of inconsistency in the interpretation of the text. For, as anyone who has made any stylistic investigation will know, it is difficult enough for one man to apply the principles he has set up uniformly throughout such a long analysis, and correspondingly harder for two or three to apply the same principles as each other. However, since the task would almost certainly prove intolerable for one person, the latter course would have to be adopted with the hope that close co-operation between the participants in the enquiry would reduce inconsistency to a minimum.

5

GENERAL ASPECTS OF LANGUAGE TRANSLATION

STEM-ENDING DICTIONARIES

LIKE an unintelligent child, the automatic computer can only translate in any sense with the aid of a dictionary. The very possibility of mechanical translation, therefore, depends upon the construction of an adequate storage device and upon our being able to reduce the vocabulary in some manner to a practical size.

Word-counts by Dewey [1] taken from newspaper material, novels, and general literature show that the 1,000 most frequent words cover 80% by volume of text. But it would be mistaken to suppose that a dictionary of 1,000 words would give a translation containing 80% of the information contained in the text being translated. In fact, it may be generally asserted that the higher the frequency of a word, the less information it gives: the infrequent words define the subject of discourse. For mechanical translation, therefore, there seems to be no option but to use as large a dictionary as possible so as to include a large number of the infrequent words. A vocabulary of at least 10^5 words would be desirable and this is rather impractical at the moment, though new forms of storage device are being developed which are capable of holding such a dictionary.

The question of reducing the vocabulary now arises. A dictionary of about 10^4 entries is desirable: how can such a dictionary be obtained? It is a platitude to say that the large vocabulary of general literature is a result of the many and complicated activities of modern civilization. But it leads to the conclusion that by choosing the literature of sufficiently restricted fields of activity a much smaller vocabulary is sufficient to provide 'reasonable' translations. In a sense the most limited fields are the exact sciences—chemistry, physics, mathematics and engineering, and it is here, too, that there is the most need for mechanical translation. The technical literature relevant to particular branches of science consists of general language occupying the largest volume of text and the isolated technical terms of that discipline. Both sections of vocabulary are limited, the general language by the more or less stylized range of expression which over the long periods of time does not vary considerably, and the technical terms by relatively slow accretion of new words reflecting the rarity of an entirely new discovery. The approximate sizes of necessary vocabulary are shown by an estimate of 2,800 words required for the translation of Russian mathematical literature, and of 4,000 words for the translation of German papers on electron optics. Vocabularies restricted in this way are known as 'microglossaries' or 'idioglossaries'. Their sizes are certainly within the reach of present-day storage techniques.

Now it will be objected that estimates of dictionary size usually ignore the fact that most languages are inflected and that word-counts often discount the inflected forms of a word. With a language like Russian where nouns, verbs and adjectives can have many different case endings, the inclusion of every form in the mechanical dictionary would vastly exceed the estimated 2,800 words for mathematics. For the current type of storage device it is therefore necessary to divide words into 'stems' and 'endings' and to build the programme for mechanical translation upon a double matching procedure. In this a foreign language word of the input text is first matched with a dictionary of 'stems'. When the stem has been located, it is removed from the word and the remainder looked up in a dictionary of 'endings'. The two pieces of information derived from these dictionaries together give the equivalent of the input word. Naturally variations of this procedure are necessary for a language in which inflections are made by means of prefixes.

It is easy to programme a computer to select from the dictionary the longest entry which is part of the input word. This part can be removed and the remainder compared with the dictionary of endings. The contents of the dictionary can be so arranged as to give the correct equivalents for both stem and ending. This simple procedure is based upon the matching of letters of a word or part of a word with the letters of the dictionary entry starting from the left and working to the right—left to right matching. The method, however, breaks down when the longest entry in the dictionary, which is part of the word, is not in fact the correct splitting of a word. There are then two possibilities:

(i) The remaining letters will not be found as an entry in the dictionary of endings. Another, shorter entry in the stem dictionary will then give correct decomposition.

(ii) The letters which remain after subtraction of the stem from the input word correspond with a dictionary entry for endings, but there is another mode of decomposition into stem and ending.

With this look-up mechanism a stem $S_1 = a_1, a_2 \ldots a_{r+1}$ will be located which, when subtracted from the word $a_1 a_2 \ldots a_{r+1} \ldots a_n$, will give a letter group $E_1 = a_{r+2} \ldots a_n$ not found as an ending when compared to the ending dictionary. An easily programmed routine can now be brought into play which removes the final letter a_{r+1} from the stem $a_1 a_2 \ldots a_{r+1}$ and adds it to the ending E_1 making it $E_2 = a_{r+1} a_{r+2} \ldots a_n$ which is placed in the temporary store. The new stem $S_2 = a_1 a_2 \ldots a_r$ is then compared with the stem dictionary by the bracketing procedure to be described in Chapter 6. Location of a new stem will be followed by comparison of the new ending E_2 with the ending dictionary. If an entry is found, then the equivalents corresponding to the decomposition $a_1 \ldots a_r / a_{r+1} \ldots a_n$ are extracted. On the other hand if E_2 is not located in the dictionary a new stem $S_3 = a_1 \ldots a_{r-1}$ is formed by the subtraction of the final letter from S_2 and a new ending $E_3 = a_r a_{r+1} \ldots a_n$ by the addition of this letter to E_2. S_3 and E_3 can now be compared with the stem and ending dictionaries and the process repeated, shortening the stem and lengthening the endings until the correct entries are found.

In the second case a special digit or set of digits must be attached to the first and longest stem entry to indicate that with a particular ending a second alternative is possible. The correct alternative to be chosen will depend upon information that cannot be derived from the input word alone. It follows that a small microglossary can be used on computers with present storage capacities, even though the language is so highly inflected as to give a large vocabulary if all forms of words were to be included in a single dictionary. In comparison with stem dictionaries, the ending dictionaries are negligible in size.

It frequently happens that words can be split into stem, joining letters and ending, instead of into stem and ending. The joining letters are redundant, at least as far as identifying equivalents is concerned. The endings in the preceding type of dictionary can then be seen to be divided into sets, each set having the same target language equivalent, and having the final letters in common but central letters different. The final letters, common to each group, are now called the ending. As an example of this type of word structure consider the inflections of regular French verbs. Table 5.1 shows the 21 endings for the future tense derived according to the

Table 5.1

Future tense of French regular verbs

Conj. *Prototype*	*1st* *donner*	*2nd* *finir*	*3rd* *vendre*	*4th* *recevoir*	*5th* *sen(t)ir*	
Person (sing.)						
1st	-erai	-rai	-rai	-evrai	-irai	-tirai
2nd	-eras	-ras	-ras	-evras	-iras	-tiras
3rd	-era	-ra	-ra	-evra	-ira	-tira
Person (plural)						
1st	-erons	-rons	-rons	-erons	-irons	-tirons
2nd	-erez	-rez	-rez	-erez	-rez	-tirez
3rd	-eront	-ront	-ront	-eront	-iront	-tiront

previous method. What characterizes the future tense, however, are the endings -rai, -ras, -ra, -rons, -rez, -ront. The entries in the new type of ending dictionary are therefore six in number, and the analysis is shown in Table 5.2. Similar splitting for some other

Table 5.2

Future tense of French regular verbs

	Joining letters						*Future ending*
Conj.	1	2	3	4	5		
Person (sing.)							
1st	-e-	—	—	-ev-	-i-	-ti-	-rai
2nd	-e-	—	—	-ev-	-i-	-ti-	-ras
3rd	-e-	—	—	-ev-	-i-	-ti-	-ra
Person (plural)							
1st	-e-	—	—	-e-	-i-	-ti-	-rons
2nd	-e-	—	—	-e-	-i-	-ti-	-rez
3rd	-e-	—	—	-e-	-i-	-ti-	-ront

tenses is shown in Tables 5.3, 5.4, 5.5, and it can be seen that, for regular French verbs, the number of endings is consequently reduced by about two-thirds. To operate a dictionary in this manner necessitates right-to-left matching once the stem has been removed and this again can be performed on a computer. Words

Table 5.3

Imperfect tense of regular French verbs

	Joining letters						*Imperfect ending*
Conj.	1	2	3	4	5		
Person (sing.)							
1st	—	-ss-	—	-ev-	—	-t-	-ais
2nd	—	-ss-	—	-ev-	—	-t-	-ais
3rd	—	-ss-	—	-ev-	—	-t-	-ait
Person (plural)							
1st	—	-ss-	—	-ev-	—	-t-	-ions
2nd	—	-ss-	—	-ev-	—	-t-	-iez
3rd	—	-ss-	—	-ev-	—	-t-	-aient

with two modes of decomposition are best dealt with by entering those words entirely in the stem dictionary and giving them two equivalents.

Where a storage device large enough to contain every form of a word is available, this will minimize the time spent consulting the dictionary. In the next chapter a mechanism of dictionary look-up will be explained which selects the correct entry with a minimum number of operations. For a dictionary with N entries this 'bracketing' procedure yields an equivalent in p operations where p is the smallest integer greater than $\log_2 N$. Suppose the stem dictionary

Table 5.4

Conditional tense: same joining as for future tense

All conjugations

Person (sing.)	*Conditional endings*
1st	-rais
2nd	-rais
3rd	-rait
Person (plural)	
1st	-rions
2nd	-riez
3rd	-raient

Table 5.5

Past historic tense

	Joining letters				*Ending*	*I Conj. complete ending*
Conj.	2	3	4	5		
Person (sing.)						
1st	—	-i-	-u-	-i-	-s	-ai
2nd	—	-i-	-u-	-i-	-s	-as
3rd	—	-i-	-u-	-i-	-t	-a
Person (plural)						
1st	—	-i-	-u-	-i-	-mes	-ames
2nd	—	-i-	-u-	-i-	-res	-ates
3rd	—	-i-	-u-	-i-	-rent	-erent

to contain N_i entries, each having m_i possible endings, where $i=1, 2, \ldots n$. The bracketing procedure now gives the equivalent of an input word in p operations, where p is the number of operations required to locate a stem plus the number to locate an ending, that is,

$$p = \log_2\left(\sum_{i=1}^{n} N_i\right) + \log_2\left(\sum_{i=1}^{n} m_i\right)$$

$$= \log_2\left(\sum_{i=1}^{n} N_i\right)\left(\sum_{i=1}^{n} m_i\right).$$

If the stem-ending dictionary is expanded into a single dictionary in which all forms occur, the number of entries would be $\sum_{i=1}^{n} N_i m_i$. The number of operations required to locate an input word would therefore be $P = \log_2\left(\sum_{i=1}^{n} N_i m_i\right)$, but

$$\left(\sum_{i=1}^{n} N_i\right)\left(\sum_{i=1}^{n} m_i\right) \geqslant \left(\sum_{i=1}^{n} N_i m_i\right),$$

therefore, $p \geqslant P$ and the number of operations saved is

$$p - P = \log_2 \frac{\left(\sum_{i=1}^{n} N_i\right)\left(\sum_{i=1}^{n} m_i\right)}{\left(\sum_{i=1}^{n} N_i m_i\right)}.$$

For example, suppose a stem dictionary to contain 1,000 nouns each taking 10 different forms, 1,000 verbs each of 10 forms, 1,000 adjectives of 10 forms and 1,000 other words each of 1 form. Then $\sum_{i=1}^{n} N_i = 4{,}000$, $\sum_{i=1}^{n} m_i = 31$, $\sum_{i=1}^{n} N_i m_i = 31{,}000$. The number of operations saved by having the expanded dictionary is thus:

$$p - P = \log_2 \frac{4{,}000 \times 31}{31{,}000} = \log_2 4 = 2,$$

but since the total number of operations involved in locating a word in this dictionary is $\log_2 31{,}000 \approx 13$, this is not a large economy, although in practice a little more time than this will be saved since the stem-ending procedure requires an additional operation to change the search mechanism from the stem to the ending dictionary. The proportionate saving is, however, relatively small, and if a larger stem dictionary is used the proportionate saving is also decreased. For, suppose the number of words in the stem dictionary to be increased by a factor λ, by doubling the number of nouns, adjectives, etc., which would not increase the number of endings, the saving in the number of operations is unaltered. The new saving will then be:

$$p^1 - P^1 = \log_2 \frac{\left(\sum_{i=1}^{n} \lambda N_i\right)\left(\sum_{i=1}^{n} m_i\right)}{\left(\sum_{i=1}^{n} \lambda N_i m_i\right)}$$

$$= \log_2 \frac{\lambda\left(\sum_{i=1}^{n} N_i\right)\left(\sum_{i=1}^{n} m_i\right)}{\lambda\left(\sum_{i=0}^{n} N_i m_i\right)} = \log_2 \frac{\left(\sum_{i=1}^{n} N_i\right)\left(\sum_{i=1}^{n} m_i\right)}{\left(\sum_{i=1}^{n} N_i m_i\right)}$$

$$= p - P.$$

It should be noted that the total number of operations is altered by the addition of $\log_2 \lambda$ and that the storage space for both types of dictionary is increased by the factor λ. The latter is the more serious since the increase in size is at least of the same order as the size of the stem dictionary.

COMPOUND WORDS

Another problem, similar in many respects to that of splitting into stem and ending, is the splitting of compound words. In German and allied languages, nouns, and less frequently nouns and other

parts of speech, can be freely combined. Thus, for such a language, a vocabulary of N nouns can give rise to approximately ${}^{N}C_2 = \frac{1}{2}(N^2 - N)$ compound nouns. All of these compounds will not, of course, be found in actual texts. The construction of technical microglossaries is of no help here, since in scientific fields full use is made of compound words. It is therefore necessary to make provision for the splitting of compounds.

The German compound constructed from two nouns has the structure

$$noun^1 - X - noun^2.$$

The symbol X denotes a group of letters which could formally belong to the ending of $noun^1$ giving the splitting

$$noun^1 - X / noun^2$$

or together with $noun^2$ yield another word in the dictionary $noun^3 = X - noun^2$. The latter instance giving a splitting

$$noun^1 / X - noun^2 = noun^1 / noun^3.$$

The letters X are analogous to the joining letters occurring in stem-ending analysis, but here they are of some semantic significance. In many German compound-nouns X is simply the letter '*s*' and $noun^1$ '*s*' is then the genitive of $noun^1$. For instance

Widerstand-s/bewegung
= resistance (genitive)/movement
= resistance movement.

An 's', however, does not invariably have this function. It is possible for it to be the first letter of the following word as in

Ein/sicht = insight.

Frequently, the letters X may be absent so that the compound is simply

$$noun^1 / noun^2$$

as in 'Einsicht' above.

A dictionary containing a German microglossary must clearly contain the simple nouns which when juxtaposed give the compound words. It must also contain those compound words, the equivalents of which are not directly derived from the equivalents of the components. Thus dictionary entries 'ein = in' and 'sicht = sight' will correctly give the equivalent of 'Einsicht' and also the correct meanings of the components in other contexts: on the other hand, the entries 'Tat = deed' and 'Sache = thing' are not by themselves sufficient to give a reasonable equivalent to 'Tatsache = fact'.

Unlike the division of a word into stem and ending, which necessitates reference to two separate dictionaries, the splitting of compound words entails more than one reference to the same dictionary. The programme for effecting the splitting must make provision for the division of the components themselves into stem and ending so that the complete structure of the compound word is

$$\text{stem}^1 - \text{ending}^1 - X - \text{stem}^2 - \text{ending}^2$$

A further complexity occurs when a word is compounded of more than two others but this contingency is relatively infrequent.

Reifler[2] has given a full discussion of the construction of a matching procedure and a dictionary suitable for the resolution of German compound substantives.

THE PROBLEM OF MULTIPLE MEANING

From the inception of projects for mechanical translation, it was realized that ambiguity would be a major problem. The type of ambiguity that causes difficulty is not necessarily that usually encountered within a language: here, for instance, an English word is ambiguous if it has more than one 'meaning' in an English dictionary. This raises no difficulty if both target languages share similar ambiguities. The difficulty occurs where the areas of meaning of the source language word do not coincide with those of the target language word. The problem is to reduce the ambiguity to manageable proportions. Limitation of mechanical translation to the literature of highly specialized activities reduces the total vocabulary and leaves the words themselves with specialized applications. The technical words, which convey most of the information, can be assigned one target-language equivalent in the majority of cases. There still remains the problem of the surrounding general language. Although these words cannot be assigned single target-language equivalents if a fairly faithful translation is to be attained, concentration on a particular branch of science removes some ambiguity. This is because styles of writing in technical activities become fairly constant, the pattern of communication becomes conventionalized and particularly so in the exact sciences. For a microglossary it is sufficient, at the most, to give these equivalents to a general word, each equivalent being representative of the major areas of meaning of that word. If the mechanical translation programme prints out each of the alternatives then a specialist in that particular field, knowing only the target language, will certainly be able to use the results although they might appear incomprehensible to a non-specialist. But it is possible to do better than this. A computer can be programmed to investigate context and, in the next chapter, a method of using code numbers attached to target-language equivalents will be explained whereby the accumulation and compounding of these enables the general nature of the whole preceding text to be examined. This information can be used for the elimination of some ambiguity, though the sentence in which the word occurs is most important in this respect. It has been found that one or two words on either side of the word being examined are nearly as effective in reducing ambiguity as the whole sentence. A programme for examining the immediate context of a word, therefore, should effectively resolve most ambiguities.

REFERENCES

[1] DEWEY, G., 'Relative Frequency of English Speech Sounds', Harvard Univ. Press, (1923)

[2] REIFLER, E., 'Mechanical Translation', 2, (1), (1955), pp. 3–14

6

PROGRAMMING TECHNIQUE FOR MECHANICAL TRANSLATION

INTRODUCTION

THIS chapter will be concerned with the technical details of the construction of programmes for mechanical translation. The most important part of such a programme is the mechanism for looking up in the dictionary the foreign language words of the text to be translated and selecting the target-language equivalents. The dictionary, however, does not provide only the equivalents in coded form, but also certain other information which will be loosely called 'syntactical'. On the basis of the syntactical information certain other operations such as change of word order may be performed. These operations themselves may require some sort of procedure for consulting a dictionary of, for example, word types. But whatever the degree of sophistication of a programme, at least one routine for locating one stem in a large number of different items is involved.

The dictionary look-up procedure will first be examined and the mechanization of syntactical operations deferred until later.

PUNCHED CARD METHODS

Both stem-ending and ordinary dictionaries can be mechanized by the use of punched card machines and it is worth devoting a few lines to an examination of the general method.

The text to be processed is first transcribed on to cards so that each text word appears on a single card and is accompanied by a count number which defines its position in the sentence. When the whole text has been so prepared, the cards are sorted into alphabetical word order just as was done for the frequency analysis described in Chapter 3. The pack of cards is now compared with a dictionary pack by means of a collator, thus each text word finds its mate in the dictionary pack and an output card is produced on which is recorded the translation, or translations, from the dictionary card and the position in the original text from the text pack.

It is clear that, because both dictionary and text packs are in alphabetical order, only one passage through the collator is required to process the text.

After the collator operation, the cards produced are sorted into order using the text-occurrence numbers and the ordered pack is then reproduced, either on a tabulator or on a suitably arranged electric typewriter.

The punched card method can also be used to mechanize the use of a stem-ending type dictionary. Here, however, it is necessary first to collate the text pack with the stem dictionary pack and thus to produce output cards bearing:

1. Stem translation or translations.
2. Ending remaining after removal of stem.
3. Any grammatical data derived from 1.
4. Position number of word original text.

The new pack is now sorted into alphabetical order on 2 and the resulting array is collated with an ending-dictionary pack. The result is now to produce a new set of cards which contain:

1. Stem translation prefixed and affixed by any ending.
2. Any grammatical data.
3. Position number.

If no rearrangement of word order is required the pack of cards just produced is sorted into original word order using 3 and is then reproduced in printed form. The only real difficulty is the mechanical one of associating output stems and endings together so that, for example, the word 'having' does appear as 'hav ing'. This problem can be solved if an electrical typewriter is used as the output device.

Exactly the same machinery can be used to produce rearrangement of word order, except that now, instead of typing out the contents of the pack just produced, a further collation operation takes place, this time using the grammatical data punchings and a pack of sentence structure cards. It is also necessary to insert, into the stem-ending processed pack, cards bearing punctuation symbols to define structural units.

The advantage of using punched card machinery for these purposes lies in the effectively unlimited storage which is available on cards. This means that the restriction to microglossary and micro-grammar can be removed. The disadvantage lies in the complexity of the card handling procedures and in the inflexibility of the equipment.

DICTIONARY SEARCH

The first method to be suggested for using a computer as a mechanical dictionary was the naïve one in which the translation of any word was simply held in that storage location whose location number was equal to the code number of the foreign language word itself. Thus the word 'et' has the code number (5, 20) and so the translation would appear in storage location 520. This method is quite impracticable for the following reason. If it is assumed that no foreign language word exists having more than ten letters, then the number of such words which could occur is 26^{10}, or $1{\cdot}4 \times 10^{14}$. This number is larger by a factor of about 10^7 than the capacity of any conceivable storage device, and even though the number of actual words in a language is only about 10^7 it would still be necessary to keep the space available.

In the second method to be proposed, the letters of the alphabet are again represented in the five-digit binary code described in Chapter 3. The dictionary of words is stored in ascending order of numerical magnitude in consecutive positions of the machine store, and it may be noticed that, from the standpoint of frequency occurrence, this is tantamount to a random arrangement.

The unknown word is then sent to the accumulator of the computer and then compared with each of the dictionary entries, in order, from the numerically greatest and backwards. This comparison process involves the successive subtraction of dictionary words from the unknown word, and it is clear that the result of the subtraction will be negative until the exact equivalent or the nearest stem is reached. At this point, in the former case the result will be zero and, in the latter, positive. A simple programme for effecting this comparison is given below:

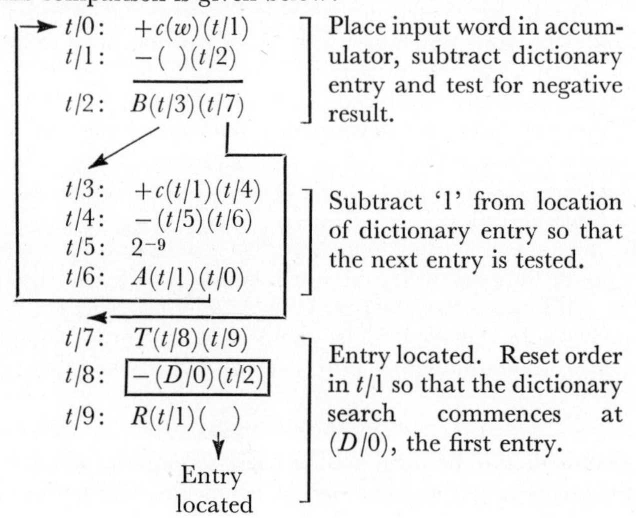

It will be seen that this method of dictionary search will involve, on the average, the examination of $N/2$ entries to locate each unknown word. A variant of the method makes use of the known frequency distribution of words in large texts. Let the most frequent word be numbered 1, the second most frequent 2 and so on, so that the rth most frequent word is said to have rank r. If now the frequency of the rth word is f_r then, for a large text in which the frequencies are governed by Zipf's law:

$$r \times f_r = k$$

where k is constant.

The number of occurrences of word r is thus k/r, so that the total number of words to be looked up, if it is assumed that the dictionary used contains N words, is approximately:

$$\int_{r=1}^{N} \frac{kdr}{r} = k \log_e N.$$

Consider now a dictionary in which words are arranged in order of decreasing frequency of occurrence; that is, in increasing order of rank r. If the look-up procedure is one of successive comparison, then the word of rank r will require exactly r look-up operations and, since this word occurs k/r times, the total number of look-up operations required to locate it is simply k. Thus, for the N words contained in the dictionary, kN look-up operations are required.

Since it has been shown above that the total number of words to be looked up is $k \log_e N$ it follows that the average number of look-up operations per word is simply $N/\log_e N$, and this compares favourably with the $N/2$ operations which would be needed under the scheme of alphabetic arrangement previously described. For example, in a dictionary of 10,000 words the first method requires, on the average, 5,000 look-up operations whereas the second requires only $10{,}000/\log_e 10{,}000 \simeq 1{,}080$ operations.

In the preceding discussion it has been assumed that there is exactly one word having rank r. It may happen that, in actual texts, there are several words which have the same frequencies and which must, in consequence, be given the same rank numbers. In this event Zipf's law does not apply directly and it is difficult to make analytical predictions; it appears likely, however, that the overall effect is to reduce the average number of hunting operations still further.

The simplicity of the first programme depends upon the numerical order of the dictionary entries. The latter method complicates the comparison procedure since, on subtraction of an n-letter dictionary entry, a test must be made to determine whether the first $5n$ digits of the accumulator are all zeros and, in any case, the method will only work when exact equivalents are stored in the dictionary. This increases the time taken for each operation and also the amount of programming space. Suppose the time taken is increased by a factor α. Then the average time taken to locate an entry is $(\alpha N)/\log N$ but since, for sufficiently large N, $\log N \gg \alpha$, this method of organization is still preferable.

Another method of operating a dictionary is to arrange it in sections, each of which contains words which have the same initial letter or letters. The first letters of an input word are then used to form the address of that section of the dictionary through which search has to be made. If the dictionary is supposed to be divided into n sections the average number of look-up operations is reduced to $N/2n$ in the case first considered, and to $(N/n)/\log_e (N/n)$ when the section contents are assumed to be arranged in order of decreasing frequency. For the dictionary of 10,000 words previously considered, these figures become: 193 and 65 for division into 26 groups, and 7·4 and 5·5 when 676 $(=26^2)$ groups are considered.

THE BRACKETING METHOD

A method which is more efficient than any of the preceding is as follows: Suppose that the dictionary contains N entries arranged in ascending order of numerical magnitude in locations 1, 2, . . . N and that N is some power of two. The incoming word is first subtracted from the entry in $N/2$. Then, if the result is positive, the required entry is in the 'first half', i.e. between 1 and $N/2$. If negative, however, it is between $N/2$ and N. Now, assuming a negative result at the first stage, subtract the word from the middle entry of the last half, i.e. that in $N/2+N/4$. If the result is negative, the equivalent must lie between entries $N/2$ and $N/2+N/4$ and, if positive, between $3N/4$ and N. This comparison process is repeated until the correct location is isolated and it is seen that this requires $\log_2 N$ steps. The superiority of this method over all others is that relatively few look-up operations are required. In other cases the number of operations increases linearly with dictionary size whereas here the increase is logarithmic. Thus doubling the size of the dictionary only increases the number of operations by 1. For instance, with a dictionary of 10^4 words 14 operations $(4 \log_2 10)$ are required; for 2×10^4 words, 15 operations and for 10^6 words 20 operations. For a machine of which the combined access and subtraction time is 1 m.sec., the search time in this last example is about 20 m.sec.

Consider next what further improvement in numbers of look-up operations can be obtained by dividing the dictionary into two parts the first containing the more and the second the less frequent words. Suppose that there are γN entries in the first dictionary. The number of operations involved in searching for a word in the first dictionary is $\log_2 \gamma N$. If the word does not occur in the first dictionary then the full number $\log_2 \gamma N$ of searches in it must be made before the second dictionary with $(1-\gamma)N$ entries is searched. The number of operations involved in locating an entry in the second dictionary is therefore $\log_2 \gamma N + \log_2 (1-\gamma)N$.

On p. 79 it was shown that the number of words to be looked up, for a distribution which obeys Zipf's law, was $k \log_e N$, thus for the first part of the dictionary $k \log_e \gamma N$ words must be hunted and, for the second, $k(\log_e N - \log_e \gamma N)$. Thus, the total number of hunting operations is:

$$n = k \log_e (\gamma N) . \log_2 (\gamma N) + k[\log_e N - \log_e (\gamma N)] [\log_2 (1-\gamma)N + \log_2 (\gamma N)]$$
$$= k \log_e N . \log_2 (\gamma N) + k[\log_e N - \log_e (\gamma N)] \log_2 (1-\gamma)N,$$

which gives as an average number of look-ups per word:

$$\bar{n} = \log_2 (\gamma N) + \left(1 - \frac{\log_e \gamma N}{\log_e N}\right) \log_2 (1-\gamma)N$$
$$= \log_2 N - \frac{\log_2 \gamma . \log_2 (1-\gamma)}{\log_2 N}.$$

The number of operations is thus reduced by

$$\frac{\log_2 \gamma . \log_2 (1-\gamma)}{\log_2 N}$$

which can be shown to be a maximum when $\gamma = \frac{1}{2}$ and this produces a saving of $1/\log_2 N$ in the average number of look-up operations*. In practice it is not worth while programming this division of the dictionary since the saving decreases as N increases and the increase must be weighed against the time taken to alter the mechanism to refer to the other part of the dictionary. Further increase in speed can be produced if, instead of merely testing the difference between the word and the dictionary entry for a positive or negative result, a test is made for identity of word and entry. Clearly not all entries require the total number of $\log_2 N$ operations to locate them.

* NOTE: A more refined analysis shows that a saving of about ·5 operations can be obtained by testing for the most frequent word separately.

In general, there are 2^{r-1} entries in the dictionary each requiring r operations before it is located; for a dictionary containing $N=2^n$ entries, the average number of operations required to locate an entry is therefore

$$\frac{1}{2^n}\sum_{r=1}^{n} r2^{r-1} = \frac{1}{2^n}[(n-1)2^n-1]$$
$$= (n-1)-2^{-n} \approx n-1.$$

Thus there is a reduction of the average number of operations by 1. On APEXC the branch order tests the contents of the accumulator for the conditions $A\geqslant 0$, $A<0$, since a test for zero is frequently used in mechanical translation, the following programme is given to indicate the method of procedure.

The programme compares an n-digit number q with the first n digits of a number p held in the accumulator where $n\leqq 32$. Suppose the n digits of q to occupy the most significant positions of the storage location. Then p can be represented by $a+\beta$, where a is an n digit number and β is a thirty-two digit number, the first n digits of which are zero, so that $2^{-(n-1)}\geqslant\beta$. If q is now subtracted from p, the number $(a-q)+\beta$ is formed in the accumulator, and $a-q$ is still an n digit number. Then, if $(a-q)+\beta\geqq 0$ and $(a-q)-2^{-(n-1)}+\beta\leqq 0$, we have $a=q$. That is, if the accumulator changes sign on subtracting $2^{-(n-1)}$, then $a=q$. The programme is:

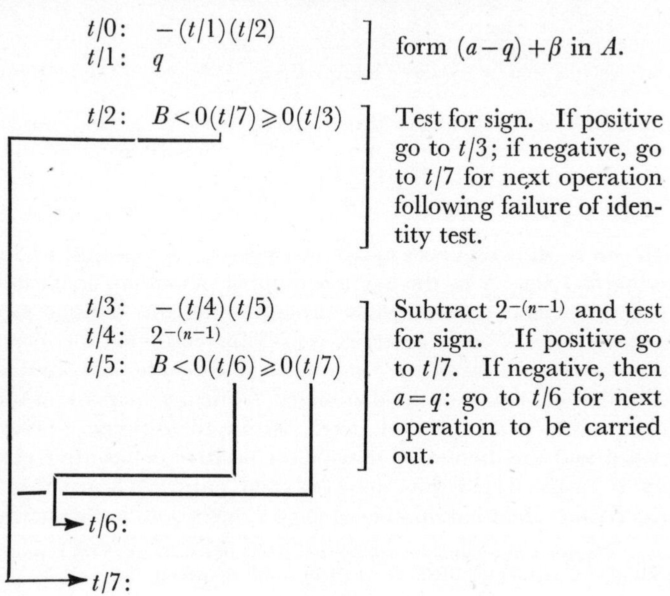

In particular, if $n = 32$, so that 2^{-31} is subtracted, the whole of p and q are compared which is equivalent to testing the accumulator for zero.

AN EXAMPLE OF A DICTIONARY SEARCHING PROGRAMME

The actual dictionary search programme associated with real machine translation is complicated by the fact that it forms only a part of a complex system which may effect stem-ending decomposition and word order rearrangement. The following programme, which is considerably simpler to understand, and which was the first experimental programme used on APEXC for the 'translation' of French, is given to illustrate the method of approach. The dictionary is restricted to twenty-nine entries and input words are assumed to have not more than six letters. These restrictions, made in order to simplify the programme, are of course removed in the procedures used in later experiments.

Each word is followed by a space symbol, (00000) or zero in the binary code given on p. 37, and each sentence ends in (11111) which causes the programme to stop.

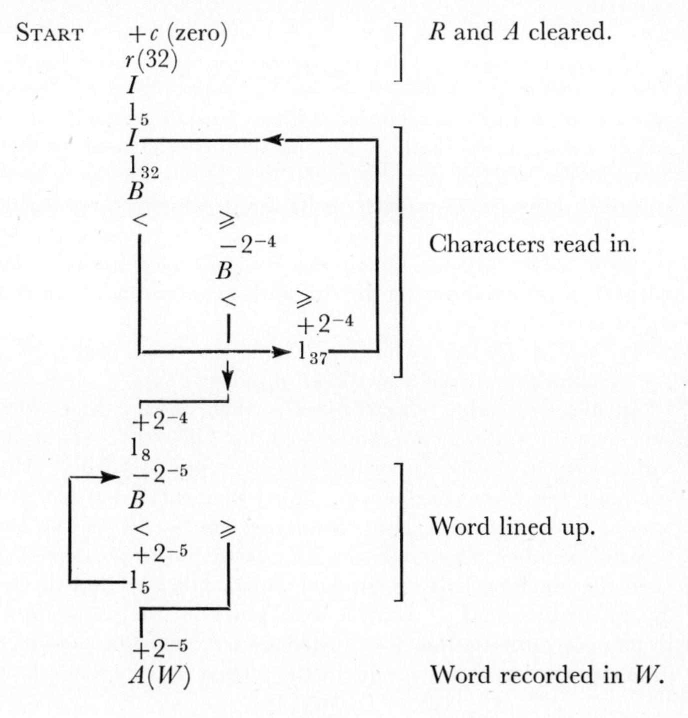

The operation of the programme is as follows:

The accumulator is first cleared to zero and the register is also set to zero by shifting the accumulator contents into it. Next, the first character from the tape is input to the register and is then shifted five places to the left to free the register to receive the next character. After this second character has been input a 32-place left shift transfers it to the leading positions of the accumulator where a test is made to see if it corresponds to a space symbol—i.e. zero. This test consists of the following parts:

1. A simple branch to see if it is negative, if so it cannot be zero and the l_{37} instruction restores the accumulator/register contents to a state in which the next character can be input from the tape.
2. If the character is positive 2^{-4} is subtracted from it. A positive result shows that it was not zero so that the operation is cancelled by the addition of 2^{-4} and the l_{37} operation is entered as in 1.
3. If, in 2, the result of the subtraction of 2^{-4} is negative the character is known to be zero so that it corresponds to a space or word-end symbol and the second phase of the programme is entered.

This second phase starts by cancelling the 2^{-4} subtracted previously and this is followed by an l_8 operation which deletes the space symbol and sets accumulator and register contents into a state where a test can be made to line-up the first character of the input word at the head of the accumulator. The lining-up process consists of l_5 shifts and tests for zero characters which, if present, indicate that the first alphabetic symbol has not yet reached the leading position. The process terminates in the cancellation of the 2^{-5} which is subtracted during the test and the recording of the lined-up input word in location W.

As soon as the foreign language word has been sent to the store the programme proceeds as shown opposite.

An iteration index, consisting of a single binary digit, 2^{-5}, is set into a probe position p and the look-up order 0_1 is restored to its initial form to ensure correctness after any previous run. After this the main test cycle commences. First the probe digit is sent to the accumulator and the l_{63} and B instructions test to see that the permissible number of look-ups (in this case five) has not been exceeded. If so the machine halts at Stop 1, which indicates that the word is not in the dictionary. If all is well, however, the probe digit is set to its new value by the $A(p)$ instruction. Next the look-up order, 0_1, is executed and this results in the setting of the foreign language

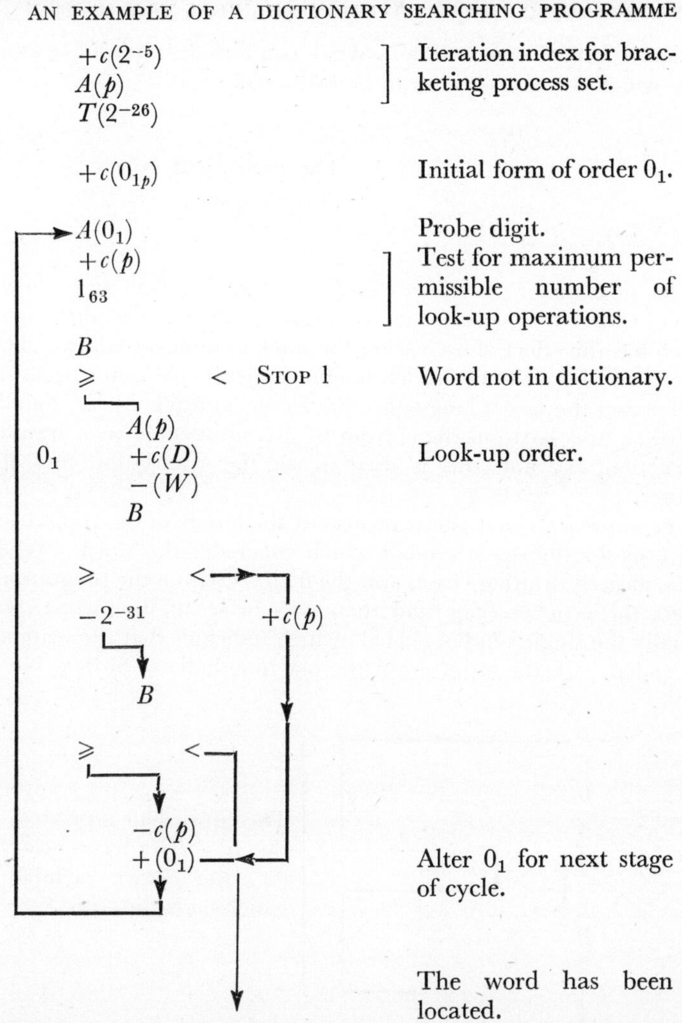

dictionary entry, D, into the accumulator, the foreign language word W is then subtracted from D and the result is tested. If this result is negative the probe digit, p, is added to (0_1), thus making the next hunting operation select the partition word in the upper portion of the dictionary from D. If, however, the result is positive a test is made for zero, and if this is not satisfied the probe digit is subtracted from 0_1 so that the next test takes place on the lower portion of the dictionary from D. If the result is zero, D is identical with the foreign language word and the order 0_1 contains the relevant location from which the translation can be extracted.

	$+c(0_1)$	
	$+2^{-4}$	The equivalent is sent
	$A_{1-10}(0_2)$	to the register.
0_2	$T(E_1)$	

The mechanism for the extraction of the equivalent is shown above. First 0_1 is sent to the accumulator, then 2^{-4} is added to it, which has the effect of increasing the track number by unity. This is necessary because the foreign language dictionary words occur on track n and the target language equivalents on track $n+1$. Finally the track and location digits from 0_1 are substituted in a transfer instruction, 0_2, and this is used to set the translation into the register.

The sequence given below prints out the letters of the translation and tests for the space symbol which concludes the word. When this is located printing ceases and the final section of the programme spaces the type carriage and then tests to see if the 'word' was actually the single symbol (11111) which indicates that the sentence has ended. In the latter event the machine halts at Stop 2, but if

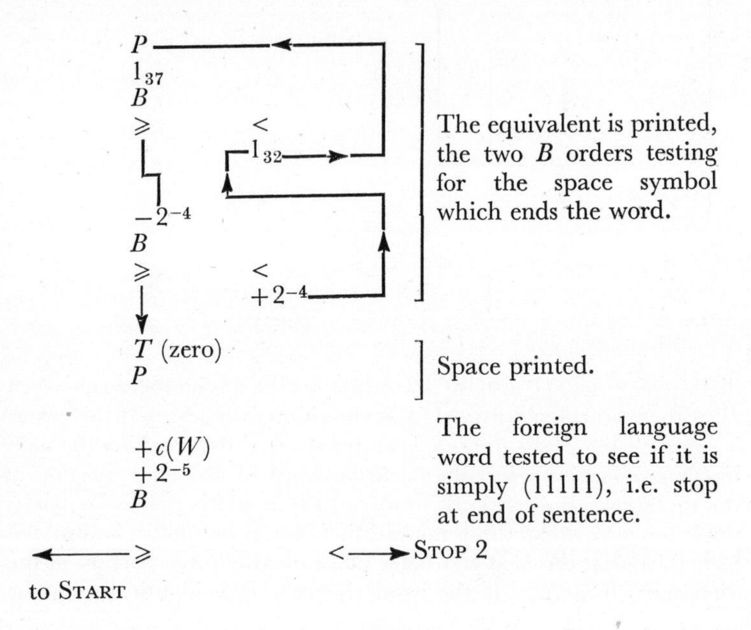

the 'word' differs from (11111) the programme returns to the start and reads in the next word.

WORD LENGTH COMPRESSION

When input words have a length which is greater than that which can be accommodated in a single computing machine storage location, several procedures are available. The most obvious is to use several machine words to store each real-language word; this is trivial but wasteful in space and in programme time. An alternative is to compress the input foreign language, and the foreign language dictionary words so that they occupy only a single machine word. Several methods are available for doing this and amongst these the following are probably the simplest.

The first is to add together the code numbers of each six-letter group in the input word and to treat the resulting code number as the equivalent of that word. For example:

resultant = 18, 5, 19, 21, 12, 20, 1, 14, 20
= 10010, 00101, 10011, 10101, 01100, 10100, 00001, 01110, 10100
= 10010, 00101, 10011, 10101, 01100, 10100,
+00001, 01110, 10100
= 10011, 10100, 00111, 10101, 01100, 10100

The second is successively to collate groups of code numbers so that, for the word considered previously:

resultant = 10010, 00101, 10011, 10101, 01100, 10100
col.: 00001, 01110, 10100
= 10011, 01011, 00111, 10101, 01100, 10100

There is little to choose between the two techniques and a choice between them will generally involve a consideration of the arithmetical speeds of the machine in use.

Both methods are related to the well-known *S*, or parity digit check of computing and telegraphy. There is always some risk that two different words may give rise to the same compressed version, but this danger is small and, in any case, can be anticipated when the dictionary is being constructed. Compression has the disadvantage that the stem-ending decomposition can no longer be used, at least in its most elementary form.

WORD ORDER

Few languages have identical word order and two major classes exist. In the first relations between words depend critically upon position and in the second they are almost entirely governed by endings. English is an extreme example of a positional language and Latin is typical of an inflectional one. Between the two extremes lie the gamut of modern languages with German and Dutch having one set of similar structures, and English and French and, to some extent, Russian another.

To produce a change in word order between an input foreign language text and the target-language output it is necessary to store at least some of the input words or their equivalents in the machine prior to producing an output. In the very simplest case, which is typified by the noun–adjective inversion which exists between French and English, it may be necessary only to examine the functional class of each input word before typing its translation. Then, suppose that the dictionary entry for French words consists of the following configuration:

(French word or stem) (English equivalent or stem) (Function number)

and that the function numbers 1, 2, and 3 apply to nouns, adjectives and verbs respectively.

If the phrase:

équation est

is presented to the machine, on receiving the word *équation* the dictionary entry located contains:

(équation) (equation) (1)

and upon inspecting the last component, (1), the machine decides that it is not directly possible to produce an output because the next word may be an adjective. The entries (equation) (1) are therefore held in store and the next word is called for. In the present example this is:

(est) (is) (3)

and, since a test shows that (3) is not the adjective code number, the translation:

equation is

is immediately typed out.

The phrase:

équation différentielle est

however, results in *équation* being stored as before, but the following word has the entry:

(différentielle) (differential) (2)

which the code number (2) shows to be an adjective. It is thus output directly and is followed by the noun already in store. The verb, which is the next word to be read, is now output directly and the translation appears as:

differential equation is.

This simple procedure can only be used when there are few word patterns which require order change, and in general a more sophisticated approach is needed. Two cases arise, the first in which blocks of words needing order change are of limited length, and the second where a whole sentence must be available before translation can begin. If a block of *n* words is known always to be adequate, the method of choice is to use a set of *n* filter positions, so that the progression of words between input to the machine and reproduction at the output involves the storage of *n* of them within the machine. Thus:

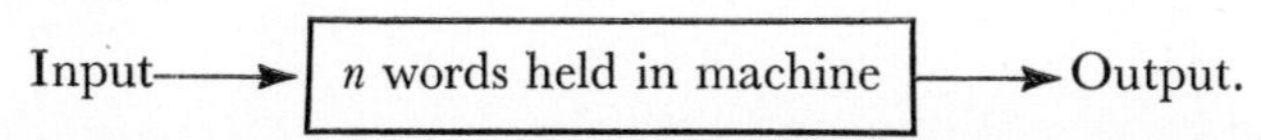

Actually to save storage space, it is sometimes advantageous to hold in the filter positions not words, either foreign or target, but the locations of the dictionary positions in which these words are to be found. This has the advantage that location numbers have far fewer binary digits than the words which they contain. On the other hand, it is difficult to deal with stems and endings by this simple method. A variant is to assemble together stems and endings so as to construct the translations of input words in one set of locations whose addresses are simply *n* consecutive words in the store. At the same time the function numbers are assembled in *n* other positions, and the two sets of data are processed simultaneously:

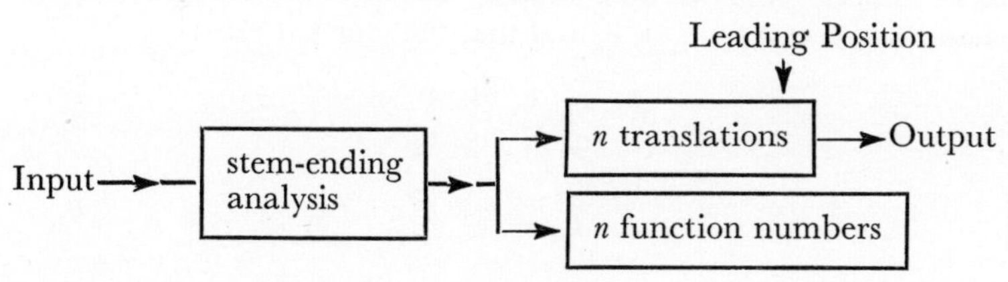

The operation of the filter is as follows:

The function number in the leading position is examined. If it is *not* one which can start a sequence needing rearrangement the leading word in the translation filter is typed out and both sets of data are shifted forward one place, a new word being read in from the input.

If the function number is one which *can* start a sequence which needs rearrangement, following numbers are associated with it to decide if the sequence actually does need rearrangement, if not, typing and shift follow and the process is repeated on the next word. When a rearrangeable sequence is encountered, its constituent words are typed out in appropriate order. This process is followed by a number of shifts of translations and function numbers to bring the next word, following the group already output, to the leading position. Two distinct methods exist for programming the filter. In the first, the filter contents are actually transferred from position to position in the store; whilst in the second, the positions of words already in the filter remain unaltered, but the instructions which make reference to them are modified so that they refer to later locations in the sequence. The latter process is simply achieved by adding an

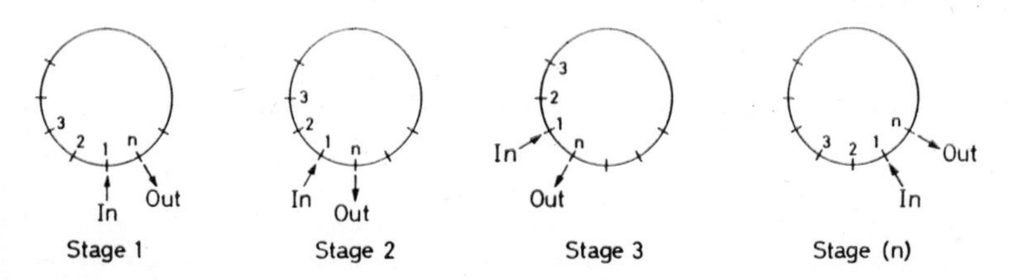

appropriate number to the operand address of instructions after each use of the filter, and by treating additions as being Mod n. In this way only n storage locations are needed for the filter and these remain fixed.

The way in which patterns of function numbers are recognized depends upon their extent. If few exist, a sequence of recognition tests suffices. For example, suppose that there are five possible function numbers: a, b, c, d, e, and that the four patterns:

$$\begin{array}{l} a,\ c,\ e,\ d,\ b, \\ b,\ e,\ d,\ c_1,\ c_2, \\ b_1,\ e_1,\ e_2,\ c,\ b_2, \\ d,\ a_1\ a_2,\ e,\ b, \end{array}$$

lead respectively to the rearrangements:

$$\begin{array}{l} c,\ e,\ a,\ d,\ b, \\ e,\ b,\ c_2,\ d,\ c_1, \\ e_1,\ e_2,\ b_2,\ c,\ b_1, \\ a_1,\ e,\ b,\ a_2,\ d, \end{array}$$

Then the detection programme operates as follows:

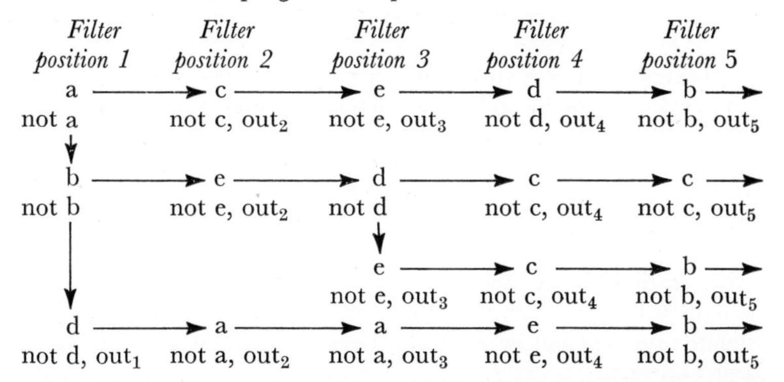

where each arrow on the right-hand side indicates that the particular pattern is present, and leads to a programme segment which performs the required rearrangement. The expressions 'out' indicate that the word sequence contains none of the functional patterns which require rearrangement and so with:

out_1—one word is typed at the output and the filter contents shifted one place,
out_2—two words are typed etc.,
out_3—three words are typed etc.,
out_4—four words are typed etc.,
out_5—five words are typed etc.

When there are many different configurations to be recognized, it is better to use a dictionary of configurations and a look-up procedure of exactly the same type as that employed in translating the language words. Where no-recognition is detected, the difference between the nearest dictionary entry and the input function number group gives the number of words which can be ouput from the filter corresponding to the out_1, out_2 etc. given above.

With languages such as German it may be necessary to rearrange, not only individual words, but also whole blocks of words, and in this event the filter technique becomes complicated. The correct approach under these circumstances is to input complete sentences which can be analysed in blocks and in words using separate programmes or dictionaries.

IDIOMS

The foregoing discussion of rearrangement of word-order leads naturally to an elucidation of the method by which idioms can be correctly translated. The actual process is simpler if the programme makes use of successive examination of function numbers rather than dictionary comparison.

Essentially the sequence of operations is as follows:

Each word which can form a part of an idiom is given a function number which is characteristic of that idiom, the machine, on detecting this number on any word proceeds to examine following words to see if they too bear the same number, if so the sequence of comparisons terminates in the printing out of an appropriate translation.

Naturally, in a programme which is to deal with idioms as well as with rearrangement, words will be accompanied not by a single function number but by several. Thus suppose that parts of speech bear numbers:

1 = noun	2 = pronoun
3 = adjective	4 = adverb
5 = verb	6 = preposition
7 = conjunction, etc.	

and that the two French idioms:

1. il-y-a   2. boîte de nuit

are under consideration. The entries in the machine dictionary will be:

French	*English*	*Function* (1)	*Function* (2)
a	has, there is	5	1
aura	will have, there will be	5	3
boîte	box	1	2
de	of	6	2
est	is	5	—
il	he	2	1, 3
nuit	night, night-club	1	2
savon	soap	1	—
y	there	4	1, 3

It should be noted that the meanings associated with the words given in this table have been deliberately restricted in order to make the method clear; in practice other meanings, for example *it* for *il*, would be given.

When the word *il* is presented at the input its dictionary entry is removed and stored, the contents of the Function (2) location are examined and they are seen to be non zero, thus indicating a possible idiom. The particular idiom sequence associated with Function (2) number 1 is then examined and it is seen to need three successive words each bearing the same Function (2) number to define the idiom. The sequence of operations is thus:

$$\begin{array}{llll} \text{Word 1}, Fn(2) = 1 \rightarrow & \text{Word 2}, Fn(2) & = 1 \rightarrow \text{Word 3}, Fn(2) & = 1 \rightarrow \\ & & \neq 1 \downarrow & \neq 1 \downarrow \\ & & \quad (1) & \quad (2) \end{array}$$

where the horizontal arrow leads to a programme which ignores the first two words and prints out the second translation associated with the third word. Thus, if *il-y-a* is presented to the machine, all of the above tests are satisfied and the second meaning associated with *a*, viz. *there is* is output, *il* and *y* being ignored. If, on the other hand, *il a* had been presented the first two tests would be satisfied but the third would fail, so that the programme branch associated with the vertical arrow (2) would be initiated and this would lead to the printing of *he has*. Finally, if the expression *il est* were presented the test would fail at *est* and the output via the vertical arrow (1) would lead to the printing of *he is*.

Exactly the same process applies to the idiom *boîte de nuit*. Here, however, the sequence of words must have their Function (2) numbers equal to 2 and it is seen that the output *night-club* which is the second meaning given under *nuit* will be produced. The expression *boîte de savon*, on the other hand, would lead to disagreement on the third comparison and this would lead to the un-idiomatic translation: *box of soap*.

Many words such as *il* in the above example can start several idioms and in this case the Function (2) locations will contain more than one idiom number. When this happens, the tests are made for the first idiom and, if these fail, they are repeated for the second. Thus if *il y aura* were presented, the test for idiom 1 would fail at *aura*, *il*, however, bears the idiom Function (2) number 1 and this also occurs on words *y* and *aura* so that the correct translation *there will be* is produced.

This process can be carried out just as easily using a dictionary of idiom structures but, since the only information which is needed is the presence or absence of the Function (2) idiom number on succeeding words and the number of such words which need to be examined, it is less advantageous here than in word rearrangement.

It is to be remarked that as words are read in the first test to be made is that involving the Function (2) idiom digits. If this fails, the Function (1) word order rearrangement digits are processed.

MULTIPLE MEANING AND AMBIGUITY

So far, except where a second meaning was associated with idiom, it has been assumed that words held in the dictionary have only one meaning. This is generally untrue and means are required for deciding which of the alternative meanings is to be output. Two distinct classes of ambiguity exist: grammatical and contextual. The first is typified by the word *est* which occurred in the previous section. The true dictionary entry corresponding to this word should have been:

French	*English*	*Function* (1)	*Function* (2)
est	is, east	5, 1	—

where the Function (1) number 5 indicates the verbal meaning *is* and the number 1 the substantive meaning *east*. Which of these meanings is appropriate will depend only upon the local context so that the rule can be set up that if a word having possible categories 5, 1 (verb) (noun) is preceded by a pronoun, category 2, the meaning 5 is to be adopted, whereas if it is preceded by an adjective or a preposition having categories 3 and 6 the substantive meaning, 1, is to be output.

The second type of ambiguity is not so easily resolved since, in general, the functional numbers of the various alternatives are identical. An example of this is provided by the word *noyau* which can take the meanings: *kernel*, *nut*, *centre*, *nucleus*, all of which are substantives. To clear up this kind of ambiguity it is necessary to add a third function class to the two already predicated, and this will contain numbers which define the fields in which the alternative meanings are appropriate. Thus:

French	*English*	*Function* (1)	*Function* (2)	*Function* (3)
Noyau	Kernel	1	—	1
	Nut	—	—	2
	Centre	—	—	3
	Nucleus	—	—	4

where the Function (3) numbers are defined as:

1. Mathematics. 2. Botany. 3. Sociology. 4. Physics.

There are two methods of using these numbers. In the first, where the subject of translation is known, the machine is simply programmed to ignore all meanings except that which falls into the required category. In the second, where the subject is unknown, the machine is programmed to keep a running count of the numbers of unambiguous words which fall into each of the categories. After some part of the text has been processed it will be found that one of the categories has been used more frequently than the others and this is taken as the indicator for deciding between the alternative meanings which occur. This method involves, in general, a preliminary run through the text.

Where the text deals with two subjects, for example the social implications of atomic energy, the situation is more difficult and the only solution is to keep a record, both of gross and of local context and to use these, if possible, to resolve the difficulties. It is the opinion of the authors, however, that almost all ambiguities can be treated by reducing the entries to that single word which best represents the sense of all of them. In the example given, *nucleus* would probably suffice.

LITERARY TRANSLATION

It has been said by Rabelais that:

> 'Les traductions sont comme les femmes. Si elles sont belles, elles ne sont pas fidèles, et si elles sont fidèles, elles ne sont pas belles'

and this holds the key to the possibility of literary translation by machine. The principle of operation is simple: a library of phrases, sentences and paragraphs is built up for the language into which translation is to be effected; and these are either constructed by persons of taste and attainment or taken from classical authors. These expressions are stored in a dictionary whose 'foreign language' content consists not of words but of category numbers which define the tense mood and subject of the passage to which they refer. When a foreign language text is presented to the machine the first operation is one of analysis using a dictionary of the sort described in previous sections of this chapter. The result of the analysis is not, however, a set of words but rather a set of category numbers. From the category numbers of each phrase of the foreign language text a composite category number is built up and this is compared with the dictionary of category numbers for the target language. When the nearest equivalent has been found the relevant passage is printed out.

This process is very similar to the one by which schoolboys (and others) are able to write a 'poem' in the style of Swift or Pope. It is eminently suitable for mechanical handling and has the sole disadvantage that no existing machine has adequate storage facilities to make it a practical possibility. It may be noted, in passing, that translation is a vector operation, that is one which possesses direction. Thus it is theoretically possible to translate the works of Shakespeare into modern French, which possesses all of the background of ideas to receive them; but the reverse process of, say, translating the works of Sartre into Shakespearean English is not generally possible.

7

THE MECHANICAL TRANSCRIPTION OF BRAILLE

THE BRAILLE SYSTEM

BRAILLE is a system of language representation for the blind which consists of embossed characters formed by using combinations of six dots arranged and numbered thus:

```
1 •   • 4
2 •   • 5
3 •   • 6
```

Each dot is known by its number, so that in writing about Braille characters we simply specify these quantities, for example, '2-3-4' stands for the character

```
      •
•
•
```

63 combinations of dots are possible, and in Braille used for languages employing Roman characters, the alphabet absorbs 26 of these signs, 10 are used for international punctuation marks, and the remaining 27 are used for the special needs of individual languages, such as accented letters or the making of contractions. Numbers are represented by the first ten letters preceded by the numeral sign (3-4-5-6). Some of the conventional representations are shown in Table 7.1.

For a number of languages, two grades of Braille have been established. Of these Grade I is a letter-wise transcription of Roman Print. The problem of automatic transcription is here, of course, quite trivial: it could very well be done by a kind of typewriting equipment in which the keys are labelled with Roman letters, and, on depression, produce the appropriate Braille character. Grade II is the form of the system for general use in Braille journals, books and letter-writing. Its primary purpose is to reduce the bulkiness of Braille books by the use of abridged signs expressing more or less frequent combinations of letters, including conjunctions, prepositions, pronouns, prefixes and suffixes.

A few languages have developed very highly-abbreviated systems,

Table 7.1

Line 1	A	B	C	D	E	F	G	H	I	J
Line 2	K	L	M	N	O	P	Q	R	S	T
Line 3	U	V	X	Z	Y	and	for	of	the	with
Line 4	ch	gh	sh	th	wh	ed	er	ou	ow	W
	,	;	:			!	( )	“ ?		”
Line 5	ea	be bb	con cc	dis dd	en	ff	gg		in	
Line 6	Fraction-line sign st		ing		Numeral sign ble	Poetry sign ar		Apostrophe		Hyphen com
Line 7	Accent sign					Italic or decimal-point sign		Letter sign		Capital sign
Used in forming contractions										
Compound signs	*	Dash	Square brackets [ ]	Inner inverted ‘commas’						

usually called ‘grades’. Such systems resemble shorthand, in that the original full text is scarcely recognizable. They are too difficult except for the expert, and few books are printed in Grade III Braille.

The relation between the letters of the alphabet and the Braille symbols is not simple: an alphabetic character may be represented sometimes by one symbol and at other times by another. The symbol chosen to represent a printed character depends upon what precedes and follows, so that the process of transcribing into Braille involves context. Some of the Braille symbols are used to represent certain frequently occurring groups of letters such as 'th', 'wh . . .', 'the', 'with', 'com . . .' etc. Such symbols are known as contractions.

In the following paragraphs, a group to be contracted is represented by capitals and two neighbouring contracted groups are separated by a bar '/'. Thus the word company is transcribed to 'COMpany' showing that 'com' is represented in Braille by a contraction, whilst 'disingenuous' is transcribed to 'DIS/INgENuOUs'.

RULES OPERATED BY A DICTIONARY

The production of Braille texts is governed by rules. A few of these determine the layout of the text on the page, but most concern the conditions under which contractions can be made. They show that transcription on an inkprint character or group of characters into Braille symbols depends both upon the context of letters immediately preceding or following the group concerned, and upon the wider context of the whole sentence in which the letters occur.

Considered solely as a context-dependent transformation of one series of data (inkprint symbols) into another (Braille symbols) the problem of mechanical transcription is analogous to mechanical translation. On the other hand it differs in that the numbers of elements making up the inkprint text and the numbers of Braille symbols are such that they can be treated by means of a digital computer of limited storage capacity. Ignoring capitals, italics and changes of type, inkprint practice employs just over 30, and the Braille system 63, symbols. Furthermore, rules for the production of Braille are available in the form of guides for hand transcribers; but the rules for translation of languages are the subject of discovery, not pronouncement. In contrast to the system of inkprint symbols and Braille, actual languages are not so conveniently restricted. Ambiguities in language cannot always be resolved by examining a limited context of the word concerned. The number of different words in a text, even in technical papers with highly conventional styles, cannot easily be reduced to such an extent that they may be dealt with by a computer of ordinary capacity.

Although Braille rules are quite clear in their intention, they are not immediately suitable for programming because they are not always expressed formally in terms of the structure of the sequence of symbols preceding or following the group whose contraction is to be made. Typical rules which are not formalized are:

'Contractions forming parts of words should not be used when they are likely to lead to obscurity in recognition or pronunciation, and therefore should not overlap well-defined syllable divisions. Word signs should be used sparingly in the middle of words unless they form distinct syllables. Special care should be taken to avoid undue contraction of words of relatively infrequent occurrence. . . .'

'Contractions should not be used which would upset the pronunciation of syllables: e.g. "asTHma" not "aSThma", "poSTHumOUs" not "posTHumous", "daCHshund" not "daCH/SHund", etc.'

'Contractions should not be used to bridge the components of compound words, e.g. "LONGhAND", "grasshoppER", "cARthorse", "kettledrum", "STateroom". . . .'

The non-formal terms in the first rule are 'obscurity in recognition', 'pronunciation', 'syllable division', and the success with which an automatic computer can be programmed to operate a rule involving these terms depends upon how accurately they can be expressed in terms of patterns of alphabetic characters. In many languages the classification of the alphabet into vowels and consonants enables the syllable divisions to be deduced. English, however, has no such direct connection and a dictionary procedure must be used for syllable division. The entries will consist of the most frequent words accompanied either by their Braille equivalents, or by an indication of their correct syllable division. This procedure amounts to giving an extensional definition of 'syllable' and is an expensive method of solving the problem because the routine to operate the dictionary would be relatively slow and the dictionary itself would take up a large amount of storage.

The operation of the dictionary is as follows:

Coded letters of the text to be transcribed are fed into one of the registers of the computer so that at any time a group of, say, twelve consecutive letters is available to the machine. Each time a letter is fed in, the previous letters are shifted by one place so that the initial letter is lost.

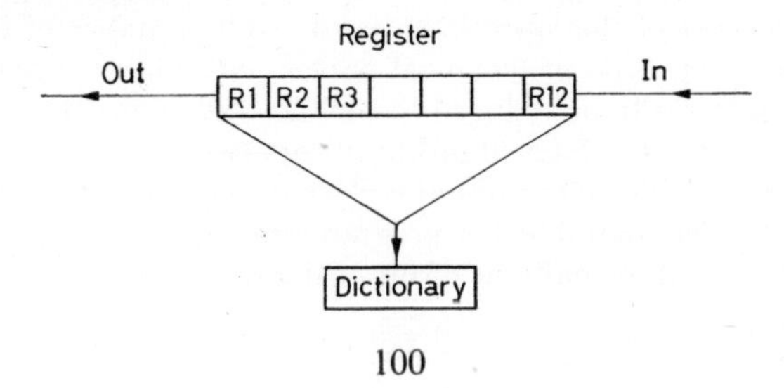

The contents of the register starting from R1 are then compared with the dictionary so that the longest entry which is part of those contents is selected. The dictionary entries are so arranged that an entry is always found even if it consists only of a single letter. When the equivalent of the entry has been printed, the letters in the register which have been contracted are discarded by shifting up the remaining contents and reading in new letters at R12. As soon as the register is full the process is repeated.

As an example, suppose that the register contains the letters 'bters . . .'. A comparison with the dictionary will show that the longest entry contained in these is the letter 'b'. The Braille equivalent of 'b' is then printed and the contents of the register shifted so that the 'b' is removed leaving 'ters' in the leading positions. Again, if the register contains the letters 'thers . . .', the longest entry in the dictionary which is part of the scanned sequence is 'the'. The contraction representing 'the' is then printed and the first three letters discarded to leave 'rs . . .' in the positions previously occupied by 'thers . . .'.

Consider next the rule for syllable division. This can be operated by including as entries at least those frequently occurring words where the indiscriminate use of contractions would bridge syllable divisions or disobey some other non-formal requirement. For instance, the word 'asthma' must be entered in the dictionary with the correct Braille equivalent 'asTHma'. If the word is not entered in the dictionary, the longest entry which is part of the group will be 'a', so that the Braille equivalent of 'a' will be printed and the letters 'sthma . . .' remain. Another comparison will show that 'st' is the longest group of letters in the register which is a dictionary entry, so that the contraction for 'st' is produced, thus yielding the incorrect transcription 'aSThma'.

Some other rules which, if they could be adequately formalized, would best be operated by means of a dictionary are the following:

'A contraction may be used when a prefix is followed by letters which form no recognized English word, by an English word that is not the same part of speech as the derived word, or by an English word the meaning of which is other than that of the derived word,' e.g. "dEDuce", "EDict", "prEDict", "prEDicaMENT", "prERogative", "DENomINator", "rENew", "prOFile", "prOF/OUND", "prOFuSION".

'A contraction should not be used when a prefix is followed by an English word of cognate meaning and being the same part of speech as the derived word', e.g. "denATIONalize", "denote", "predesST/IN/ED", "predomINate", "prerequisite", "react", "readmit", "sublet".

'"MIS"—the contraction for ST and SH should not be used in such words as "mistranslate", "misterm", "mishear", "mishap". The ST may be used in common words such as "mistake".'

'It is usually not advisable to take advantage of a prefix, in order to use a contraction which could not have been used in the simple word', e.g. "unblemiSH/ED", "unfulfillED", "unlessonED", "DIS/INgENuOUs".

'Generally speaking, a contraction may bridge a word and its suffix', e.g. "freEDom", "borEDom", "agreEA/ble".

'Exceptions to the above rules are such words as "dukedom", "kniGHthood", "orangeade".'

Again, the dictionary method will work well if it includes as entries those words which are not transcribed correctly by the indiscriminate use of contractions. But to operate the first two rules would require a large number of entries such as those illustrated. Even taking the most frequent words would make the dictionary too large. The third rule requires the entries

mistranslate
misterm
mishear
mishap
m,

so that, for instance, if the word 'mistake' occurred, the longest dictionary entry which is part of this word is 'm' and hence the Braile equivalent of 'm' would be printed and the correct transcription 'miSTake' would be made. The remaining rules may be treated similarly. Generally this dictionary structure will operate rules which, when formalized, will read:

'Contract the group of m letters A_m to the group of l Braille symbols B_l unless A_m is preceded by the letter group C_p and followed by the letter group D_q. In the latter event transcribe the whole combination $C_pA_mD_q$ to the Braille group E_r.'

This rule will be effected by entries

$$A_m \longrightarrow B_l$$
$$C_pA_mD_q \longrightarrow E_r$$

showing that $C_pA_mD_q$ is in effect an exception to the rule that A_m is to be transcribed to B_l.

Another type of rule which is conveniently operated merely by making entries in a dictionary is that which can be interpreted as a priority rule. That is, a rule which decides arbitrarily which contraction must be made where two possible methods of contraction are at hand. The general rule is:

'In cases where a word may be contracted in two or more ways, each saving the same amount of space, that way should be selected which produces the most readable combination of dots. For instance, when "d", "r", and "n" follow "one", contract "ed", "er", "en" in preference to "one".

'Ex: "tonED" is better than "tONEd", "prisonER" than "prisONEr".

'Avoid using Double Letter signs where there is an alternative single cell contraction, e.g. "mEDdle" not "meDDle".'

In this case the correct transcription can be obtained by the above dictionary mechanism if the entries

oned ——→ onED
oner ——→ onER
one ——→ ONE

are made in the dictionary showing that ER and ED have priority over ONE. Again the group 'oundd' should be transcribed as 'OUnDD', while 'ound' must be rendered as 'ouND'. Dictionary entries

oundd ——→ OUnDD
ound ——→ OUND
ou ——→ OU

in this order are required. Any group of letters beginning with 't' that can be contracted to a two-celled sign has priority over 'ST'. The contraction of 'st' in the natural order would prevent the contraction of the longer group, thus wasting space. Consequently, any of the groups, 'through', 'these', 'those', 'their', if preceded by an 's' are rendered by a group beginning 'ST . . .'. The correct transcriptions can be obtained by the entries:

sthrough ——→ sTHROUGH
sthose ——→ sTHOSE
sthese ——→ sTHESE
stheir ——→ sTHEIR
sthe ——→ sTHE

also

stion ——→ sTION

The number of entries may be reduced by making 'sth' a conditional entry, that is an entry whose equivalent has to be selected by means of a special routine. If 'sth' is recognized by means of the dictionary then the Braille equivalent of 's' is printed and a special sub-routine discards only the 's' although a three-letter group has been found. Thus the next operation of the dictionary compares the letters 'th' and those following. The dictionary entries beginning with the letter 't' are

through
those
these
their
the
th
t

so that at least 'th' is contracted. This gives priority to those contractions beginning with 'th' over those beginning with 'st'.

A similar procedure applies to groups beginning or ending with the letter 'e', e.g. 'herence' is transcribed correctly as 'h/ER/ENCE'. This can be achieved by dictionary entries

herence ——→ h/ER/ENCE
herenc ——→ h/ER/EN/c
here ——→ HERE

Alternatively, 'herenc' can have an equivalent 'h' and the same condition as for 'sth'. Similar combinations occur when three groups are juxtaposed.

It will be noticed that 'word' is a purely formal term since a word (as far as mechanical transcription is concerned) is defined as the group of symbols including 'space' between two neighbouring punctuation marks. By proper choice of the code for letters the special Braille rules concerned with the making of contractions at the beginning or end of words can be programmed either by making entries in a dictionary or by special recognition sequences. Thus there is a rule stating that 'com' can be contracted only at the beginning of a word. By making 'com' a conditional entry in the dictionary a preceding punctuation mark can be recognized and the correct transcription produced.

RULES OPERATED BY A FILTER ROUTINE

The preceding considerations show that a transcription programme based upon a dictionary is quite capable of formalizing most of the rules for transcription into Grade II to any required degree of refinement. Some of the rules, however, require an examination of too large a context for operation by means of a dictionary. These must be handled by means of a filter technique somewhat analogous to that used for mechanical translation. An example of this is provided by the rule governing the use of the contractions for the letter groups 'a', 'and', 'for', 'of', 'the', 'with'. These contractions can be used wherever the letter groups occur, but where the contractions stand for words and where they occur together the space between them can be eliminated 'where the sense permits'. There is no exact way of converting this to a formal rule, but formalization can be achieved to a certain extent at the expense of certain anomalies. Examples of elimination of the space between the words 'a', 'and', 'for', 'of', 'the', 'with' are:

He is *with the* boy.
He is *with the* officer *of the* watch.
The end *of a* perfect day.
but Him we think *of and* love.

Formalization of 'sense' can be partly achieved by a grammatical analysis of these words. Their grammatical functions are given below:

and	conjunction (*c*)
a, the	article (*a*)
of, with	preposition (*p*)
for	preposition or conjunction (*pc*)

The combination of word-types that can formally be said to make sense are:

(i) *c*/*p*/*a*
... *and with the* other group ...

(ii) *a*/*p*/*a*
... *the for the* most part thickly wooded slopes ...

(iii) *c*/*a*
... *and a* large house ...

(iv) *p*/*a*
... but *with the* sunset came ...

(v) *c*/*p*
... *and with* more than one ...

This analysis covers most cases but is not complete. Series of four such words can occur, but these are infrequent and can be treated as pairs of words. Thus, although *a*/*p* does not occur, the rule that space elimination can occur between pairs *c*/*p*, *c*/*a*, *p*/*a*, *a*/*p* will enable any series of this type of words to be analysed correctly. The difficulty is that 'for' can be both a conjunction and a preposition, so that we may consider 'for' to be in a class by itself. The conditions for space elimination now in question are:

c/for, for/*p*, for/*a*, *a*/for.

For/*a* is quite legitimate, since it can be either *c*/*a* or *p*/*a*. The others lead to forbidden combinations. In any particular instance of its

Combination	*Syntactical analysis*	
	Permissible combination	*Impermissible combination*
c/for	*c*/*p*	*c*/*c*
for/*p*	*c*/*p*	*p*/*p*
a/for	*a*/*p*	*a*/*c*

occurrence there is no means of deciding which function 'for' is taking without a complete analysis of the whole sentence in which it occurs. If it is decided without further programming to eliminate space between *a*/for, for/*p* and *c*/for, cases will arise which contravene the rule. For instance,

'Him we live *for with* joy and . . .'.

Space elimination here is not permissible, since the italicised words are not connected by sense, whereas it is in order in the following example, where 'for' is a conjunction:

'*For with* good food and wine . . .'.

In the present context the class of conjunctions excluding 'for' is recognized simply as the class whose only member is 'and', and the class of symbols which can be either conjunctions or prepositions is the class of 'and-words' which are not articles.

There may be cases where the above classification breaks down, but it will suffice for the majority of cases.

A method of operating the rules concerned with 'and-words' is to make the contractions for the 'and-words', and then perform the space-elimination while the symbols are in the filter.

Hence the programme has to detect patterns of ‘and-word’ symbols in the filter. The best method of detecting whether a number in a given filter position belongs to this class, is to attach a code digit to the word, though this procedure is not logically necessary, since an extensional definition could be employed.

In a programme constructed for APEXC a ‘1’ in the second position in a number is used to indicate membership of the class of ‘and-words’. If such a number is placed in the accumulator and shifted one place left, the digit comes to the first position, and can then be detected by means of a branch order:

$t/0$: $+c(x)(t/1)$	Number in position x transferred to accumulator.
$t/1$: $l_1(t/2)$	And-word digit placed in most significant position.
$t/2$: $B(y)(z)$	If and-word present (i.e. accumulator negative), go to order in position y: if not, go to position x.

This method is economical and fast.

Space elimination cannot occur, if one of the ‘and-words’ forms part of another word. Thus

. . . *and a*ttention . . .

cannot be rendered as

. . . *and*/*a*ttention.

Five filter positions are sufficient to operate the rule. Suppose the symbols are transferred from position 1 towards position 5. Disregarding for the moment the provision in the rule for ‘sense’, the space may be eliminated from position 3, provided the pattern of symbols is as shown below:

	1	2	3	4	5 6
FROM SCANNED SQUARE	space or punct. mark	‘and-word’	space	‘and-word’	‘and-word’ or space or punct. mark

The elimination of the space is effected simply by shifting the number in 2 to 3 and 1 to 2, leaving 1 vacant for the next character. Using this simple scheme a series of symbols

... and   and   and   and ...

is converted to the series

... and/and/and/and/ ...

A spurious operation will only occur, if a word is present which ends with two 'and-words'. For instance 'sofa *and a*' will be converted to 'sof*a*/*and*/*a*' under this simple scheme. This confusion might be averted by using a sixth position:

	1	2	3	4	5	6
FROM SCANNED SQUARE	space or punct. mark	'and-word'	space	'and-word'	'and-word'	space or punct. mark

If 5 contains an 'and-word', space elimination can only occur if 6 contains a space or punctuation mark.

This method, however, provides space elimination only between sets of three 'and-words'. Thus the set

... and   and   and ...

is transformed to

... AND/AND/AND   AND/AND/AND ...

If space elimination is permissible when there is either an 'and-word' or punctuation mark or space in 6, then removal of the space will always be legitimate, provided either that no word ends in three 'and-words' or that no word is a combination of two 'and-words'. There is no definite solution to this problem, it is a matter of indefinite refinement with a decreasing probability of error according to the number of filter positions.

CONCLUDING REMARKS

The preceding treatment, and some practical experimental trials, suggest that an ideal Braille transcription programme would consist of a dictionary used in conjunction with a filter routine. The size of the dictionary is the limiting factor on the practicability of the system. At least two hundred contractions can be made in Grade II

Braille, and a dictionary containing only these entries will lead to the indiscriminate use of the contractions. A more refined transcription can be obtained by increasing the number of entries, the degree of perfection depending upon the number of 'exceptions' covered by the increased number of entries. There is no definite limit, an exact representation of Braille as produced by hand transcribers would probably require a dictionary of about a thousand entries to deal with the problems of syllable division. This necessitates a storage space out of all proportion to the advantage gained over the straightforward procedure of making contractions whenever they occur.

The results of experiments have shown that the speed of output is not such as to make the machine production of Braille text an economic possibility. This is particularly the case at present when computing machine time is expensive and many skilled and willing workers transcribe books into Braille on a voluntary basis.

8

FRENCH

THE purpose of this chapter is to describe an experimental scheme for translating from French into English devised specifically for operation on APEXC, the electronic computer of Birkbeck College. When it is known that the storage capacity of APEXC is at present only large enough to permit the use of 250 foreign words and their English equivalents (assuming that space is to be left for programming or syntactical instructions), it will be realized that the primary requirement of such a scheme is that it should be as concise as possible, but at the same time by its attention to basic principles, of as universal an application as possible. This combination has to some extent been achieved, inasmuch as while leaving sufficient 'dictionary' space for about 250 foreign words and their translations, the scheme to be presented here enables the machine to perform some operations of syntactical nature and to recognize the masculine and feminine, singular and plural forms of nouns and adjectives and also all parts of the verb except the 1st person imperative and the subjunctive mood. The former of these is not included because it requires a rather periphrastic translation, which combined with its comparative rarity makes it unsuitable for preliminary experiments, the latter because certain forms of it are identical to the indicative. Whilst this is not important in the majority of instances, where the French subjunctive is translated by the indicative in English anyway, there are some constructions where the subjunctive, too, is required in English. Besides confusion of mood there is also the possibility of confusion of tense, since the 1st and 2nd person plural of the present subjunctive are the same in form as the imperfect indicative. In both cases the solution is to identify the subjunctive (where not formally identifiable) by the type of construction in which it occurs. Since this is impracticable, however, with the present storage capacity of APEXC, the subjunctive has been omitted from the scheme entirely.

THE STEM-ENDING METHOD—VERBS

The means of making the scheme so concise is the use of the stem-ending method, first employed by Booth and Richens in 1947. With this method the machine requires in most cases only one dictionary entry (i.e. the stem) in order to be able to identify all the different forms of this word. The greatest saving, of course, is with the verb,

	Present	*Future*	*Conditional*	*Imperfect*	*P. Historic*	*Imperative*	*Infinitive*	*Perfect part*	*Present part*
1.	Donn-								
1st	e	erai	erais	ais	ai				
2nd	es	eras	erais	ais	as	e		é	ant
3rd	e	era	erait	ait	a	e	er	ée	ante
1st	ons	erons	erions	ions	âmes			és	ants
2nd	ez	erez	eriez	iez	âtes	ez		ées	antes
3rd	ent	eront	eraient	aient	èrent	ent			
2.	Fin-								
1st	is	irai	irais	issais	is	is			
2nd	is	iras	irais	issais	is	isse		i	issant
3rd	it	ira	irait	issait	it		ir	ie	(issante)
1st	issons	irons	irions	issions	îmes			is	(issants)
2nd	issez	irez	iriez	issiez	îtes	issez		ies	(issantes)
3rd	issent	iront	iraient	issaient	irent	issent			
3.	Rec-								
1st	ois	evrai	evrais	evais	us	ois			
2nd	ois	evras	evrais	evais	us	oive		u	evant
3rd	oit	evra	evrait	evait	ut		evoir	ue	(evante)
1st	evons	evrons	evrions	evions	ûmes			us	(evants)
2nd	evez	evrez	evriez	eviez	ûtes	evez		ues	(evantes)
3rd	oivent	evront	evraient	evaient	urent	oivent			
4.	Vend-								
1st	s	rai	rais	ais	is				
2nd	s	ras	rais	ais	is	s		u	ant
3rd	—	ra	rait	ait	it	e	re	ue	(ante)
1st	ons	rons	rions	ions	îmes			us	(ants)
2nd	ez	rez	riez	iez	îtes	ez		ues	(antes)
3rd	ent	ront	raient	aient	irent	ent			

which has over thirty such forms (excluding the subjunctive and compound tenses), but before discussing this in detail the meanings of stem and ending should be explained. A stem is not necessarily a stem in the sense known to grammarians, but is defined as the longest part of a word common to all forms (inflections) of that word. For example, the stem of 'dormir' is 'dorm-', and what remains of each inflected form of 'dormir' after the subtraction of the stem 'dorm-' constitutes an ending. This rule, however, is not universal, for there are instances where a single stem would account for all forms of the verb, but more than one is chosen for the sake of utility (e.g. the stem 'acqu-' would cover all forms of 'acquerir', but in addition 'acquier-' has to be used in order to comply with the general system covering all verbs). Utility may in fact be considered the only principle of grammar in mechanical translation.

If verbs are divided, then, into stems and endings, the results for the latter will be found to account for each of the four regular conjugations (see previous page). If the French verb stems and their English translations are entered into the machine's dictionary together with an instruction that each word fed in for translation is to be identified with the stem in the dictionary which it most closely resembles, the basic meaning of every verb in the passage to be translated will be supplied in the output. In order to give the translation of the verb its correct tense, however, it is necessary to refer to the endings. These must also be included in the dictionary, though apart from the stems, since otherwise confusion will result (e.g. between the singular present indicative of 'avoir' and the endings characteristic of the singular Past Historic of the 1st conjugation). Neither should they be included as they appear above for the following reasons: Firstly the use of different inflections to indicate difference in person and number is almost entirely a linguistic redundancy, so that in actual fact where two identical endings occur it is necessary to make only one entry in the dictionary; secondly, since the purpose of the endings is solely to denote tense, there is no need to enter the whole ending but only enough to make the distinction in tense possible (e.g. the '-rai' part of the endings '-evrai' in 'recevoir' is sufficient to show that the tense is future). These distinctive endings are 46 in number (see p. 113). Here one or two explanatory remarks need to be made. The =stem means that there is no ending (e.g. 'il *vend*'). The feminine and plural forms of the present participle can be disregarded because they really come under its adjectival function. Those forms in parentheses, though characteristic of the tense under which they are included, are also found in another tense, of which they are regarded as primarily characteristic. The reason for this is that the limited capacity of the machine prevents instructions being included (assuming of course that they could be formulated) to enable it to differentiate between these formally identical tenses. For the present one translation must serve for both, and this is best determined by the tense in which the disputed form occurs the more frequently. For example, the ending '-is' represents the present indicative only in 'finir' type verbs, the past historic not only in 'finir' but also in 'vendre' and 'sentir' type verbs. It is therefore taken as primarily characteristic of the latter tense.

Obviously, however, the fewer there are of these identical tense forms, the less the confusion is likely to be. Hence the stem 'fin-' instead of 'fini-' for the 'finir' type of verb in the present scheme.

Present	*Future*	*Conditional*	*Imperfect*	*P. Historic*	*Perfect part*	*Infinitive*	*Present part*
e	rai	rais	ais	ai	é	r	ant
s	ras	rait	ait	as	ée	re	
z	ra	rions	ions	a	és		
t	rons	riez	iez	mez	ées		
ois	rez	raient	aient	tes	i		
oit	ront			rent	ie		
				is	(is)		
				it	ies		
				us	u		
=stem				ut	ue		
(is)					(us)		
(it)					ues		

Had the stem been 'fini-' the following difficulties would have arisen:

1. Endings= -s and -t: 1st, 2nd, 3rd pres. indic. = 1st, 2nd, 3rd pers. sing. past historic.
2. Ending=-is: 1st, 2nd, pers. sing. and past historic=perf. participle masc. plural.
3. Ending=stem: Perf. participle masc. sing. = 3rd pers. sing. pres. indic. of 'vendre' type verbs.
4. Endings= -e and -es: Perf. participle fem. sing and plural= 1st and 2nd pers. sing. respectively pres. indic. 'donner' type verbs.

With the stem 'fin-', on the other hand, only the first two of these apply. In the present scheme, therefore, 'fin-' is the best stem. As the dictionary is enlarged and a greater number of irregular verbs included, it is possible that ambiguities will occur which can be solved by making the stem 'fini-' instead of 'fin-' (e.g. unless the -i is added the verb 'saisir' will have a stem identical in form to the 1st and 2nd pers. sing. pres. indic. of 'savoir'). It is clear that there can be no one optimum system for all translation programmes, because although their general principles may possibly remain the same the details will always vary according to the size of the dictionary and the nature of its contents. This is particularly true of verbs, the stems of which will have to be modified continually in order to avoid ambiguities (e.g. 1st, 2nd, 3rd pers. sing. pres. indic. of 'vivre' = 1st, 2nd 3rd pers. sing. past historic 'voir', which in the 1st and 2nd persons is liable to be confused with the stem of the verb 'viser'). Since correspondences of this kind are by no means uncommon, it may be more advantageous in a larger dictionary to revert to the conjugational classification with each conjugation having its separate procedure, in order to reduce the likelihood of confusion.

To come back to the table of endings, the reason for the forms representing the present indicative being written as they are in the table lies in the rule already mentioned, in accordance with which the machine identifies every incoming word or part of a word with the nearest equivalent (meaning the nearest shorter equivalent) contained in the dictionary. Hence if '-s' is entered in the dictionary as a present indicative ending, the machine will identify with it not merely the bare '-s' of 'vendre' and 'sentir' type verbs, but also the '-es' of the first and the 'ions' of all conjugations, simply because this is the only entry in its dictionary with which it can identify them. For the same reason the 1st/2nd and 3rd pers. sing. pres. indic. endings of 'recevoir' type verbs ('-ois', 'oit') have to be entered in full, as otherwise they would be identified with the past historic forms '-is' and '-it' instead of the present '-s' and '-t'.

The system described above covers not only the regular but also the irregular verbs in most of their forms, the only difference being that many of the latter require several stems instead of one. 'Aller', for example, must have the following five: 'vais', 'va-', 'vont', 'all-', 'i-'. Difficulties do arise of course, just as with the regular verbs, but they are relatively few in number. There are five main types:

1. One or two verbs such as 'valoir' and 'vouloir' have a 1st and 2nd pers. sing. pres. indic. with the ending '-x', while some like 'prendre' and 'asseoir' have 3rd pers. sing. ending in '-d'. The solution to this is to add '-x' and '-d' to the list of endings indicative of the present tense.

2. Some verbs have a past historic form resembling none of the other tenses (except in one or two instances the perfect participle)

and consequently requiring a stem peculiar to itself. It would be natural to assume that since this stem is peculiar to a past tense, its translation in the dictionary could also be a past tense. Taking 'eus' the past historic of 'avoir' as an example, the stem would be 'eu-' and the translation 'had'. This works for the singular with its present endings '-s' and '-t', but the plural endings '-mes', '-tes' and '-rent' are marked in the system as characteristic of the past historic, so that the translation of the plural will come out as the past tense of 'had'. The problem is solved in this instance by making the stem 'e-' instead of 'eu-', so that all the endings lie in the past historic list, not half in this and half in the present indicative list. Then all that is required to ensure a completely correct result is to regard 'e-' as a regular stem with a present tense translation.

Besides 'avoir' this solution can be applied only to a few other irregular verbs (e.g. 'croire', 'croître', 'plaire'), not to all to which it seems applicable at first sight (e.g. 'être', 'voir', 'savoir', 'mouvoir', 'pouvoir', 'boire', 'faire', 'lire', 'prendre', 'mettre'). The reason for this is that any stem devised for the past historic of these verbs will be ignored in accordance with the rule that incoming words must be identified with the longest similar stem in the dictionary. This may be illustrated as follows: For the past historic of 'voir', i.e. 'vis', 'vis', 'vit', 'vîmes', 'vîtes', 'virent', it is possible to find stems to cover only 'vit', 'vîmes' and 'vîtes' (i.e. 'vit-' and 'vim-'); the other three forms are bound to be confused either with the stem of the verb 'vis-er' or with the verb 'vir-er'. A possible solution in such cases is to enter the ambiguous forms in the dictionary as they stand with an instruction to the effect that when they have no ending they belong to a different verb and consequently have a different translation than when found with an ending. So the word 'vis' without an ending would be recognized as belonging to 'voir', whilst in any longer form it would be recognized as a form of 'viser'. The 3rd person 'virent' would have to be distinguished from the same form of the verb 'virer' by context. Other verbs with past historic forms incapable of being treated like that of 'avoir' are 'tenir' and 'venir' ('tins' and 'vins') and those which, like 'finir', have forms identical in the singular to those of the present tense (e.g. 'dire', 'rire', 'suffire', 'confire', 'circoncire', 'conclure'). The solution for 'tenir' and 'venir' is again to enter the forms concerned into the dictionary in their entirety; for 'dire', 'rire', etc. as for 'finir' an examination by the machine of the context is necessary to resolve the ambiguity. This, however, does come within the scope of our present discussion.

3. The perfect participle of several verbs (e.g. 'dire', 'faire', 'écrire', 'conduire', 'craindre') is identical in form to the 3rd pers. pres. indic. In the compound tenses no confusion arises because the accompanying auxiliary serves to distinguish the participle as such, but used adjectivally the masc. sing., masc. plural and the feminine forms will all be interpreted by the machine as present indicatives. Only the masc. plural with its unique ending '-ts' (e.g. 'conduits') can be solved by distinction of form, the other three being homomorphic with other tenses, namely the masc. sing. with the 3rd pers. sing. pres. indic., the fem. sing. ('-te') with the 1st and 3rd pers. sing. pres. indic. of 1st conjugation verbs like 'jeter' which double the 't' (i.e. 'jette'), and the fem. plural with the 2nd pers. sing. pres. indic. of the same verbs (i.e. 'jet-tes') or the 2nd pers. plural past historic of all verbs. Again, although an extra stem (i.e. 'jett-') for the 'jeter' type verbs helps a little, a complete solution requires the machine to be able to take account of the syntactical context of these adjectival perfect participles.

4. Two of these verbs, 'faire' and 'dire', present a somewhat more complicated problem, since the fem. plural form of their perfect participle is not only identical with the 2nd pers. plural of the pres. indic. ('faites', 'dites') but also has itself a past historic ending '-tes'. If, however, 'faites' and 'dites' are entered in the dictionary as they stand, the second half of the problem is solved, leaving the first to be dealt with as suggested in 3.

5. (*a*) The masc. sing. perfect part. of 'asseoir' ('assis') and 'acquerir' ('acquis') are identical with the 1st and 2nd pers. past historic, but the fem. forms of the same have endings marked in the above scheme as primarily characteristic of the present indicative.

(*b*) All perfect participle endings in the '-u' or '-i' form in the masc. sing. will be '-us' and '-is' in the masc. plural—again forms characteristic of the past historic. These too can be solved in the way suggested in 3. No difficulty need be encountered as regards this similarity of perf. part. and past historic in a simple programme, however, because it can limit itself to indicating in translation of the verb merely past, present or future, no distinction being made between the various forms of the past tense.

THE ELIMINATION METHOD

In the method just described the meaning of the verb is first obtained from its stem, then the tense is found from the ending. A perusal of the table of endings reveals, however, that a second method is available, using only a particular letter or letters instead of the whole ending. The most obvious example of this is the letter 'r' which is sufficient to indicate that the tense is either conditional or future indicative. In place of an ending dictionary, therefore, it is possible to have a set of instructions like the following:

1. If the ending is 'r' or 're' the verb is an infinitive, so that ('to') must be inserted before the translation of the stem. The parenthesis denotes that the insertion of 'to' is not always necessary in the English translation—for example, in that of 'puis-je sortir?', whereas 'il va partir' does require it. Larger storage capacities will make it possible to incorporate instructions enabling the machine itself to make this distinction.

2. If the last three letters of the ending are '-ant', indicating that the word is a present participle, 'ing' should be added to the translation of the stem. Again, given a large storage capacity an instruction requiring the machine to deduct the mute '-e' from words ending so before adding '-ing' could easily be included.

3. If the ending contains 'r' not followed by '-ent' (in which case the tense is past historic) the verb is either future or conditional. If the letter '-i' occurs in any position but the last after this '-r' the verb is conditional, and the word 'would' must be placed in front of the stem meaning. Otherwise the tense is future, and the word 'will' is to be inserted. The English irregularity of 'shall' with the 1st person and the interchange of this and 'will' with a change of emphasis could also be accounted for with more dictionary space available.

4. If the first letter of the ending is 'e' (not followed by 'a'), 's' (not followed by 'a' or 'i'), 't' (not followed by anything) 'x', 'o', 'n', 'l', 'd', or there is no ending at all (i.e. a bare stem) and neither 'avoir' nor 'être' precedes it, the tense is the present indicative. In this case the stem meaning is adequate for the translation. (Note: What has been said about refinements in the above sections applies here also to the suffix '-s' in the 3rd pers. sing. present tense of the English verb.) If there is no ending and 'avoir' or 'être' does precede, the verb is in the perfect tense (see 5, p. 118).

Why 'e', 's', 'x', 'o', 'd', 't' should be indicative of the present tense is not difficult to see. Why, on the other hand, the same should be true of 'n' or 'l', and why 'e' should not be followed by 'a', 's' by 'a' or 'i', or 't' by any letter may not be so obvious. The reasons are as follows:

(I) 'n' enables some irregular verbs which double the final consonant of their stem in the 3rd pers. plural (e.g. 'venir'—'viennent') to be given one stem (i.e. 'vien-' instead of two);

(II) 'l' performs the same function for the first conjugation verbs in '-eler' (e.g. 'atteler'—'attelle');

(III) 't' is not followed by another letter because 'tes' is an ending characteristic of the past historic. (Note: This means that two stems are required for 1st conjugation verbs in '-ter', e.g. 'jet-', 'jett-');

(IV) 'e' not followed by 'a' because the 'e' is retained before 'a' and 'o' by first conjugation verbs ending in '-ger' (e.g. manger). The precaution is necessary, therefore, to prevent the imperfect and past historic of these verbs being translated as the present tense;

(V) 's' not followed by 'a' or 'i' as happens in the imperfect of 'finir' type verbs, if the stem 'fini-' is preferred to 'fin-' (i.e. '-issais', '-issait', 'issions', '-issiez', '-issaient'). (Note: With the present method the stem 'fini-' is preferable to 'fin-', because if the 'i' were not included in the stem, it would appear as the first letter of all the endings of the present indicative, which would in consequence be translated as a past historic. As it stands, only the singular forms of the past historic are confused with those of the present indicative.)

5. Everything not accounted for by the previous instructions is in the past tense and '(e)d' can be added to the translation of the stem*.

ADVANTAGES AND DISADVANTAGES

The two ways of ascertaining the tense of a verb may be called the stem-ending and elimination method respectively. The question of which is the better can only be answered definitely if the size of the dictionary required, the nature of the text to be translated, and the quality of the translation desired are known. The eliminating method, for example, assumes that the person receiving the translation will be content to have all past tenses translated simply as such, using the context and his own judgement to decide where the sense requires a perfect, imperfect, or past historic. For a more precise translation the stem-ending method is preferable.

Regarding the nature of the text, if this is written in the past tense, the stem-ending method will probably prove quicker than the eliminating method, which arrives at the past tense only as the last possibility. If, on the other hand, the tense is present or future the elimination method may well provide the quicker translation. This,

* NOTE: Again the rule is not adequate because of the existence of the English strong verbs—e.g. 'sang', 'sung'—but it is only the present restricted storage capacity, as we have said before, which prevents the inclusion of these strong forms alongside the regular form ('sing') together with the instructions necessary for their application.

however, is more in the nature of a guess than anything, as indeed would be any remarks about the amount of dictionary space likely to be taken up by each method. Two facts, however, are quite definite, namely, (*a*) the elimination method is better than the stem-ending method for translating perfect participles, because with it only the first letter of the ending, which is the one distinctive of the perfect (i.e. 'e', 'i', 'u',) need be considered, whilst for the stem-ending method all the forms (feminine and plural) have to be included in the dictionary and (*b*) for the treatment of irregular verbs the stem-ending method is the more economical because the fact that it can ignore the middle part of some of these verbs, enables them to be covered by one stem less in each case than with the elimination method.

Consider, for example, the verb 'asseoir'. With the elimination method this requires three stems, namely 'assied-' (for present indicative sing.), 'assey-' (for the imperf. and plural of pres. indic.) and 'ass-' (for future, past historic and conditional). In contrast, only two are needed with the stem-ending method, which can ignore the '-ied-' in the sing. pres. indic. and thus use 'ass-' for this too. This economy proved possible for seventeen irregular verbs out of the seventy examined. They are 'acquérir', 'bouillir', 'tenir', 'sentir', 'partir', 'servir', 'asseoir', 'savoir', 'pouvoir', 'écrire', 'joindre', 'craindre', 'mettre', 'battre', 'suivre'. To this list may be added their compounds and all similarly conjugated verbs, though care must be taken with the latter, since with some a verb similar in stem prevents the reduction of the number of stems. The only stem needed for 'dormir', for instance, would be 'dor-' if the verb 'dorer' did not exist, but it does exist and so not only has the stem to be 'dorm-', as with the elimination method, but also the singular forms of the present indicative (dors, dort) must be entered in the dictionary in full.

NOUNS AND ADJECTIVES

The treatment of verbs now completed, we can pass on to discuss the scheme for nouns and adjectives. The two are taken together because they may both have feminine and/or plural forms, and these can be dealt with by one and the same procedure. Nouns and adjectives fall into the following classes:

Type 1—If the feminine is formed simply by adding extra letters to the masculine without changing it, the masculine form (so marked) is entered in the stem dictionary and the extra letters denoting the feminine form (so marked) in the ending dictionary (e.g. 'chien-ne', 'joli-e').

Type 2—If the feminine form is a result of first altering the masculine form and the adding to it (e.g. 'chameau', 'chamelle'), the letters common to both forms (i.e. 'chame-') are entered in the stem dictionary, those peculiar to the masculine and feminine (i.e. '-au', '-lle') in the ending dictionary. The gender of a noun having identical forms for feminine and masculine must be determined in another way (e.g. by examination of the gender of an accompanying article or adjective).

It is easy to recognize the plural forms, both masculine and feminine, of those adjectives and nouns which have plural forms distinct from the singular, inasmuch as the ending will have either '-x' or '-s' added to it. Apart from irregularities the only class of nouns and adjectives not following this 'rule' is that ending in '-al' or '-ail' which drops the 'l' before adding 'ux' (e.g. 'cheval', 'chevaux', 'travail', 'travaux'). This class can be indicated in the same way as the feminine form described under *Type 2*, that is putting the letters common to both singular and plural (i.e. 'cheva-') in the stem dictionary and the letter 'l' which is dropped in the ending dictionary. Calling this class *Type 3*, we have now the following scheme for regular nouns and adjectives.

		Stem	*Ending*	*Plural*
Type 1	noun	chien (m.)	-ne (f.)	-s
	adj.	joli (m.)	-e (f.)	-s
Type 2	noun	chame-	-au (m.)	-s
			-lle (f.)	
	adj.	bre-	-f (m.)	-s
			-ve (f.)	
Type 3	noun	cheva-	-l (m.)	-ux
	adj.	principa-	-l (m.)	-ux
			-le (f.)	-s

Whilst all plurals which are genuine forms and not the same as the singular can be recognized by the three suffixes '-s', '-se', '-ux', the difficulty remains of enabling the machine to distinguish where these suffixes occur after the ending and where directly after the stem. The latter applies to masculine forms of *Type 1* nouns and adjectives and to masculine adjectives and all nouns of *Type 3*, the former to *Type 2* nouns and adjectives and the feminine adjectives of *Type 3*. A solution can be achieved by a set of simple instructions, which do not even require the machine to distinguish between the three suffixes:

1. The machine looks in the stem dictionary. If (*a*) the incoming noun or adjective can be identified exactly with one of the stems, it is a *Type 1* masculine noun/adjective and can be translated immediately; (*b*) the incoming noun or adjective cannot be identified with a stem, because there is an extra letter or letters present, it cannot be translated immediately, so,

2. The machine searches the ending dictionary. If the extra letter or letters are (*a*) identified exactly with an ending in the dictionary, the incoming word must be either a fem. sing. noun/adjective of *Type 1*, a masculine or feminine singular noun/adjective of *Type 2*, or a masculine or feminine singular noun/adjective of *Type 3*, and it is translated accordingly (see below); (*b*) identified with an ending contained in the dictionary, but there is still an extra letter left over, the incoming noun/adjective is the plural of the stem + ending word and the gender is that marked after the ending. An '-s' is added to the English translation to denote the plural; (*c*) not identified with an ending in the dictionary, the incoming noun/adjective must be the plural of the stem word and its gender is that marked after the stem in the dictionary*.

Although the scheme described allows rapid identification of all regular nouns and adjectives, it has the drawback of being not too economical as regards storage space, requiring as it does an ending dictionary even larger than the stem dictionary, since the majority of stems have at least one and often two endings. However, a consideration of the different endings for regular adjectives and nouns reveals that they are relatively few in number, say about 16 (i.e. 6 masculine, 10 feminine)—masculine: '-eur', '-au', '-l', '-il', '-f', '-se'; feminine: '-euse', '-rice', '-lle', '-ne', '-te', '-sse', '-e', '-ve', '-se'. A feasible arrangement, therefore, would seem to be to have an ending dictionary consisting of only these 16 endings, yet capable of producing a correct translation of all regular French adjectives and nouns. This might in fact be so, if English did not have a completely different feminine form of a noun where French has only a partially different form (e.g. 'fils-fille', 'son-daughter'), or an irregular plural where French has a regular one, (e.g. 'homme-s', 'man-men'). A reasonable solution can be achieved, however, by dividing all nouns into two classes:

(*a*)—Those which have a completely different word for masculine and feminine (e.g. 'cheval-jument'), those which have no gender in

* Note: The identification of number in adjectives is, of course, not directly relevant to their actual translation, but can nevertheless be useful in determining the number and gender of nouns with identical masculine and feminine or singular and plural forms.

English (nouns like 'le village', abstract nouns etc.)—all those, in fact, not requiring a distinction in gender in translation*.

(*b*)—Those which have a feminine or plural form requiring a different translation from the masculine or singular form respectively.

Nouns of the first class, where the ending serves only for identification and not for actual translation, may be dealt with in the way mentioned above, that is, by means of an ending dictionary of only 16 endings (32, if plurals are included for the purpose of getting immediate recognition and dispensing with instructions to the machine). In this way the speed of identification is preserved and, at the same time, combined with a reasonable economy.

For the second class the unmodified system can be retained. In this every noun is accompanied by its feminine and plural endings, each with its appropriate translation if different from that of the masculine singular. For cases where the feminine is simply a lengthened form of the masculine, the two translations will be marked alongside the stem and ending respectively (e.g. 'chien=dog', ending='-ne'=dog (bitch)). If, however, a change in the masculine form is involved, the two translations will accompany the two endings, as for example in 'act-' (no translation), endings: '-eur=actor', '-rice=actress'.

Before leaving the section on nouns and adjectives, it should be said that the remark made in connection with verbs applies equally well here; namely that if two words of different meanings are confused by the regular stem-ending procedure, the stems must be altered where possible in order to create a means of distinction. If this should prove impossible, the forms in question must be treated as irregular and entered in the dictionary as they are.

PRONOUNS

The only other part of speech requiring instructions for its identification is the pronoun; to be more precise, the personal (unstressed) and the possessive pronoun. Here there are four difficulties to be overcome, namely those of distinguishing the accusative of the 3rd personal pronoun ('le', 'la', 'les') from the definite article, the dative plural of the 3rd personal pronoun (leur) from the identical possessive form, the nominative 'nous' and 'vous' from the accusative/dative, and finally that of removing the oblique forms of the personal pronouns from their position before the verb in French to their normal English position after the verb.

The first problem can be solved by interpreting 'le', 'la', 'l'',

* NOTE: All adjectives can therefore be included here.

'les' before a pronoun or verb as forms of the personal pronoun not the definite article. Similarly in the second case when 'leur' precedes a verb, it may be taken as the personal pronoun.

The other two can be treated as follows:

Type 1—The sequence is:

pronoun^1 + pronoun^2 + pronoun^3 + verb.

If 'nous/vous' is the first pronoun, then it is nominative and the order of translation is:

pronoun^1 + verb + pronoun^2 + pronoun^3

(e.g. 'nous le leur donnons' = we give it them).

Type 2—The sequence is:

pronoun^1 + pronoun^2 + verb.

Here there are several possibilities:

(*a*) if pronoun^1 is a nominative form ('je', 'tu', 'il', 'elle', 'ils', 'elles') pronoun^2 is oblique, and the order of translation is then:

pronoun^1 + verb + pronoun^2

(e.g. 'je le donne' = I give it);

(*b*) if pronoun^1 is oblique, pronoun^2 is also oblique. Then the order of translation is:

verb + pronoun^1 + pronoun^2

(e.g. 'le berger le lui donne' = the shepherd gives it him);

(*c*) if pronoun^1 is a form which cannot immediately be identified as either nominative or oblique (i.e. 'nous' or 'vous'), the verb ending must be examined to see whether it agrees with the 'nous' or 'vous'. Thus:

1. if the verb ends in '-ons' or '-mes', 'nous' is nominative;
2. if the verb ends in '-z' or '-tes', 'vous' is nominative.

} Translate in order given in (*a*)

If there is no congruence, the 'nous' or 'vous' is oblique and the translation order is that of (*b*).

Type 3—If the sequence is:

pronoun + verb,

the procedure is exactly the same as for *Type 2*.

CONCLUSION

This, then, is the outline of a basic programme for translating from French into English. It is concerned almost entirely with grammar because this and the problem of multi-meaning (distinguishing between the various meanings which a word may have) are the only sources of any real difficulty for mechanical translation. Syntax, apart from a few minor things such as word order where nouns and adjectives or, as we have discussed above, pronouns are involved, is similar enough to that of English and need not concern us at this stage. As for the problem of multi-meaning which we have mentioned, this and its possible solution will be dealt with in the next chapter.

9

GERMAN

SECTION I

PUNCTUATION, CO-ORDINATION, WORD-ORDER, NOUN

THIS chapter, which deals with the possibilities of translating German by electronic computer, is not an exact counterpart to the chapter on French, inasmuch as it does not aim to present a complete, though small scheme for incorporation in an existing machine. The size of the programme required to deal with the vastly more complicated syntax of German makes this impossible at the present time. What is presented is not a scheme—it is too rambling and has too many loose ends to be called that—but rather a conglomeration of the main problems to be faced in translating German together with one or two suggestions on how to overcome them.

The basis of our own treatment is some work already done by Oswald and Fletcher* on the subject of German syntax. This we have endeavoured to extend a little, while adding something about the co-ordinate problems of grammar and lexicography.

INPUT OF FOREIGN LANGUAGE TEXT

The machine must have a fixed segment of text to read in at a time, and for obvious reasons the most suitable unit in translating German is the sentence, as defined by a period, semi-colon, colon, exclamation or question mark. Although each sentence is to be read in as a whole, this does not mean that the machine necessarily deals with it all at once. On the contrary it is more convenient—especially with the more complicated types of sentence—if the machine can break it up into smaller units and treat each of these in turn. Should it be wondered why these units are not read in one at a time in the first place instead of the whole sentence, the answer is simply that the smaller units cannot always be treated separately: to decide whether they can be so treated requires an examination and analysis of the actual text, which is not possible, unless this—in the form of

* Proposals for the Mechanical Resolution of German Syntax Patterns—'Modern Language Forum', Vol. XXXVI, 1951.

the whole sentence—is already present in the machine's store. Defining marks of the subdivisions within the sentence as given by Oswald and Fletcher are:

1. Any period, semicolon, colon, exclamation or question mark, is the terminal boundary of a grammatical clause.

2. The comma can be recognized as the initial boundary mark of a subordinate clause whenever it occurs immediately before a relative pronoun, subordinating conjunction, interrogative adverb, or interrogative pronoun; or before a preposition followed by any one of the aforementioned elements.

3. The comma can be recognized as the terminal boundary mark of a subordinate clause when it precedes either 'so' or 'dann', or whenever it occurs after a finite verb in a clause introduced by a subordinating element.

4. The comma can be recognized as the terminal boundary mark of any infinitive clause when it occurs immediately after an infinitive preceded by 'zu' or an infinitive with 'zu' infixed.

5. Except in the environments outlined in 2, 3, and 4, the comma serves only as a mark of co-ordination, i.e., marks the linkage of like functional units, or the linkage of like partial clauses, or the linkage of complete independent clauses—to which perhaps may be added

6. The comma is the terminal boundary of a co-ordinate clause, when followed by 'und/oder'.

The preceding subdivisions of the sentence can be recognized by the machine without reference to the contents of the text, but two remain which undoubtedly require this reference, one concerning co-ordinate clauses, the other interrupted clauses(i.e. by the insertion of other clauses or phrases). The general rule for co-ordinate clauses is of course that, if the second of the two clauses is capable of being separated from the first and standing on its own as a complete and independent unit, this is denoted by an intervening comma. If, on the other hand, it is not capable of being separated, having an intrinsic connection with the first, no comma intervenes. Since in the former case, in order to be able to stand on its own, the clause must obviously have its own subject, it is reasonable to conclude that a comma between two co-ordinate clauses indicates that the subject of the second is different from that of the first, e.g.

'In der Diskussion um das Frühwerk Thomas Manns in den zwanziger Jahren spielte der Gegensatz Bürger—Künstler eine gewisse Rolle, und die Interpreten können sich, indem sie besonders dieses Motivfeld in den Vordergrund rücken, auf den Dichter selbst berufen.'

If this were an inviolable rule, the machine would have no difficulty in dealing with a sentence like the following:

'Wenn Hegel in dem genannten Aufsatz auf die Überwindung der „Entgegensetzung" dringt, und die Versöhnung von Geist und Natur erstrebt, dann ist für ihn Abraham jene Gestalt, die unter Betonung der schlechthinnigen Exklusivität Gottes das Unheil der „Entgegensetzung" verschuldet hat.'

Where, though '*die Versöhnung*' may be either subject or direct object according to its form, the comma before the '*und*' would definitely prove that it must be the subject, there being no other possible subject form in the clause. It should be an inviolable rule—both logic and uniformity demand it; unfortunately authors cannot have their arms twisted, so that occasional exceptions to the rule like the above, where no comma should exist before the '*und*', will continue to crop up, and the machine must be prepared to deal with them.

In contrast with co-ordinate clauses separated by a comma, it is not possible to state categorically of those not separated by a comma that they must have one and the same subject. The grammar-book rule is that already stated: regardless of whether the two clauses have the same subject or different ones, if they are interdependent and not capable of standing alone, no comma is placed between them. It is clear, however, that it is only with two subordinate clauses that the subjects can be different and the clauses still remain unseparated by punctuation, e.g.

Daß diese Fremdheit aber auf die Dauer nicht bestehen kann *und* eine Auseinandersetzung gesucht werden mußte, ist in der Geschichte der bürgerlichen Gesellschaft leicht zu belegen.'

In fact, since two co-ordinate subordinate clauses are by nature interdependent and inseparable, they should always be connected by a conjunction without a comma. Instances like,

'Da eine Woche meines Urlaubs vergangen ist, so daß ich bald an die Rückreise denken muß, *und* daß ich außerdem befürchte, sie bei meiner Rückkehr nicht mehr anzutreffen, möchte ich . . .'.

are only apparent contradictions to this rule, the explanation lying in the intervention between the two co-ordinate clauses of a third clauses (*so daß ich . . . muß*). If this were omitted, the result would be,

'Da eine Woche meines Urlaubs vergangen ist und ich außerdem befürchte . . .'.

True exceptions like the one quoted at the beginning are rare. With co-ordinate main clauses, on the other hand, it is equally clear, that whether they are capable of standing alone depends simply on whether they have the same or different subjects. If they have the same subject they are interdependent and will therefore not be separated by punctuation; if they have different subjects they are independent and will be separated by punctuation. But just as exceptions can occur in the case of subordinate clauses, so too they can occur here, e.g.

'Darin ist diese Stoffwahl gerechtfertigt und es liegt kein Grund vor, demgegenüber irgendwelches Befremden zu äußern.'

The question of punctuation as a guide in co-ordination may be summed up, therefore, by saying that with subordinate clauses punctuation is of no assistance in deciding whether the clauses have the same subject or different ones, and with main clauses, where it could be of assistance, it is not because authors do not always follow the rules laid down in grammar books. Punctuation being unreliable, some other means of discovering whether two co-ordinate clauses have the same subject or different ones must be used. If the clauses connected are main clauses, there is fortunately no difficulty, because the nature of the word occurring immediately after the conjunction will indicate whether the clauses have the same or different subjects. When the word is a verb, the former will be true, e.g.

'Im Zauberweg verliert der Tod diese Eindeutigkeit und erhalt das Gepräge von etwas verwirrend-Zweideutigem.'

When a substantive, the latter, e.g.

'Darin ist diese Stoffwahl gerechtfertigt und es liegt kein Grund vor, demgegenüber irgendwelches Befremden zu äußern.'

If, on the other hand, the clauses connected are subordinate clauses, there may or may not be a difficulty, depending again in most cases on the nature of the word (or to be more precise, the syntactical unit) following the conjunction. Where it has a uniquely nominative form, the clauses clearly have different subjects, e.g.

'Etwas von diesem Mut ist vor allem in Hans Castorp lebendig, da am Ende des Romans die Stunde der Bewährung schlägt und *der Tod* nicht mehr in der begrenzt-persönlichen Erfahrung des „Zauberbergs" an ihn herantritt, sondern . . .'.

The same is true where the syntactical unit has a nominative/accusative instead of a uniquely nominative form, but the verb is passive or transitive, e.g.

'Daß diese Fremdheit auf die Dauer nicht bestehen kann und eine Auseinandersetzung gesucht werden mußte, ist in der Geschichte der bürgerlichen Gesellschaft leicht zu belegen.'

Where the syntactical unit has a nominative/accusative form and the verb is active a decision cannot be made without first examining the rest of the clause. Then, if a second syntactical unit either of the same type (i.e. nom./accus.) or uniquely accusative is revealed, it may be assumed that the one immediately following the co-ordinating conjunction is the subject of the clause, e.g.

'Wenn Thomas Mann diese Thematik nun wieder aufgreift, dann geht es auch bei ihm vor allem darum, daß der Tod in die Fülle und zugleich in die Leere hineinführt und *die Begegnung* mit ihm nicht nur *Steigerung* bewirkt, sondern auch Zersetzung und Auflösung.'

It will be noted that in this instance the second syntactical unit is neither nom./accus. nor uniquely accusative. When such units are found their function has to be deduced from various features of the surrounding text. In this instance, for example, we could put together the facts that the verb is of the type usually requiring an accusative direct object, that there is no other unit capable of fulfilling this function besides '*Steigerung*', and that the position of '*Steigerung*' prevents it being interpreted as a dependent genitive, to arrive at the conclusion that '*Steigerung*' is the direct object. We might be wrong, of course, because we have not eliminated the dative case, but the latter is so rare, except with personal pronouns, that the odds are all in our favour. More will be said about this type of procedure later on in connection with change of word order*.

If, on the other hand, when searching the rest of the clause for a second nom./accus. or accusative syntactical unit, none is found, it is most likely that the first is the direct object, not the subject of the co-ordinate clause, e.g.

'Dieser tritt aber unerbittlich für das Leben gegen die Zweideutigkeit und Verführung des Todes um so überzeugender ein, als er selbst nicht gegen die Verlockung der Schwermut und des Todes gesichert ist und *sie* zunächst in sich selbst zu überwinden hat.'

Since transitive verbs are often used intransitively, there is theoretically no reason why a co-ordinated subordinate clause should not be found in which there is only one nom./accus. syntactical unit (i.e. immediately following the conjunction) and this unit is the subject. In practice, however, it is not common to find such a clause.

* NOTE: When considering any problems involving nominative/accusative forms, precautions must be taken to ensure that the machine does not identify the various phrases denoting duration of time as such (e.g. '*einige Tage, die ganze Zeit*'). This is made easier by the fact that such phrases occur in the main with intransitive verbs.

In a subordinate clause introduced by a relative pronoun any nom./accus. syntactic unit in a co-ordinate clause must of course be accusative, if the relative is the subject of the first clause, e.g.

'Will man die tiefere Einheit des Romans verstehen, dann ist darüber hinaus vor allem noch auf das Motiv hinzuweisen, das alle übrigen in sich begreift und *die Thematik* des Romans im Ganzen formt.'

Before leaving the subject of co-ordination two general remarks may be made about distinguishing the different types of co-ordination, followed by a description of the method proposed by Oswald and Fletcher for dealing with the same problem.

1. If there is a finite verb before and after the co-ordinating word, then two clauses are linked, and the translation of the first can be completed before passing on to the second. It makes no difference if the second clause has no subject of its own (i.e. shares it with the first clause), except that in this case an auxiliary or modal verb will probably occur only with the second of the two participles/infinitives,

'. . . sondern in ihm kommen Spannungen und Gegensätze zum Ausdruck, die in der Situation der bürgerlichen Gesellschaft selbst angelegt sind und immer wieder von ihr ausgetragen und zum Ausgleich gebracht werden mußten.'

2. If there is only one finite verb, the co-ordinating word merely connects two words or phrases, which must be taken together as belonging to one clause.

In order to understand Oswald and Fletcher's solutions to the problem of co-ordination—solutions which they themselves wished to be regarded as tentative—it is necessary to be acquainted with their system of coded syntactical units. For this purpose the table of such units given by them is reproduced here.

Table of Coded Syntactical Units

1. 'der'; 'dieser'-words in '-er'; descriptive adjectives in '-er'.
2. 'des'; 'dieser'-words in '-es'; 'ein'-words in '-es'.
3. 'dem'; 'dieser'-words in '-em'; descriptive adjectives in '-em'.
4. 'den'; 'dieser'-words in '-en'; 'ein'- words in '-en'.
5. 'die'; 'dieser'-words in '-e'; 'ein'-words in '-e'.
6. 'das'; 'ein'-words in zero; descriptive adjectives in '-es'.
7. Descriptive adjectives in '-en'.
8. Descriptive adjectives in '-e'.
9. Comparative of descriptive adjectives in zero.
10. Comparative of descriptive adjectives in '-er'.
11. Comparative of descriptive adjectives in '-es'.
12. Comparative of descriptive adjectives in '-em'.
13. Comparative of descriptive adjectives in '-en'

Table of Coded Syntactical Units—(contd.)

14. Comparative of descriptive adjectives in '-e'.
15. Present/past participle in '-er'.
16. Present/past participle in '-es'.
17. Present/past participle in '-em'.
18. Present/past participle in '-en'.
19. Present/past participle in '-e'.
20. Masculine noun.
21. Feminine noun.
22. Neuter noun.
23. Plural noun.
24. Genitive singular of masculine and neuter nouns.
25. 'ich'; 'wir'; 'er'; 'man'.
26. 'mir'; 'ihm'; 'ihnen'.
27. 'mich'; 'ihn'.
28. 'uns'.
29. 'es'.
30. 'sie'.
31. 'sich'.
32. 'wer'.
33. 'wessen'.
34. 'wem'.
35. 'wen'.
36. 'was'.
37. 'deren'; 'dessen'.
38. 'denen'.
39. 'haben', present singular.
40. 'haben', present plural infinitive.
41. 'haben', past singular.
42. 'haben', past plural.
43. 'sein', present singular.
44. 'sein', present plural.
45. 'sein', past singular.
46. 'sein', past plural.
47. 'sein', infinitive.
48. 'werden', present singular.
49. 'werden', present plural infinitive.
50. 'werden', past singular.
51. 'werden', past plural.
52. Modal verbs, present singular.
53. Modal verbs, present plural, infinitive.
54. Modal verbs, past singular.
55. Modal verbs, past plural.
56. Other verbs, present singular; past participle of verbs in '-ieren', past participle of weak verbs with inseparable prefix.
57. Other verbs, present plural, infinitive.
58. Other verbs, past singular.
59. Other verbs, past plural.
60. Past participle in zero.
61. Present participle in zero.
62. Infinitive with '-zu-' infix.
63. 'worden'.
64. Non-prepositional prefix, unattached (to be attached to finite verb of clause in which it occurs).
65. Adverb; descriptive adjective in zero.
66. Adverbs of quantity; numerals (to be attached to word immediately following).
67. 'denn'; 'sondern'.
68. 'und'; 'oder'; 'aber'; 'auch'.
69. Subordinating conjunction.
70. Preposition.
71. Preposition compounded with 'da-'.
72. Interrogative adverb.
73. 'zu'.
74. 'um'; 'ohne'; 'anstatt'.
75. 'als'.
76. 'wie'.
77. 'so'; 'dann'.
78. 'nicht'.
79. Contraction of preposition with article.
80. 'ihr'.
81. Absolute adverbs.
82. Explanatory conjunction.

On locating a co-ordinating element ('und', 'oder', 'aber', and the comma) the procedure is simply to search the text on either side of it for syntactical units with similar codings in the code table. As an example of a 'linkage of like elements', as the authors call it, is given,

'"Wir denken uns eine bestimmte Anzahl konkreter Gegenstände, z.B. aus einem vor uns stehenden Obstteller etwa 5 Äpfel, 2 Birnen, und 1 Aprikose."

66—23—66—23—66—23.

The apposition of the sequences 66—23, 66—23, 66—23 indicates linkage of like elements.'

Naturally Oswald and Fletcher did not believe that all correspondences between units with similar syntactical function would be so precise. As they stated, if the elements linked are nouns or noun phrases, a check must be made to determine whether one noun, which may have a dependent genitive or prepositional phrase, is attached to another which has an adjective fulfilling the same role, e.g.

'"Die Anekdote weist Züge auf, die wir oft in der Volksdichtung finden: episodenhafte Kürze, Betonung der Handlung, Beschränkung auf das Notwendige."

(The linkage indicated is 8—21+21—1—21+21—70—6—22).'

When the syntactical units connected were verbs, only six combinations of the code numbers applied. These were given as:

56+	co-ordinating	element	+56
57+	,,	,,	+57
58+	,,	,,	+58
59+	,,	,,	+59
60+	,,	,,	+60
56+	,,	,,	+60

and illustrated by

'Er sucht und findet eine algebraische Lösung.'
56 56

'Wir suchen und finden algebraische Lösungen.'
57 57

Nos. 58 and 59 were identical to the above, but with perfect in place of the present tense verb forms.

'Wir haben algebraische Lösungen gesucht und gefunden.'
60 60

'Er hat das Problem studiert und gelöst.'
56 60

This tentative scheme was completed by a rule requiring the machine, when no linkage of like units was indicated by the code table, to scan the sentence for the existence of two identical clauses, one on each side of the co-ordinating conjunction.

Slight though it be, the scheme obviously points the way to a complete solution of the problem—perhaps not *the* solution, but at any rate one solution—by a dictionary of co-ordination patterns.

The second problem encountered when dividing up a sentence concerns clauses or phrases occurring within a clause, the difficulty here being to get the machine to re-unite the two halves of the thus divided clause. The part of speech to be found in the second half is usually—along with prepositional phrases, etc.—the verb (in a subordinate clause the whole of it, in a main clause the whole, if uncompounded or without modal verb, otherwise the infinitive or past participle) but the direct object, subject and predicate (in sentences with the verb 'to be') are also found, e.g.

'Ein so zusammengesetztes Licht wird natürlich im allgemeinen ein kontinuierliches Spektrum geben, *nur müssen an den Stellen*, die den fehlenden Wellenlängen entsprechen, *Lücken vorhanden sein*, die betreffenden Spaltbilde müssen fehlen. *Die Umkehr des Satzes*, nämlich daß ein beobachtes kontinuierliches Spektrum notwendig von einem im festen oder flüssigen Zustande befindlichen leuchtenden Körper herrühre, *ist aber nicht zulässig*.'

In one way or another the machine must be capable of realizing that a certain clause is incomplete. This is not so difficult, because in the overwhelming majority of instances (99 out of 100 would not be a bad guess) the remaining portion of the divided clause occurs immediately after one intervening subordinate clause. All that is necessary is to inform the machine that in a clause it must expect to find:

(*a*) a subject.
(*b*) a finite verb.
(*c*) if a modal verb is present, an infinitive.
(*d*) if an auxiliary is present, an infinitive or past participle.
(*e*) if the verb can be used transitively, a direct object.
(*f*) if the verb is 'sein', 'werden', 'bleiben' etc., a predicative noun, adjective, or prepositional phrase.

The mere fact that one of these is missing, when theoretically it ought not to be, will not help the machine to decide that the clause is incomplete, since certain clauses for example do not have their subject expressed, e.g.

'Trotzdem darf an der anfänglichen Aussage festgehalten werden.'

'Sein', 'werden', 'bleiben' etc. do not always have a predicate, or modal verbs an infinitive, and, as was mentioned above, verbs which are normally transitive are not invariably so. If, however, any is missing, and if after usually one, but occasionally more subordinate clauses, a second defective clause is found containing the part of speech missing from the first, it may reasonably be concluded that the two belong together as one. It is not impossible in some cases for this to lead to the fusion of two clauses which are really independent, but it is hardly conceivable that such an occurrence could be anything but rare.

Once the machine has succeeded in separating off a piece of text which it can deal with as a unit, two processes have to be carried out. Firstly, the functions of all the syntactic units and blocks in the sentence must be determined, in order that they may be arranged in translation in a prescribed sequence. Secondly, the English equivalents of the German words must be looked up in the dictionary and printed out. This method of dealing with the variable word order of German by isolating the syntactic units in each sentence and then rearranging them in a fixed sequence in English constitutes the basic idea of Oswald and Fletcher's plan* for resolving German syntax patterns.

REARRANGEMENT OF SYNTACTIC UNITS AND BLOCKS

The English sequence of syntactic units and blocks is shown in Table A. This serves for both dependent (subordinate) and independent (main) clauses, the first two items naturally not applying to the latter. Table B shows the sequence for an infinitive clause.†

Experiments with these fixed sequences have shown that in the majority of cases they give a readily intelligible, if not completely faultless, translation. This is particularly so with sentences arranged in German in the 'normal' instead of the inverted order. Apart, however, from the obvious drawbacks of a stereotyped form of sentence in English, together in some cases with a change of emphasis, it is not difficult to find in practice a large number of

* NOTE: Oswald and Fletcher, 'Modern Language Forum', Vol. XXXVI, p. 3: 'Words that can be syntactically isolated are called . . . syntactic units; word-blocks that can be syntactically isolated are called . . . syntactic blocks.'

† NOTE: When more than one element is predicated for the same position in any sequence, it is to be understood that these elements are mutually exclusive.

Table A

1	2	3	4	5	6	7	8	9	10	11
Preposition	Rel. pronoun	Prepositional phrase (occuring before any nominal or pronominal unit)	Subject	Verb	Indirect object (pronoun)	Absolute adverb	Direct object	Ind. object (noun)	Adverb	Unattached prepositional phrase
	Interrogative adverb						Predicative noun		Predicative adjective	
	Interrogative pronoun									
	Subordinating conjunction									

Table B

1	2	3	4	5	6	7	8
Infinitive predicator (e.g. 'um', 'ohne')	'zu'+ infinitive	Indirect object (pronoun)	Absolute adverb	Direct object	Indirect object (noun)	Adverb	Unattached prepositional phrase
				Predicative noun		Predicative adjective	

sentences which produce an odd-looking translation if treated in strict accordance with this method. By way of illustration may be quoted one affecting the stipulation that a prepositional phrase occurring before a noun or pronoun block at the beginning of the clause be left there in the English translation. This is desirable if the same emphasis as in the original is to be preserved, with, e.g.

'Von Anbeginn spielt das Land der Ägypter eine wichtige Rolle.'
'From the very beginning the land of the Egyptians plays an important role.'

In some cases, for example where a relative clause follows the subject, it is even necessary that the prepositional phrase should precede, so as not to separate the noun and its relative, e.g.

'Unter diesen beiden Bestimmungen läßt sich alles zusammenfassen, was in den Romanen für die alte Generation charakteristisch ist.'
'In these two definitions can be comprehended everything which is. . . .'*

However, although in the majority of instances it is advisable that the prepositional phrase should be retained at the beginning of the sentence, there are occasions when the opposite is true. Sometimes there is a fairly obvious reason for this—the prepositional phrase functioning as direct object after certain verbs is a case in point, e.g.

'In der Handlung der zwei ersten Romane ragt in gewisser Weise noch die vorbürgerliche Welt hinein',

but there are many others where only extensive research into this problem of the relation of German to English word-order will find a solution. Translation into correct English is not possible by means of Oswald and Fletcher's fixed sequences alone. They form the foundation for a method, but other model sequences are required to cover all the varieties of sentence, such as the above, which cannot be satisfactorily accounted for by the basic sequences.

To enable the machine to recognize whether a clause is independent, dependent, or infinitival, so that the appropriate word

* NOTE: Of this instance it may further be remarked that it is also preferable for the subject to follow the verb, though this is not in accordance with Oswald and Fletcher's fixed word-order, and for the relative clause in the German to be replaced by an adjectival phrase in English, i.e.

'In these two definitions can be comprehended everything characteristic of the older generation in the novels.'

This latter modification is one that frequently has to be made in translating from German.

sequence may be followed, Oswald and Fletcher recommend the following routine:

1. If a German finite verb form (code numbers 39 to 59 inclusive, see p. 131) occurs either immediately before the subject or immediately after it, the clause can be identified as an *independent clause.*

2. If the first verbal form encountered in the German text is a prepositional infinitive (code numbers 62 or 73+40, 47, 49, 53, 57), the clause can be identified as an *infinitive clause.*

3. If the appearance of the finite verbal form is postponed until after the occurrence of one or more of the following syntactic units or blocks: pronominal indirect object, absolute adverb, direct object or predicate nominative, nominal indirect object, predicate adjective, unattached prepositional phrase, then the clause can be identified as a *dependent clause.* This, however, appears to be rather more complicated than necessary, and can probably be replaced by something like:

1. If the clause begins with (*a*) a relative pronoun or subordinating conjunction, (*b*) an interrogative adverb or pronoun (provided that the sentence is not a question), (*c*) a finite verb (provided the sentence is not interrogative, imperative or exclamatory, i.e. followed by ? or !), it is subordinate.

2. If the clause contains only 'zu'+infinitive as its verb, it is infinitival.

3. All other clauses are independent*.

* NOTE: If it appears remarkable that Oswald and Fletcher's syntactic sequence is only for statements, it should be remembered that interrogative sentences are generally rare in scientific literature. For the sake of completeness, however, a few simple rules might be included in a programme to alter the sequence for an interrogative sentence, should one occur.

1. If the verb is simple, (*a*) place the verb 'do' in the same tense before the subject; (*b*) change the verb to the present infinitive form, if not already so, e.g.
'What had been achieved showed this to be true.'
'Did what had been achieved show....'

2. If the verb has an auxiliary or modal verb with it, place the auxiliary or modal before the subject, e.g.
'The combinations, though complex, can be prescribed as follows.'
'Can the combinations, though complex, be prescribed as follows?'

3. The negative 'not' is placed immediately after the auxiliary, modal or verb 'do', unless (*a*) it negatives a particular part of the sentence, in which case it precedes this part, e.g.
'Was the man not in the best of health at the time?'
(*b*) the sentence involves the idiomatic 'double subject' construction with 'it' which it follows, e.g.
'Is it not the case that...?'
(*c*) the subject is a pronoun, in which case it follows this, e.g.
'Do we not want peace?'

4. Negatives like 'never' follow the subject.

The distinction between adverb and absolute adverb, though not mentioned specifically by Oswald and Fletcher, is clearly one of form only, that of the latter being adverbial only, e.g. '*untereinander*', '*noch*', whilst the former's permits it to function as either adverb or adjective, e.g. '*endlich*', '*nämlich*'. Why they are given different positions in the syntactic sequence is not so clear.

It should be stated that Oswald and Fletcher did not intend that adverbs should invariably be placed in one of the two positions prescribed; on the contrary, they declare: 'Adverbs of quantity are to be attached to the word immediately following them. Adverb/adjectival forms and absolute adverbs are to be attached to any adjective, article or other adverb that they immediately precede. Otherwise they are to be placed in the position prescribed for them in the sequence of functional units.'

This adverb routine, however, is one of the less satisfactory parts of Oswald and Fletcher's syntactic sequences. Though correct positioning of the adverb is not as essential to a readily intelligible translation as that of other units, it is nevertheless desirable in the interests of good English. To this end the English equivalent of each German adverb in the dictionary should be given a code number indicating the position or positions in a sentence usually occupied by it. This, of course, would mean a complete analysis of all common English adverbs—something after the manner of that of Palmer and Blandford (*A Grammar of Spoken English*). The authors divide the adverbs into five classes in accordance with the position which they occupy in the sentence, i.e.

(*a*) Pre-subject position,
(*b*) Pre-verbal position*,
(*c*) Post-verbal position,
(*d*) Pre-qualificative position (e.g. before adjectives and other adverbs),
(*e*) Miscellaneous†.

A list of 373 of the commonest adverbs in English (of which only 37 are denoted as 'miscellaneous') is given. A calculation from it shows that 130 of the adverbs can occupy one position only, the distribution in the alternative position being (*a*) 18, (*b*) 1, (*c*) 87, (*d*) 23,

* Note: This refers only to the main part of the verb, when an auxiliary or modal is involved.

† Note: Meaning that an adverb may occur in a large variety of positions throughout the sentence.

(*e*) 1; 160 can occupy two positions only, the distribution being (*a*) or (*b*) 1, (*a*) or (*c*) 40, (*a*) or (*d*) 1, (*b*) or (*c*) 67, (*b*) or (*d*) 27, (*c*) or (*d*) 24. The remainder of the adverbs (83) can occupy three or more positions.

One third of the adverbs, then, have only one possible location. Of those which may occupy two positions 52 likewise cause no difficulty, because one of the positions is the 'prequalificative' (i.e. the same as in the German text). These together constitute half the adverbs. The remaining half can be used in two or more positions. Of each of them we may ask these questions:

(*i*) Does the position or the collocation of words in which it stands make any difference to its sense? If not, we can adopt one position as standard for the purposes of mechanical translation.

(*ii*) If difference of position or context does affect the sense, can rules be discovered for determining in which of its possible positions the adverb should in each particular instance be placed? According to Palmer and Blandford (*A Grammar of Spoken English*, p. 184) it makes no difference as regards meaning in what position the adverbs for which positions (*a*) or (*c*) and (*a*) or (*b*) are possible occur. As illustrations they quote:

'I went there yesterday—Yesterday I went there.'
'I sometimes go there – Sometimes I go there.'

If there is in fact no difference, it means that 41 more adverbs may easily be accounted for.

By contrast, say these authors: 'To shift an adverb from the pre-verbal to the post-verbal position generally means converting it from an incidental into an essential component, e.g.

'We quietly went away.' (Incidental)—'We went away quietly.' (Essential)

The difference in meaning can be wider; for example with 'well', which is used in the pre-verbal position with various connotations according to the intonation (e.g. 'He might well do this'—which is ambiguous in print, 'He could well afford to buy it'), whilst in the post-verbal position it has its commoner meaning of 'In a good manner'.

It would appear, then, that some of the adverbs left to be dealt with provide affirmative answer to question (*ii*) above. Since an adverb's meaning can differ according to its position, it will presumably occur more than once in our dictionary as the translation of different German words, and for each of these it will have only one possible position in the sentence. Should, however, the German possess the same ambiguity as the English adverb which translates it, thus requiring its two (or more) meanings as equivalents, the only solution is to establish positional criteria for it (as with the English), which can then be equated with these equivalents.

Finally, it should be remarked that, although a classification as simple as that above would succeed in placing the translation of each German adverb in something like its correct position in the sentence, the adverb system of a language—usually the last thing to be mastered by foreigners learning the language—is obviously too complicated to be disposed of so easily. The aim must be not to tell the machine to place a particular adverb before or after the verb, but to tell it exactly whereabouts before or after the verb to place it.

A second problem arising from the tables of word sequences concerns what Oswald and Fletcher call the 'unattached prepositional phrase'. The problem is not so much where to put it—the position allocated to it at the end of the clause is adequate for the majority of instances—but how to identify it. Most prepositional phrases that occur are in fact 'unattached' (namely about 90%), but the machine should be prepared to deal with the others as well.

There is no difficulty if the prepositional phrase is attached to a noun other than the subject, because these follow the verb in any case in the rearranged syntactical sequence. Take for instance these prepositional phrases dependent on the direct object, the most usual noun block after the subject to which they are attached:

1. 'Der Tod vermittelt in den „Buddenbrooks" in unmittelbarer Weise *den Zugang zum Grunde des Seins.*'

2. 'Auch Jaakob hatte einst *die Fahrt ins Reich der Toten* unternommen.'

3. 'Niemals allerdings um ihrer selbst willen, sondern weil sie in irgendeiner Weise *einen symbolischen Bezug zum Leben des Helden* haben.'

'Not for their own sake, of course, but because in some way they have *a symbolic relation to the life of the hero.*'

There is likewise no difficulty, if in a main clause the subject occupies its normal position in front of the verb, since any dependent prepositional phrase will also precede the verb, e.g.

'Die herrlichen Ergebnisse in dieser Richtung beruhen auf nichts anderem als auf einer Untersuchung des Lichtes, das die fernen Himmelskörper uns zusenden.'

The difficulty arises in main clauses with inverted order of subject and verb and in subordinate clauses, rigid application of Oswald and Fletcher's syntactical sequences resulting in a separation of the prepositional phrase from the noun block to which it belongs by the verb. Sometimes this has no great affect on the translation, but more often it produces an odd word-order or—worse still—one that appears correct but has a meaning in some degree different from that intended. As an example of the first case may be given:

'Da entfacht sich in den „Buddenbrooks" *ein Streit zwischen dem alten Johann Buddenbrook und seinem Sohn Jean.*'

which in accordance with the syntactic sequence would come out as

'In the "Buddenbrooks" a quarrel starts between old Johann Buddenbrook and his son Jean;'

of the second:

'Zusammengefaßt wird diese Erfahrung in jenem visionären Erlebnis, darin sich in zwei Bildern *die Einsicht in die Zweideutigkeit verdichtet.*'

the translation of which would be

'. . . in which in two pictures insight is condensed into the contradiction.'

(instead of '. . . in which insight into the contradiction is condensed into two pictures.')

and of the third:

'Dadurch werden aber auch *die Bewegungen innerhalb der Bestandteile der Moleküle* gestört.'

which would be translated as

'By this the movements are also disturbed within the constituents of the molecules.'

instead of

'By this the movements within the constituents of the molecules are also disturbed.'

Whether Oswald and Fletcher observed this problem of the 'unattached prepositional phrase' is not clear, since they do not mention it. On the other hand there is in the explanation of their syntactic sequence tables an instruction which reads: 'Any prepositional phrase or any genitive construction which immediately follows a noun or a nominal block is to be attached to the noun or nominal block.' This seems to be evidence at least of recognition of the problem. Unfortunately, if this rule were put into operation, more mistakes would ensue than if one regarded every prepositional phrase as 'unattached'. We have already quoted the relative frequency.

The question still remains, then, of how the problem of distinguishing an 'attached' from an 'unattached' prepositional phrase is to be solved. There appears to be no single solution, and it may be, no complete solution, though whether the latter is actually so and how far short it falls will only be able to be established empirically. The procedure must be to regard any prepositional phrase immediately following the subject of a clause (except, as mentioned above, in main clauses, with normal sequence) as unattached. In many cases this can be verified by such criteria as:

1. Existence between the subject and the prepositional phrase of an adverb or particle, e.g.

'Dadurch werden aber die Bewegungen *auch* innerhalb der Bestandteile der Moleküle gestört.'

2. The preposition being of a type that cannot be attached to a noun, e.g.

'Aber wenn Leukippos *trotz* seines ursprüngliches Zusammenhangs mit der Elcatik weit von einem Parmenides abwich. . . .'

3. The subject being a pronoun, e.g.

'Wenn man von dieser Novelle absicht, ist *er in dem Spätwerk* fast völlig in den Hintergrund getreten . . .'

Prepositional phrases are regarded as attached to the subject only when the preposition is of a type regularly constructed with the noun (subject) in question, and an indication to this effect is marked alongside the noun in the mechanical dictionary. For instance, in the clause

'. . . und *die Begegnung mit dem Tod* nicht nur Steigerung bewirkt, sondern auch Zersetzung und Auflösung.'

the prepositional phrase would be attached to the subject in translation, because '*Begegnung mit*' is a regular construction, whereas in

'Und wie sich auf dem Berge *seine Gedanken mit der Erinnerung* an den Alten dem Tod zukehren, so auch dieser merkwürdigen Form der Zeiterfahrung.'

the prepositional phrase would remain unattached, '*Gedanken mit*' not being a regular construction. Again, in a clause of similar sequence to the last the subject and prepositional phrase are connected

'(. . . in jenem visionären Erlebnis), darin sich in zwei Bildern *die Einsicht in die Zweideutigkeit* verdichtet.'

and are recognized by the construction '*Einsicht*+accusative', while in one resembling the first clause above in structure they are unconnected.

'(Es ist im Grunde Ausdruck der gleichen Tatsache), wenn *das Leben in jeder hinsicht* noch den Charakter der Gebundenheit und der „Komplexität" trägt.'

This clause, however, reveals something of a flaw in the system, because although many nouns do have what may be called a 'regular construction'—similar in most cases to that of the verb from which they are derived, there are just as many that do not. Here 'das Leben' is a good illustration of this point, since it is possible to write a clause in which the prepositional phrase is connected to it, the preposition itself not having changed e.g. '. . . wenn das Leben in jedem Gefängnis noch den Charakter der „Gebundenheit" und der „Komplexität" trägt.'

In some cases a solution is afforded by some minor feature, like the position of an adverb, e.g.

'Anders als der alte Hans Lorenz Castorp steht allerdings die alte Generation in den „Buddenbrooks" *schon* am Rande dieser Ordnung.'

(if the prepositional phrase had been unattached the position of the adverb would have been after '*Generation*') but the presence of such a 'tell-tale' in every instance cannot be relied upon.

In lieu of a complete solution the best procedure in these ambiguous cases would seem to be to assume that the prepositional phrase is 'unattached' and in the translation to have some symbol placed at the end of the clause concerned to indicate that it may after all be attached to the subject*.

* NOTE: If future experience in translating from German to English showed that there exist a number of ambiguities of various types incapable of being resolved mechanically, this method of getting the machine to place a certain symbol at the end of the relevant clause or sentence might prove useful. Each type of ambiguity would be represented by its own particular symbol, and a pamphlet explaining the significance of the symbols issued to the recipient of the translation, who, being forewarned of the type of mistake liable to be made by the machine, could act as his own post editor.

A second problem involving the prepositional phrase is the relative order when more than one occurs in a clause, since the German order is often not that customary in English. The difficulty is to get the machine to know when the original order should be retained, e.g.

'Bevor wir uns aber an die Lösung der Frage nach dem äußeren Bau des Weltalls wagen dürfen, . . .'

and when it should be reversed, e.g.

'So vorbereitet, trat Athen mit der Philosophie in nächste Berührung.'

In some cases it makes no great difference to the English whether the original order is retained or reversed, e.g.

'In dieser Weise verändert sich das Problem des Todes von den „Buddenbrooks" bis zum „Zauberberg" in entscheidender Weise.'

though this—as often elsewhere—depends very much on the words chosen for the translation. If, for example, '*in entscheidender Weise*' is rendered by 'in a decisive fashion', it is possible to place either it or 'from the "Buddenbrooks" to the "Zauberberg"' first. If, on the other hand, it is translated by 'decisively' one is more or less obliged for reasons of euphony and rhythm to place it in front, i.e.

'In this way the problem of death changes decisively from the "Buddenbrooks" to the "Zauberberg".'

In others there is no possibility of altering the order, since the second prepositional phrase depends on the first, e.g.

'Man wußte, daß sie auch innerhalb Körper von ungeheuren Ausmaßen zu sehen waren.'

With this, however, compare another sentence of an apparently similar syntactical pattern,

'. . . weshalb man auch innerhalb der Geistesgeschichte von „Blutezeiten" zu sprechen pflegt.'

where the second prepositional phrase is dependent directly on the verb instead of the first prepositional phrase and their order must be reversed in translation. To this problem too there is no simple or complete solution, though the methods advocated in the previous case prove fairly satisfactory. In the majority of instances the original order of the prepositional phrases can be retained in English, and in some has to be, the construction making this necessary being recognisable mechanically in the same way as before, e.g.

1. 'Der Zauberberg und der andere Roman entsprechen sich in dem Interesse für den Motivkreis der Zeit.'
2. 'Sie steht in dauernder Spannung zur religiösen Umwelt.'
3. 'Wiederum geht es um die Brunnenfahrt in das Reich des Todes.'

Für, zu+dative and in+accusative would be denoted in the mechanical dictionary as the regular constructions with '*Interesse*', '*Spannung*', and '*Fahrt*', respectively, so that wherever they occurred together, they would be regarded as an inseparable combination for translation purposes.

The basic rule of retaining the original order of the German is dispensed with only when one of the prepositional phrases is closely dependent on the verb (as with those verbs constructed with the so-called prepositional direct object) and instead of being in the first place, e.g.

'Und noch zur Zeit, da Joseph *in Verbindung* mit der Krone *tritt*, trugen die Höflinge als Ehrenbezeichnung die Titel dieser ehemaligen Gaukönige.'

is in the second, (cf. the sentence already quoted: 'So vorbereitet, trat Athen mit der Philosophie in nächste Berührung') this being the normal order when the verb (or part of it) is at the end of the clause and the second prepositional phrase is not dependent on the first as in the preceding example, e.g.

1. 'Darum möchte er sich in ekstatischer Weise mit ihm einen, um auch seinerseits des Segens der Vermittlung teilhaft zu werden.'
2. 'Wenn Hegel in dem genannten Aufsatz auf die Überwindung der „Entgegensetzung" dringt, . . .'

The procedure is exactly the same as that for distinguishing 'attached' from 'unattached' prepositional phrases. With each verb in the machine's dictionary to which this system may be applied a symbol is included indicating with which preposition it is usually constructed, so that should two or more prepositional phrases occur in a clause with this verb, the one beginning with the preposition specified will be placed first after the verb in the English translation. Thus for the two illustrations just given the constructions specified would be '*einen mit* . . . unite with' and '*dringen auf* . . . insist on'. Where a verb is regularly constructed with only one preposition no difficulty is encountered, but when it may be joined equally well with two, three or more, there is a danger of the machine being confronted with a clause containing two prepositional phrases each with a preposition 'regularly' constructed with the governing verb. Such a verb is 'sprechen'. In the example quoted earlier it was constructed with '*von*', but '*über*' and '*mit*' are equally liable to occur, and in the same clause. For this reason it would seem to be advisable in such cases to have the prepositions denoted in order of preference (e.g. here '*mit*' before '*uber*', since the regular sequence is to talk *with* someone *about* something)*.

Another type of construction may also be included here, inasmuch as it has a formal similarity to the preceding, but at the same time needs to be distinguished and treated differently from it. The reference is to the combination of verb and prepositional phrase usually represented in English simply by a verb, e.g.

'In all dem *kommt* nichts anderes *zum Ausdruck* als was oben die Komplexität genannt wurde.'

'By all this *is expressed* nothing else but . . .'

and 'Er ist aus dem Ausland *nach Hause gekommen*.—He has *come home* from abroad.'

The method of dealing with most of these expressions is to regard them as idioms and incorporate them in the dictionary, though some (e.g. the latter example) are also amenable to the above treatment.

To the reader with any experience at all of translating from German it will be immediately obvious that the above is but a mere outline of the main problems posed by the prepositional phrase. In fact it is no exaggeration to say that a satisfactory account of the subject, supposing one could be given, would alone fill a sizeable volume. The greatest difficulty, of course, concerns the correct location of the prepositional phrase in the clause, and in this respect the sequences of syntactic units prescribed by Oswald and Fletcher cannot pretend to be more than temporary makeshifts. Not only are they bound to produce English translations of a stereotyped form, but inflexibly applied would also have the fault of treating each clause as an independent unit, which it is not. On the contrary, it is quite clear that the syntactic sequence in any clause is liable to be affected by the clause or clauses adjacent to it, and the awkward thing about this from the point of view of mechanical translation is that this influence is not always the same in English as in German, nor even in English

* Note: This procedure applies in exactly the same way to adjectives governing prepositional phrases, e.g.

'Versucht man zu benennen, was nun im Gegensatz zu dieser noch vorbürgerlichen Ordnung für die Welt des Bürgertums charakteristisch ist, dann . . . '

from one sentence to the next. By way of illustration we may compare

'Es wird darin offenbar, *wie sich in diesem Werk die Hinwendung zu jenen Bereichen vollzieht*, die in einem rein zweckbezogenen Dasein ausgeschieden werden mußten.'

with

'Zusammengefaßt wird diese Erfahrung in jenem visionären Erlebnis, *darin sich in zwei Bildern die Einsicht in die Zweideutigkeit verdichtet*; in dem Bild der ihr Kind stillenden Mutter am Anfang und in dem von den Hexen.'

The syntactical construction of the second clause in each sentence is identical, but whereas in the former the prepositional phrase 'in diesen Werk' can be left at the beginning (in accordance with Oswald and Fletcher's sequence pattern), because the following relative clause refers to the subject, in the latter '*in zwei Bildern*' must be transferred to the end of the clause, English syntax requiring the subject of a relative clause or, in this case, an apposition to stand immediately or at as short a distance as possible before it, i.e.

'. . . in which insight into the contradiction is condensed in two pictures: in the picture of the mother comforting her child at the beginning and in that of the witches.'
not
'. . . in which in two pictures insight into the contradiction is condensed: in the picture of . . .'

This difficulty of correct sequence applies, of course, to other syntactic units besides the prepositional phrase, but considerations of space and the reader's patience forbid further continuation of this topic.

DETERMINATION OF FUNCTIONS OF SYNTACTIC UNITS AND BLOCKS

The two components of the sentence causing the greatest difficulty are the noun and verb blocks respectively. Of the former Oswald and Fletcher remark: 'The function of the noun is so diverse and the number of elements that may be attached to a noun so unpredictable, that nominal blocks must be identified in terms of possible combinations of first and last elements.' A slightly corrected form of their chart is reproduced here. Combined with the 'Table of Coded Syntactic Units' already given it becomes self-explanatory, the column of figures on the left being the code numbers of the first elements in a noun block, those on the right the code numbers of the last element entered under their appropriate function. Two minor criticisms should perhaps be made here. The first is that the chart

	Subject function	*Possessive function*	*Indirect object function*	*Direct object function*
	Nominative	*Genitive*	*Dative*	*Accusative*
1+	...20	...21; ...23	...21	
2+	...22	...24		...22
3+			...20 ...22	
4+			...23	...20
5+	...21; ...23			...21; ...23
6+	...22			...22
7+		...24	...23	...20
8+	...21; ...23			...21; ...23
10+	...20	...21; ...23	...21	
11+	...22	...24		...22
12+			...20; ...22	
13+		...24	...23	...20
14+	...21; ...23			...21; ...23
15+	...20	...21; ...23	...21	
16+	...22	...24		...22
17+			...20; ...22	
18+		...24	...23	...20
19+	...21; ...23			...21; ...23

could have been much compressed, because Nos. 1, 10, and 15 of the first elements or predeterminers are functionally identical, as are Nos. 3, 12, and 17, Nos. 7, 13, and 18, Nos. 2, 11, and 16, and

Nos. 5, 8, 14, and 19. The second concerns the Table of Coded Syntactic Units which contains a Code No. 23 representing plural nouns. This would be unexceptionable if all nouns had plural forms distinct from their singular forms, but unfortunately they do not, thereby laying all the combinations including the number 23 in the Combinatory Chart for Nominal Blocks open to doubt.

Oswald and Fletcher supplemented the chart with the following propositions:

1. A nominal block is a sequence of units, the first of which is a descriptive adjective or an article or a '*dieser*'-word or an '*ein*'-word or an adjectival participle (Code Nos. 1–19), and the last of which is a noun (Code Nos. 20–23).
2. Predicable elements which may occur between the first and last element of a noun block are: numerals, descriptive adjectives, and adverbs which modify the adjectives occurring in the block.
3. Prepositional phrases are nominal blocks of the types predicated under the genitive, dative and accusative functions preceded by a preposition (Code Nos. 70, 73, 74).
4. Any prepositional phrase or any genitive construction which immediately follows a noun or a nominal block is to be attached to this.

In addition the authors gave formal recognition to that monstrosity of German syntax known as the participial construction and recommended a word sequence on the lines of those for clauses permitting the rearrangement of the syntactic units making up the participial construction into something like acceptable English. This sequence was:

1	2	3	4	5	6	7	8	9
Preposition	Article etc.	Noun (plus immediately following genitive/prepositional phrase)	Participle or adjective immediately preceding the noun	Indirect object (pronominal	Direct object Predicate nominative	Indirect object (nominal)	Adverb Predicate adjective	Unattached prepositional phrase

Before passing on to consider the adaption of Oswald and Fletcher's nominal block routine to the stem-ending method outlined in the chapter on French, it would be advisable to examine one or two of the statements made above in some detail, lest what were undoubtedly intended as generalizations are interpreted as universal truths.

The first statement concerning the definition of a nominal block takes no account of what may be termed the defective nominal block, that is, a nominal block with its last element—the noun itself —omitted. This omission is due to one of two causes; either the noun is the common '*Ding*' or the noun has already been mentioned shortly before. In the first case the defective noun block is used as a signpost to a continuation of the sentence, e.g.

'„Ernst" sei er gewesen, und jeder Zug des Humors sei ihm abgegangen; und ein zweites verbindet sich damit: in dem Bilde, das ihm in der Ratsherrentracht verflossener Jahrhunderte darstellte, sei er „wirklicher" gegenwärtig gewesen als in seiner alltäglichen Erscheinung.'

In the second case there are two main types, one where the predeterminer (first element) of the noun block is qualified by an adjective or participle, the other where it is qualified by a dependent genitive. In the first the most frequent usage is that with '*ander*' to form a comparison, e.g.

'So ist etwa das Sterben Johann Buddenbrooks ein anderes als das des Hans Lorenz Castorp.'

Other uses may be exemplified by the following:

1. 'Auch der tote, in eben dieser Tracht aufgebahrte Lorenz Castorp sei „wirklicher" gewesen als der lebende.'
2. 'Das Problem der „Antinomie" wird berührt: ob die geschichtliche Deutung der Zeit gegen eine mehr mythische gesetzt wird.'

The usual alteration to be made when translating into English is to transfer the noun from the preceding complete nominal block to the defective block, as in instance No. 2, i.e. instead of '. . . whether the historical interpretation of time is opposed to a more mythical (one)' we write: '. . . whether the historical is opposed to a more mythical interpretation of time'. That this alteration is not applicable to all instances is amply demonstrated by example No. 1 above. Here the participial construction is to blame, because without it we should have been able to write

'The dead had become "more real" than the living Lorenz Castorp:'

whereas with the participle tacked on it has to be

'The dead Lorenz Castorp, laid out in this very costume, had become "more real" than the living.'

With this order, of course, there is nothing wrong; it is merely that it is slightly less elegant than that where the noun can be removed from the preceding to the defective nominal block. On the other hand it has the advantage of retaining the original order of the German, the only modification required being the addition of the word 'one' to take the place of the noun in the defective block, when this noun represents an inanimate object, not a person. Even this is unnecessary in many cases—for instance, where the defective nominative block is in apposition

'Faßt man die weit verstreuten Aussagen des Erzählers zusammen, dann scheint ein doppelter Aspekt maßgebend, ein politischer und ein religiöser.'

and where the complete nominal block, to which the defective one refers, lies in a preceding instead of the same sentence, e.g.

'Daß diese Fremdheit aber auf die Dauer nicht bestehen kann und eine Auseinandersetzung gesucht werden mußte, ist in der Geschichte der bürgerlichen Gesellschaft leicht zu belegen. Wo immer im Verlauf dieser Geschichte die „Entgegensetzung" von Geist und Existenz fraglich wurde, mußte eine solche (sc. Auseinandersetzung) unternommen werden.'

Another type of defective noun block mentioned above was that consisting merely of the definite article, but qualified by a second noun block in the genitive. The reason for the deficiency is exactly the same as in the former case, namely, to avoid repetition of the same noun. It occurs most frequently in comparisons and appositions, e.g.

'So ist etwa das Sterben Johann Buddenbrooks ein anderes als das des Hans Lorenz Castorp.'

'Hans Castorp dagegen geht den anderen Weg, den der Steigerung'

but commonly too in most of the constructions in which the ordinary noun block can be used—in co-ordination, e.g.

'Schon diese Metapher zeigt, wie sich die Thematik der Zeit und die des Todes verbinden.'

as a predicative, e.g.

'Der Geist dagegen ist der der deutschen Romantik.'

as the object of a verb, e.g.

'Die Sphäre des Privaten entzieht sich der der Repräsentation.'
and so on*.

A variation of the above type of defective nominal block is that where the dependent genitive is replaced by a prepositional noun block, the commonest of course being that introduced by that 'understudy' for the dependent genitive, 'von'. By way of illustration may be quoted

'Und noch ein letztes, vom „Zauberberg" vertrautes, Thema klingt wieder an: das von der Zeit.'

'Und beides, die Begegnung mit der Frau und die mit dem Osten, finden den gemeinsamen Sinn.'

With the preceding should not be confused another, much less common defective nominal block, where the missing noun is to be located not in a previous block, but in the following dependent genitive. Examples are:

'Er spielt vor allem in zahlreiche der Novellen hinein.'
(i.e. 'in zahlreiche Novellen der Novellen'.)

'Der edelste dieser Helden steht jetzt bevor uns.'

Oswald and Fletcher's fourth statement concerning the attachment of a prepositional phrase to the noun which it follows has been dealt with. We come, therefore, to the last of their supplementary rules to the Combinatory Chart for Nominal Blocks, which is the syntactic sequence recommended for rearranging the German participle construction in translation to English.

More or less the same faults are inherent in it as in the sequences for clauses. The two most important are (*a*) occasional incorrect positioning of the adverb in the translation, e.g.

1. '. . . daß die zwischen P_1 und P_2 *tatsächlich* durchlaufene Bahn sich vor allen anderen Bahnen dadurch auszeichnet, daß. . . .'

2. 'Wenn es erlaubt ist, diesen in der heutigen Biologie *so* bedeutsamen Begriff im Zusammenhang mit gesellschaftlichen Tatbestanden analog zu gebrauchen—'.

(in both of which the adverb must precede not follow the participle/adjective, when translated),

* NOTE: Naturally, if the noun of the dependent genitive noun block is also a repetition, it too can be omitted, so that a double defective noun block is left, e.g.

'Auch dieses Zeichen dafür, wie die alte Generation des zweiten Romans nicht anders als die des ersten für die „Umwelt" gegen die „Welt" plädiert.'

and (*b*) the assumption again that any prepositional phrase following the final noun in the participle construction is connected with this. Obviously this is no more true here than in the case of the sequences for clauses, nor is there here the consolation that confusion only results when the noun to which the prepositional phrase gets attached is the subject; it happens whatever the noun's function, as the last example above will show.

The solution is the same as before, namely, to have the machine regard all such prepositional phrases as 'unattached' unless lexicographical considerations join the syntactical in indicating a connection. For instance, in this clause

'... um dieses Prinzip mit dem aus der Lichtoptik bekannten Prinzip von Fermat zu vergleichen'.

the combination of the fact that '*Prinzip*' is regularly constructed with '*von*' with the fact that the verb is not passive (so that '*von*' cannot represent the agent), nor of a type indicating separation leads to the conclusion that '*von*' is possessive. By contrast, in the clause

'... in welchen der Brechungsindex also nur an gewissen, von uns beliebig wählbaren Flächen von einem Wert auf einen anderen Wert springt.'

though '*Flächen von*' would be a regular construction, the nature of the verb (expressing separation) gives it preference, especially in view of the relation of the two prepositional phrases to each other. Sometimes the decision is an easy one, as for instance when the participle construction is a dependent genitive and the following prepositional phrase belongs not to it but to its governing noun, e.g.

'Dies erhalten wir durch *Rotation* der die Potentialverteilung in einer Meridianebene darstellenden Figur *um die z-Achse*.'

The other problem connected with the prepositional phrase, the relative order when two occur together, appears here too. Sometimes it makes no difference what order is adopted in the translation, as in

'Auf das im Feld E mit der Geschwindigkeit v bewegte Elektron wirkt die Kraft K.'

either: 'The force K acts on the electron moving in the field E with the velocity v.'

or: 'The force K acts on the electron moving with the velocity v in the field E.'

Other times the original order has to be retained, because the second phrase depends on the first, e.g.

'So ist z.B. in *Fig. 8* jede der beiden Zylinderelektroden durch je zwei in gleichem Abstand von der z-Achse verlaufende Geradenstücke dargestellt.'*

To complete the picture, there are instances where the order must be inverted, because the second prepositional phrase goes clearly with the participle, e.g.

1. 'Weder der Drehimpuls noch das magnetische Moment des Elektrons spielen in den für uns *in Frage kommenden* Feldern eine Rolle.'
2. '. . . welche das unter dem Winkel α_1 *auf die Ebene* F_1 *einfallende* Elektron erleidet.'

The solution is the same as before: retain the order of the German unless information included with the dictionary entries indicates a special connection between the participle and one of the prepositional phrases, as for example their being equivalent to a single verb in English ('*für uns in Frage kommenden*'—concerning us), the prepositional phrase standing in place of a direct object with an intransitive verb, etc. (cf. 2 above).

A minor fault in Oswald and Fletcher's rearrangement sequence is its failure to allocate a position to the attributive adjective so often found in addition to the participle. When it precedes a prepositional phrase, it is separated from this by a comma, e.g.

'Dies sagt aus, daß die Bahn eines Elektrons in einem *elektrischen*, durch die Funktion $v(x, y, z)$ gegebenen Feld identisch ist mit einem Lichtstrahl in einem *lichtoptischen*, durch den Brechungsindex $n(x, y, z)$ beschriebenem Medium.'

but when it precedes an adverb, it is not, e.g.

'Deshalb zeigen wir in *Fig. 8* das Feld zwischen zwei *koaxialen* hintereinander angeordneten Hohlzylindern verschiedener Durchmesser.'

Occasionally the adjective is found between the participle and the noun (cf. the example immediately below). Wherever it occurs in

* Note: Oddly enough precisely the opposite is true of some pairs of adverbs, inversion being necessary, because the former is dependent on the latter, e.g.

'Dieses wird im Zylinderkoordinatensystem durch drei *aufeinander senkrecht* stehende Komponenten bestimmt.'

the German, its correct position in English is between the article and the noun.

Finally, although no difficulty arises from the fact, it should be noted that two co-ordinate participles can occur in the same participial construction, e.g.

'Es ist das ebenfalls von der Romantik umworbene und oft in ihre Gestaltungen einbezogene spät mittelalterliche Motiv vom „Venusberg".'

Having outlined Oswald and Fletcher's method of dealing with noun blocks, we can now proceed to discuss the combination of a somewhat modified and compressed version of it with the stem-ending procedure. Taking first of all the last element in the non-defective noun block, the noun itself, it appears that German nouns fall into eight main classes, as follows:

	Class	*Ending characteristic of* *		
		(*a*) *singular*	(*b*) *plural*	(*c*) *both sing. and plural*
A	Feminines in '-nis' and '-sal' Feminine monosyllables like 'die Frucht'.	- u } N, A, G, D	e eu se seu } N, A, G en enu sen senu } D	
B	Masculines like (*a*) 'der Garten' (*b*) 'der Forst' Neuters like 'das Auge'	(e)s G e D - N, A, D	u (e)n } N, A, G, D	
C	Masculine monosyllables not modifying in plural. Masculines in '-ig' '-ich', '-icht' '-ing'. Neuters in '-nis', '-sal', 'icht'.	(e)s (e)su ses sesu } G - u } N, A, D	en enu sen senu } D	e se eu } Sing. D Plur. N, A, G

* Note: N=nominative, A=accusative, G=genitive, D=dative these being the cases of which an ending may be characteristic. A dash indicates that there is no ending, and 'u' represents the umlaut. Why this is regarded as an ending is explained later. The 'e' in parenthesis occurs only when the nominative singular form of a noun ends in a consonant.

	Class	Ending characteristic of		
		(*a*) *singular*	(*b*) *plural*	(*c*) *both sing. and plural*
D	Masculine proper nouns in '-e'.	- u } N		(e)n } Sing. A, G, D (e)nu } Plur. N, A, G, D
	Masculines like (*a*) 'der Held', (*b*) 'der Student', (*c*) 'der Name'.	(e)ns G		
E	Feminine nouns in '-heit', '-keit', '-schaft', '-in', '-ung', '-el', '-er'. (Except 'Mutter' and 'Tochter'.)	- u } N, A, G, D	(e)n (e)nu neu nenu } N, A, G, D	
F	Masculine monosyllables like 'der Topf'. Neuters 'das Floß', 'das Kloster'. Masculines and neuters in '-tum'. Neuter monosyllables like 'das Bild'. Masculines like 'der Vater'.	(e)s G - N, A, D e D	u er eu eru } N, A, G nu ern enu ernu } D	
G	All masculine and neuter nouns in '-el' and '-er' except those included in class *F*.	s su } G	n nu } D	- u } Sing. N, A, D Plur. N, A, G
H	All masculine and neuter nouns in '-en' except those included in class *B*.	s su } G		- u } Sing. N, A, D Plur. N, A, G, D

It will be realized that the classes in the above table do not correspond to the various declensions given in grammar books. This difference may be explained briefly as one of principle. Whereas the grammarian classifies together the types of noun according to the nature of the changes their form undergoes in declension, the mechanical translator is interested only in the positions of the change. In short, he classifies according to where not how the change is made. An illustration will make the difference clear. Normally the nouns '*Vater*' and '*Garten*' are classed together in some subdivision of the strong declension, simply because they both have '-s' added to them to denote the genitive singular and their vowels modified ('*Väter*', '*Gärten*') to signify the plural. The fact that '*Vater*' takes an '-n' in the dative plural ('*Vätern*') is not considered important, because 'Garten' too would have taken '-n' (so it is said) if it did not already have one. For the purposes of mechanical translation, however, where the aim is to obtain as much syntactical information from the words as possible, the words '*Vater*' and '*Garten*' are grammatically distinct, inasmuch as the dative plural of the former is distinguishable from the other plural forms, while that of the latter is not.

Hence in our scheme '*Vater*' is classed under *F* with nouns like '*Eigentum*'. Again, in grammars they come under different categories of the strong declension, because, whereas '*Vater*' forms its plural by modifying a vowel, '*Eigentum*' modifies the vowel and adds the letters '-er' as well ('*Eigentümer*'). As far as mechanical translation is concerned, however, they are nouns of the same type, because the cases where a change of form occurs are the same in both, i.e. one form for nominative, accusative and dative singular, another for genitive singular, a third for the nominative, accusative and genitive plural, and a fourth for the dative plural. The fact that these changes are of a different nature is, as we have said, of no consequence whatsoever. At the same time it does mean that some care must be taken in interpreting the table above. An illustration will again make this clearer. If we take class *F*, it will be seen that the endings characteristic of the plural are eight in number. Obviously, therefore, a noun in this class cannot be constructed with every one of these; rather the correct approach is to expect to be able to find the endings appropriate to any noun somewhere among the eight. Thus, for instance, the endings for a noun like '*Topf*' are '-e'+umlaut (N, A, G) and '-en'+umlaut (D), for '*Bild*' '-er' (N, A, G) and '-ern' (D) and so on. Similarly no confusion arises for the machine, because having come across the word '*Bilder*', say, and having identified the stem '*Bild-*', all it has to do next is to examine the twelve endings available in this class (counting (e)s as two, since they would have to be entered thus in the dictionary), whereupon it would identify the remaining letters '-er' as characteristic of N, A, G plural. For the same reason no difficulty is caused by entering both '-e' and '-' as characteristic of the dative singular.

Nouns not comprehended in any of these classes will probably have their different forms entered separately in the dictionary rather than be grouped into small classes of only two or three members. How many members a class must comprise to make its formation an economical proposition as regards dictionary space cannot be estimated before the exact details of how the programme is to be entered in the machine have been worked out.

The umlaut in German causes a little difficulty. If each of the three vowels which may take the umlaut is regarded as a different letter, when it has the umlaut, or if the umlaut is represented in the input text simply by an 'e' placed after the vowel, it will be impossible for the machine to identify a form of a word having the umlaut with another form of the same word not having the umlaut. This, of course, presents no problem, if the storage capacity of our machine is so vast that we can afford to enter every form of a word in the dictionary—the different forms are just regarded as different words. Such storage, however, is not yet available, nor, if one considers the size and complexity of the programme which must be included, quite apart from the actual dictionary, will it be for some time to come.

If, on the other hand, the umlaut is ignored, we must be prepared to use other means to identify the plural form of nouns of the '*Nagel*', '*Bruder*', '*Faden*', etc. type, to distinguish words of different meaning which otherwise have identical forms (e.g. '*der Schutz*' = protection, '*der Schütz*' = marksman), to distinguish the indicative and subjunctive forms of the imperfect tense of '*sein*', '*haben*', '*werden*', '*dürfen*', '*können*', '*mögen*', '*müssen*' and many strong verbs, and so on. Not being prepared to do this, we adopted the solution of considering the umlaut as an ending for the purposes of the stem-ending routine. This means that any noun having an umlaut in its singular form is entered in the stem dictionary without the umlaut symbol, the latter being put instead in the ending dictionary. The only other requirement is that on the input tape the umlaut symbol should be placed at the end of the word to which it belongs.

FIRST ELEMENT IN NOUN BLOCK, (*a*) DEFINITE ARTICLE, (*b*) INDEFINITE ARTICLE, (*c*) WORDS LIKE [DIESER], (*d*) ADJECTIVE, (*e*) PARTICIPLE USED AS AN ADJECTIVE

These, too, are divided according to the stem-ending principle. The stems are respectively 'd-', 'ein-', 'dies-', etc., and the uninflected adjectival or participial form. The neuter of the definite article, '*das*', has to be regarded as a separate word. The endings, five in number, are: '-er', '-es', '-em', '-en', '-e'.

If a noun occurs on its own, we can use only its own ending to determine its function, and as the preceding table shows, each ending is not sufficiently unique for this purpose. 'Bare' nouns, therefore, are not amenable to this method and must be treated in the same way as those nouns whose grammatical function still remains ambiguous, even when they are accompanied by an article, etc.

If, on the other hand, one of the five possible 'first elements' mentioned above occurs with the noun, its ending can be utilized to reduce the number of functions which the noun's ending is capable of representing. Thus we get the following table:

		-er	*-es*		*-em*	*-en*		*-e*	*das/ein*
			(*a*)	(*b*)‡		(*a*)	(*b*)‡		
A	-, u	*g, d						n, a	
	e, eu, se, seu	G						N, A	
	en, enu, sen, senu					D	D		
B	(e)s		g	g			g		
	-	n		n, a	d	a	a		n, a§
	e				d				
	u, (e)n	G				D	D	N, A	
C	-, u	n		n, a	d	a	a		n, a§
	(e)s, (e)su, ses, sesu		g	g			g		
	en, enu, sen, senu					D	D		
	e, se, eu	G			d			N, A	
D	-, u	n							n
	(e)ns		g	g			g		
	(e)n, (e)nu	G	g	g	d	a, D	g, a† D	N, A	
E	-, u	g, d						n, a	
	(e)n, (e)nu, nen, nenu	G				D	D	N, A	

* Small letters denote the singular, capitals the plural. N, n=nominative, A, a=accusative, G, g=genitive, D, d=dative.

† It is unlikely that the singular form of these nouns will occur with only an adjective or participle, since all represent living beings.

‡ With the ending '-es' section (*a*) includes the definite and indefinite articles, section (*b*) words like 'dieser', the adjective, and the participle. With the ending '-en" however, section (*a*) includes the definite and indefinite articles and words like 'dieser', section (*b*) the adjective and participle. The reason for the distinction is that 'dieser' with the ending '-es' may (like an adjective or participle) denote the nominative and accusative as well as the genitive singular of a neuter noun, whereas the articles denote only the genitive: with the ending '-en', on the other hand, it behaves exactly like the articles, signifying either accusative singular of a masculine noun or dative plural of any gender, whilst the adjective or participle ending in '-en' may indicate in addition to these the genitive singular of masculine and neuter nouns.

§ With neuter nouns the function may be either nominative or accusative; with masculine nouns it is nominative only. Since all nouns in the stem dictionary will have their gender indicated this distinction can be made by the machine.

		-er	-es		-em	-en		-e	das/ein
			(a)	(b)†		(a)	(b)‡		
F	(e)s		g	g			g		
	e				d				
	-	n		n, a	d	a	a		n, a§
	u, eu, er, eru	G						N, A	
	nu, enu, ern, ernu					D	D		
G	s, su		g	g			g		
	n, nu					D	D		
	-, u	n, G		n, a	d	a	a	N, A	n, a§
H	s, su		g	g			g		
	-, u	n, G		n, a	d	a, D	a, D	N, A	n, a§

Where two or more letters occur together in one space in the table, there exists a functional ambiguity due to identical forms. Ambiguities of this type may or may not be ultimately resolvable; it all depends on the context in which they occur. A preliminary investigation of this problem designed not to produce a comprehensive answer but to spy out the land, so to speak, showed that in a passage of about five thousand words there were nearly six hundred 'prepositionless' noun blocks or nouns whose form left their syntactical function uncertain. Of the five types of ambiguity to be found in such noun blocks (i.e. a noun with a predeterminer), namely

(*a*) (i) nominative or accusative plural of all genders.
(ii) nominative or accusative singular of feminine and neuter nouns.

(*b*) genitive or dative singular of all feminine nouns.

(*c*) accusative singular or dative plural of masculine nouns in classes D and H.

(*d*) accusative or genitive singular of masculine nouns in class D when qualified by an adjective or participle only.

(*e*) nominative singular or genitive plural of masculine nouns in classes G and H.

all occurred except (*d*). The probable reason for this has already been mentioned (*see* † note to table on p. 159). The other four types, however, are available for examination together with the various solutions that offered themselves in each case.

AMBIGUOUS NOUN BLOCKS

Type (*a*)

There can be no confusion when a noun block of the first kind (i) and one of the second (ii) occur together in a clause, inasmuch as they differ in number, and reference to the verb will indicate which is the subject. As might be expected, there are some exceptions, but these need not be enumerated here, since they can be found in any good grammar along with their appropriate explanation. Here it will be sufficient to say that they fall into two basic types:

1. The subject is plural, the verb singular, e.g.

'Da beginnt für ihn noch einmal die Fahrt in die Brunnentiefe, jene, die *Hans Castorp und Josef am Anfang* zu wagen aufgetragen *ist*.'

2. The subject is grammatically singular, the verb plural, e.g.

'*Eine Menge* Äpfel *lagen* unter dem Baume.'

The fact that such exceptions can be and are classified in grammars indicates that they can also be taken into account by the machine, that is, provided that it is desired to incorporate the necessary instructions, because the exceptions are rare enough to be disregarded without any serious detriment to the translation as regards intelligibility. In what follows, then, the two kinds (i) and (ii) will be treated together as *Type* (*a*).

Type (*a*) *in a main clause*—It was found in the passage investigated that of the noun blocks of *Type* (*a*)

104 fulfilled the function of subject.
17 ,, ,, ,, ,, direct object.
14 ,, ,, ,, ,, predicative (with verbs like '*sein*' —to be).

whilst 30 lay outside the basic construction of the clause, i.e. in apposition and the like. These last and others of a similar nature occurring in subordinate and infinitival clauses will all be considered together under 'Apposition', since not only the correct identification of their function, but also their correct location in the English syntactical sequence has to be determined.

The 104 noun blocks had their function as subject determined in one of the following ways:

1. By being the only 'prepositionless' (i.e. not preceded by a preposition) substantival block immediately before or after the verb (excluding a dependent genitive or prepositional phrase, if present) and also the only possible nominative form in the clause, e.g.

'*Die gleiche Problematik* von Entgegensetzung und Versöhnung findet sich nun auch in dem Werk Manns.'

'In dem „Buddenbrooks" gelingt *die Einung mit* dem Grunde unter Preisgabe der Person.'

There were 75 such blocks.

2. By being the only possible nominative form immediately before or after the verb, e.g.

'Von Anbeginn spielt *das Land* der Ägypter in den Mahnungen und Reden Jaakobs als das verfluchte Land des Geschlechtes, der Unzucht und des Todes ebenso eine Rolle, . . .'

These were six in number.

3. By being the only possible nominative form in the clause and —both the position immediately before and that immediately following the verb being occupied by a prepositional phrase—by being the next syntactic block after the latter of these (excluding a dependent genitive, if present), e.g.

'Im übrigen waren im Laufe der Jahre die ehemaligen Feudalherren als Hofbeamte in die Dienste Pharaos getreten.'

These were seventeen in number.

4. By being the only possible nominative form besides an interrogative pronoun with the verb '*sein*', i.e.

'Was aber ist die Lösung dieser „Antinomie" von Selbstmächtigkeit und Hingabe?'

This was the only instance of this kind.

For the 101 noun blocks comprehended under these four types there was a satisfactory solution of functional ambiguity, but for the remaining three there was not, occurring as they did in a clause with two such noun blocks, one immediately before the verb and the other immediately after. The general rule in such cases is undoubtedly that the noun block preceding the verb is the subject, and indeed two of the three clauses followed this rule, e.g.

'*Die Psychologie* verrät *das 19. Jahrhundert* und verleugnet nicht die Einsicht in einen Naturalismus Zolascher Prägung.'

the other, however, did not;

'*Besondere Gewichtigkeit* hatte *die Existenz* Abrahams sowohl für den frühen Hegel wie für Kierkegaard.'

Can subsidiary rules be formulated to account for such exceptions? In this connection, for example, either the syntactical unlikelihood of a singular noun without an article being the subject, when there is an equally good candidate with an article, or the lexicographical unlikelihood—but not impossibility, of course—of a word like '*Gewichtigkeit*' being the subject of a verb like '*haben*'. However, even supposing that adequate rules could be formulated, would it be worthwhile taking up storage space for them considering that the exceptions which they are intended to cover are not only extremely infrequent but also in all probability sufficiently intelligible, if not exactly correct English, when translated according to the general rule? In this latter respect the above may serve as an example:

'Particular importance had Abraham's existence for the young Hegel as well as for K.'

The criteria which determined the function of the remaining fourteen noun blocks as that of the direct object (three having just been discussed in connection with the subject function) were as follows:

1. The noun block in question followed the verb, which was preceded by a syntactic unit (noun or pronoun) unambiguously nominative in form, e.g.

'Dieser Roman nimmt *die Thematik* des „Zauberbergs" im Grunde wieder auf.'

or it followed the verb and was separated from it either by a nominative unit again or by one of ambiguous (nominative/accusative) form like itself, e.g.

'Im „Zauberweg" verliert der Tod *diese Eindeutigkeit.*'

and the example given under 2 of the section on noun blocks functioning as subjects. This solution applied to ten of the noun blocks concerned.

2. The noun block followed immediately after the verb in a co-ordinate clause, e.g.

'So ist etwa das Sterben Johann Buddenbrooks ein anderes als das des Hans Lorenz Castorp und kennt bereits *die Befremdung* angesichts des Todes.'

There were three of this kind.

3. The noun block occurred between the first and last elements of a participial construction, i.e.

'Wie geht dieses mit dem *die Problematik* der modernen Gesellschaft umspielenden Handlungsgeschehen der ersten Romane zusammen?'

This was the only instance.

The 14 predicative with verbs like 'sein'* were recognized in the following ways:

1. By not being immediately before or after the verb, another nominative or possibly nominative blocks being in one of these positions, e.g.

'Die „Preußin" ist in dem streng auf den Umkreis der Lübbekischen Hansestadt eingeschränkten Ordnung *die „Fremde"*.'

There were five noun blocks solved in this way:

2. By occurring in the impersonal construction with '*es*' or '*das*' and '*sein*', where '*es*' is only the grammatical subject, the English translation being 'There are . . .', e.g.

'*Zwei Momente* sind es, die den zweiten Roman in entscheidender Weise von dem ersten abheben und eine neue Ebene der Deutung verlangen.'

Eight of the noun blocks were of this type:

3. By occurring in a clause where the verb is preceded by a syntactic unit of indubitably nominative form, i.e.

'Für Hegel ist Abraham weit entfernt, Vorbild zu sein, er ist vielmehr *das schlimme und gefährliche Gegenbild*.'

This was the only such instance.

* NOTE: With verbs such as '*sein*', unlike others, the negatives '*nicht*', '*keineswegs*', etc. must be counted as separating a noun block from a position next to the verb, and in fact indicating that it cannot be the subject, e.g.

'Es kann nicht das Ziel des Schaffens sein, . . .'

This does not apply, of course, to those cases where the '*nicht*' is merely preparatory to a following '*sondern*'.

Type (*a*) *in a subordinate clause*—Besides 13 not occurring in the basic construction of the clause there were 90 noun blocks, and of these

58 turned out to have the function of subject
29 „ „ „ „ „ „ „ direct object
3 „ „ „ „ „ „ „ predicative.

The function as subject was determined as follows:

1. By the noun being the only possible nominative block in the clause, e.g.

'Wenn gefragt wird, wo zum erstenmal in der deutschen Geistesgeschichte der Neuzeit *die Einsicht* in die Zweideutigkeit des Ursprungs entwickelt wird, dann ist sowohl auf das Alterswerk Goethes wie auch auf bestimmte Erfahrungen der Spätromantik hinzuweisen.'

Altogether 44 of the noun blocks were solved this way, which proved to be the only completely sure one. A further 12 would have their function correctly identified, if it were declared a rule that the first possible nominative block in the clause is the subject, e.g.

'. . . jenes Lied, in dem *die Musik* das Vermögen hat, in der Magie des Klanges und der Melodie das zu vergegenwärtigen, was bisher als bestimmend für die Deutung des Romans erkannt wurde.'

Unfortunately this rule means incorrect identification for another noun block, which, though the first possible nominative block in the clause, is really a direct object, i.e.

'*Welche Bedeutung* dieses inzwischen für den Dichter gewonnen hat, das erweist schon die Tatsache, daß für die Entfaltung dieses Motivs von den vier Bänden des Josephs-Romans nicht weniger als ein ganzer Band reserviert ist.'

As with the similar instance already discussed in the section on the main clause a syntactical solution is probably available, inasmuch as the normal rule for subordinate clauses is that the subject precedes the object, and deviations from this rule are possible only in certain circumstances. One of these is when the clause is, as here, an indirect question. This fact can be made to serve as a caution to the machine that the normal sequence *may* occur reversed. That it need not necessarily occur so is amply illustrated by the following sentence:

'Welcher Aufgabe Joseph in diesem geschichtlichen Zusammenhang zugeordnet ist, das wird sehr schön am Anfang des ersten Teils offenbar.'

If desired, the lexicographical evidence of '*Bedeutung*' being more likely to stand as the object rather than the subject of a verb like '*gewinnen*' may also be adduced. On the other hand, as was mentioned before, no precautions may be taken at all and such exceptions left to the normal procedure, since the nature of the words themselves prohibits any ambiguity, provided that the inversion of the normal order in German had itself led to no ambiguity. The translation of the above instance would then be:

'What significance acquired this in the meantime for the writer is shown by the fact that . . .'

If it is desired to pinpoint the exact area of confusion the machine can be made to place a code symbol after such a clause (as was suggested in connection with prepositional phrases) indicating to the reader that the possibility exists of the subject and direct object having been incorrectly interchanged in the translation. Such refinements are necessary, of course, only if a possible mechanical solution to the problem in the first place is eschewed on the grounds of economy in space and time.

One noun block still remains to be discussed out of the 58 which turned out to be subjects. It too is an exception; and in exactly the same way to that just treated, since it is the second possible nominative block in its clause and yet is the subject, i.e.

'Besondere Gewichtigkeit hatte die Existenz Abrahams sowohl für den frühen Hegel wir für Kierkegaard, und von Bedeutung wird sie für die beiden Denker—wie es *das Gesamtverhältnis*, in dem sie zueinander stehen, nahelegt—in völlig konträrem Sinn.'

Again there is a reason for the inversion of the normal order, namely the impracticability—despite the theoretical possibility—of postponing the pronoun 'es' until after the subject and its dependent relative clause. That, however, does not of itself provide a solution. For this it is necessary to be able to say that in such a construction, i.e. '*es*' (or '*das*', '*dies*', etc.) followed by a nominative/accusative noun and its dependent relative clause and then the verb, the pronoun '*es*' will always be the direct object. Even if this is not true of all types of subordinate clause, it must surely be so of those which are introduced, like the example, by what might be called an 'illustrative "wie"', and this need only be specified in the programme to account for this type of exception to the general rule.

Of the 29 noun blocks with the function of direct object one has already been mentioned. A further nine depended for the resolution of their ambiguity on the hypothesis contradicted by the instance just discussed, that is, that such a noun block following another nominative/accusative unit must be the direct object. Some of the others were solved in a more certain fashion either by reason of

1. The existence in the same clause of an unambiguously nominative form, e.g.

'Will man *die tiefere Einheit* des Romans verstehen, dann ist darüber hinaus vor allem noch auf das Motiv hinzuweisen, das alle übrigen in sich begreift und die Thematik des Romans im Ganzen formt:' or

2. Lack of congruence with the verb, e.g.

'Thomas Mann steht hier am Ende einer langen geistesgeschichtlichen Entwicklung, einer Entwicklung, die im Grunde *alle entscheidenden Epochen* des 18. und 19. Jahrhunderts einbegreift.'

There were four of the first and three of the second type.

Four of the remaining 12 noun blocks occurred in co-ordinate dependent clauses, two of them relative clauses. In these an immediate solution was possible, inasmuch as the relative pronoun was recognizably the subject of the first co-ordinate clause (e.g. by form, congruence with verb, etc.) and therefore necessarily of the second one too, not being repeated after the conjunction in a possible oblique form, e.g.

'Will man die tiefere Einheit des Romans verstehen, dann ist darüber hinaus vor allem noch auf das Motiv hinzuweisen, das alle übrigen in sich begreift und *die Thematik* des Romans im Ganzen formt.'

The other two were of the type mentioned at the beginning of the chapter in connection with the problem of co-ordination,

'Wenn Hegel in dem genannten Aufsatz auf die Überwindung der „Entgegensetzung" dringt, und die Versöhnung von Geist und Natur erstrebt, dann . . .'

and the solution for such instances was discussed in the same place.

The last eight noun blocks all occurred in relative clauses. In three of these the form of the relative pronoun itself provided the solution, since it could only be either nominative (masculine) or dative (feminine) and the latter was excluded by the nature of the clause. For the relative pronoun to be dative one of two conditions would have to apply: either the verb would have to be of the type constructed with a dative direct object, or there would have to be a subject and a direct object in the clause apart from the relative. Neither of these applied in the instances in question, e.g.

1. 'Er ist—in der Kategorie der Zeit gesprochen—der Gott, der das Geheimnis der Zukunft in sich trägt.'

2. 'Anders Joseph, der zwar mit dem Vater noch die Sorge für die Priorität des Geistes teilt.'

For the other five there is no solution beyond an instruction to the machine to regard the relative pronoun as the subject and the noun block as the direct object in every case where there are not specific indications to the contrary. Since the relative pronoun here has an ambiguous nominative/accusative form the problem is essentially the same as that with a clause containing two such noun blocks and in the same way can arise only in those relative clauses which have a transitive verb. Since in such relative clauses the relative pronoun is more often the subject than not—in the text investigated by us the proportion was 17:3—the rule for the machine just suggested seems a reasonable one. At any rate it is adequate for the five noun blocks mentioned, e.g.

'Und wenn Hanno Buddenbrook, die Geschichte der Familie abschließend, sich in die Musik verliert, einer Musik, die die Nähe Richard Wagners, des Gefährten Schopenhauers, nicht verleugnet, dann ist auch in diesem Motivzusammenhang das Erbe der Romantik nicht fern.'

The three instances where the relative pronoun was not the subject do not belong to the type of noun block under discussion, but it will be convenient to quote them here as illustrations of the 'specific indications to the contrary' criterion. In the first the form of the relative pronoun is itself decisive,

'Politisch stellt sich das Ägypten, *dem* Joseph begegnet, als ein zentral regiertes Staatswesen dar.'

In the second there is an unambiguous nominative form in the clause,

'...der mangelnde Bezug zu dem, was *man* im besonderen „Welt" nennt.'

Again there is the possibility of congruence solving the problem (but not with a form like '*die*' which can be both singular and plural). This, however, might have the effect of confirming an incorrect interpretation resulting from the basic rule of taking the relative pronoun as the subject, as is shown by the third example from our text,

'Nun aber in der späten Stunde, da aller Zwang sich ihn als nichtig zu enthüllen beginnt, da beginnt für ihn noch einmal die Fahrt in die Brunnentiefe, jene, die *Hans Castorp und Josef* am Anfang zu wagen aufgetragen *ist*.'

where the verb is in agreement with only the latter of two co-ordinate subjects. The error could only be avoided if information existed in the machine's dictionary indicating that '*die Fahrt*' or '*die Brunnentiefe*', which could be recognized by the machine as the word to which the relative pronoun refers, could not possibly form the subject of a verb like '*wagen*'. This appears to be the only solution, and if such information had to be included in respect of every word in the dictionary, it would mean an extremely large storage capacity —not to mention extensive linguistic research.

Finally among the *Type* (*a*) noun blocks in subordinate clauses we have three that are predicative. It is clear that in the kind of clauses where a predicative is required these cannot be misinterpreted as accusative (except as that expressing duration of time, and a way of overcoming this difficulty has already been suggested), so that the only syntactic unit with which they can be confused is the subject. Even if this happens, however, it does not matter—in fact no distinction need be made, and it is sufficient to retain the order of the two noun blocks as they appear in the German, e.g.

'War *die Enthüllung* des Widerspruchs *die Voraussetzung* des Werkes, dann ist *das Gelingen* der Versöhnung *das Ziel*.'

Type (*b*)—*genitive or dative singular of feminine nouns*

Unlike the preceding, this type cannot have its function determined in the majority of instances by a few basic criteria. Even those with the widest application—confined exclusively to occurrences in a main clause—embraced only a small fraction of the total number, e.g.

1. The fact that the noun block in question follows a defective noun block, e.g.

'Hans Castorp dagegen geht den anderen Weg, den *der Steigerung*.'

2. The fact that the noun block occurs between the subject and the following verb, e.g.

'Der Fortgang der Zeit hält dem Stehen die Waage.'

Only six instances were solved in each of these two ways, that is 12 out of a total of 122 such noun blocks. To solve the remainder in the same fashion would require a comparatively large number of criteria, and even then the solution might not be completely unexceptionable in some cases. Fortunately this is not necessary. The problem is solved in fact by the relative frequency of the two possible functions, since dative nouns and noun blocks are of fairly infrequent occurrence—in German generally, not merely in the text investigated. In this latter the actual proportion of genitive to dative function was 1 dative to 121 genitive noun blocks. It seems reasonable, therefore, to have the machine consider all noun blocks of *Type* (*b*) as genitive, unless specific indications to the contrary are present in the clause concerned. In the instance contained in our text, for example, i.e.

'Und wie sich auf dem Berge die Gedanken Hans Castorps mit der Erinnerung an den Alten dem Tod zukehren, so auch *dieser merkwürdigen Form* der Zeiterfahrung.'

the specific indications would be the fact that the verb is of a type regularly constructed with the dative coupled with the fact that the functionally ambiguous noun block does not follow a noun block and is therefore unlikely to be a dependent genitive.

There still remains a distinction to be made in the genitive itself, since it does not always represent the dependent genitive. Again, however, since the dependent genitive function has a great preponderance over all other varieties (in our text 118 out of the 121 instances were dependent genitives), it may be taken as the basic rule in translation, to be disregarded only in the face of definite indications to the contrary. This may be illustrated by the three examples which were not dependent genitives (in the sense of being dependent on a noun), but genitive after a verb. Two were constructed with the verb 'bedürfen" e.g.

'Daß auch damit wiederum das Grundthema des Romans angeschlagen wird, bedarf keiner Begründung.'

the other with 'versichern', i.e.

'Von da aus also ist die Bedeutung des Todesmotivs zu verstehen: als Ausdruck der Angst vor dem Sichverlieren in der Weite des Weltbezugs und dem Wunsch, sich der Gebundenheit der Tiefe zu versichern.'

and in no case could they be mistaken for dependent genitives, though that is not to say that there is no possibility of a clause occurring in which their position would be such as to render their function uncertain. This might very well be, if a prepositional phrase were inserted between the verb and the genitive in the former instance and the reflexive pronoun 'sich' were replaced by a noun in the latter. In such cases a sure solution would have to be lexicographical, though a procedure based simply on the assumption that a genitive occurring with a verb of this type is always governed by it would be more often correct than incorrect.

Type (c)—accusative singular or dative plural of masculine nouns in classes D and H

Since noun blocks of this type will be accusative far more frequently than dative, the latter case being as we have said quite rare, the best procedure seems to have the machine interpret them always as accusative singular, unless one or more conditions like the following apply:

1. The verb is one regularly constructed with the dative, and no other possible dative unit occurs in the clause.
2. There is already an accusative noun block in the clause (not belonging to the class employed in expressions of duration of time), and the noun block in question is not co-ordinate with this.
3. The noun is preceded not by the definite article, an adjective, participle, or '*dieser*'-type word, but by the indefinite article (which is applicable only to the singular, so that the noun must be accusative) or qualifiers belonging to the plural only (e.g. '*unser*', '*beide*', numerals above one, etc.).
4. The noun is 'bare' (i.e. without any predeterminer). Such nouns are more likely to be plural than singular.

In the text investigated there were only three noun blocks of this type, and in all these cases the noun was accusative singular. None of the above conditions applied, e.g.

'— so geschieht es auch in dem Roman Thomas Manns, in welchem die so oft berufene „Verschlagenheit" den Helden befähigt, sich immer mehr aus dem Bann des Todes und des Elementes zu lösen'.

Type (e)—nominative singular or genitive plural of masculine nouns in classes G and H

There were nine blocks of this type in the text investigated, four in main and five in subordinate clauses. Of the four in main clauses two were subjects and could be recognized as such by reason of the fact that they were:

1. The only possible nominative block in the clause.
2. The only 'prepositionless' noun block immediately before or after the verb, e.g.

'Darauf kommt *der Dichter* auf jeder Stufe seines Schaffens zurück.'

The other two were genitives, as the existence of a possible nominative next to the verb showed (the nouns concerned being themselves separated from the verb), e.g.

'Von Anbeginn spielt das Land *der Ägypter* in den Mahnungen und Reden Jaakobs . . . ebenso eine Rolle, . . .'

Of the five noun blocks in subordinate clauses two were subjects. This was shown in the one case by the noun block being the only possible nominative block and also the first noun block in the clause,

'Um diesen Zusammenhang geht es etwa, darum, daß *der* „*Segen* der Höhe" sich wieder mit dem „Segen der Tiefe" verbindet.'

in the other by the noun block being the first possible nominative block in the clause (only the genitive of a proper noun could stand in this position, unless of course the genitive was dependent on a verb, not a noun),

'Ob *der Dichter* die Kapitel der Genesis in jeder Hinsicht richtig gedeutet hat, darüber mögen sich die Experten schlüssig werden.'

The other three noun blocks, which were genitive plural, had their function distinguished in each case by being co-ordinate with an unambiguously genitive unit, i.e.

1. 'Und es ist im übrigen kein Zufall, daß die Enstehung des „Zauberbergs" mit der Entdeckung Dostojewskis und *anderer russischer Dichter* zeitlich zusammenfällt.'
2. '. . . die Sympathie für den Osten, die im Werke des späten Schelling, des späten Friedrich Schlegel, Schopenhauers und anderer *Denker und Dichter* so bedeutsam wurde.'

This, however, is a purely accidental feature, and not one that can be regarded as a generally forthcoming criterion. The same applies to the fact that the nouns are of a type requiring an article in the singular except when predicative. As a more general criterion might be considered the fact that the noun blocks in question are not the first possible nominative blocks in the clause. Furthermore, in the second instance, the relative pronoun must be the subject, since the verb is of the '*sein*' type, though this does not at once indicate that our noun block cannot be nominative—it can, in the function of predicative. This possibility being excluded, however, by the existence of a predicative adjective ('*bedeutsam*'), the final conclusion that its function must be dependent genitive is arrived at.

Other criteria which might be used to enable the machine to distinguish between the functions are:

1. The noun block follows a verb, adverb, pronoun, etc.—so that it cannot be genitive, unless the verb is of a type constructed with this case.
2. The verb is plural and not of the '*sein*' type—the noun block cannot be nominative singular.
3. There is already a nominative noun block in the clause, the verb not being of the '*sein*' type.
4. There are two nominative noun blocks (not co-ordinate) or 1 nominative noun block and a predicative adjective (not used adverbially) in a clause with a verb like '*sein*'.

That completes the treatment of the five main classes of functional ambiguity in noun blocks (i.e. nouns with a predeterminer)—or at least the four which occurred in the text investigated. There is, however, one other type of ambiguity which has not been classed alongside the others inasmuch as it cannot occur with noun blocks containing a true noun. It arises with adverbs used substantivally with a '*dieser*'-type predeterminer, the possibilities being nominative or accusative or genitive singular, e.g.

'Und nicht nur im Werk des späten Goethe ist die Überwindung *dieses unfruchtbaren Hin und Her* der bloßen Polarität aufgegeben, sondern auch in dem Roman Thomas Manns.'

In this instance, the only one in the text investigated, the problem is solved outright by the accompanying adjective, not to mention the fact that it cannot be the subject, being separated from the verb by another possible nominative block, nor a predicative or direct object because the verb is passive and not of the type requiring a predicative. In short, such noun blocks, whether in a main, subordinate or infinitival clause, can be solved by criteria similar to those employed with the regular classes already discussed.

So far those nouns have been dealt with which, judged by form alone, are of ambiguous function even when accompanied by a predeterminer. Altogether there were 360 such noun blocks, and of these 208 had their function determined by a sure criterion (e.g. a nominative/accusative block being the only subject form in a clause), 147 by complying with a rule designed to account correctly for the majority of those instances not capable of being determined by a sure criterion (e.g. a nominative/accusative block being the first possible nominative block in a subordinate clause), whilst 5 were exceptions to the 'majority rule' and had to be recognized by more complex methods.

BARE NOUNS

We come now to those nouns which occur without any predeterminer and whose syntactical function is in consequence, needless to say, somewhat harder to determine than that of the foregoing. The increased difficulty is due to the fact that whereas with noun blocks there existed only an ambiguity of function, so that it was a simple one of two choice, the number of possible functions of a bare noun is such as to necessitate making a choice from three up to seven, except for certain cases where the form is unique (e.g. genitive singular of masculine and neuter nouns, some dative plurals, etc.—cf. the table of classes on p. 155). That is to say, not only the syntactical function but often also the number of the noun has to be determined from criteria other than its own form. Whether we can hope to solve this problem mechanically will become clearer in discussing the examples, 30 in number, found in the text investigated.

There were 12 nouns in main clauses, 15 in subordinate, and three in infinitival. Six of the first and five of the second performed the function of subject and with one exception could be so identified in the same way as were noun blocks; that is, for those in a main clause, by being the only possible nominative unit in the clause and also the only substantive in one of the positions immediately preceding or following the verb, e.g.

'Denn *Ironie* und *Humor* gedeihen nur auf dem Boden der Trennung.'

and for those in a subordinate clause, by being the only possible nominative unit, e.g.

'Wie das zu verstehen ist, dafür sind wiederum jene Kapitel aufschlußreich, darin sich des jungen Hans Castorp *Gedanken* in die Kindheit zurücktasten.'

The exception mentioned occurred in a clause containing two bare nouns in the positions immediately before and after the verb respectively, i.e.

'Denn *Zeit* in der einseitigen Deutung des Fortschrittes und der Zeitigung des Neuen bedeutet *Gefährdung* der Gebundenheit.'

Here, as with noun blocks, it may be taken as the *basic* rule that in such cases the first of the two nouns is the subject, the second the direct object, provided that it is not followed by an accusative or possibly accusative noun block (not an expression of time). In the latter circumstance the noun in question would be dative (indirect object, dative of advantage, etc.) unless of course the verb were of the type constructed with two accusative objects, e.g.

'Lehrer lehren Schüler richtige Ausdrücke.'

Besides the direct object in the example above there were two others in main and nine in subordinate clauses. The solution is the same, namely to have the machine interpret them as direct object, unless there are definite indications to the contrary. It is not usually necessary, therefore, to take account of features which indicate that a case other than the accusative is not possible, even though these features are present in the majority of instances (e.g. the fact that as a dependent genitive it could not follow a verb or a pronoun, cf., 'Es kann jedenfalls nicht bestritten werden, daß diese Kapitel für die Menschheitsgeschichte bis auf den heutigen Tag darum bedeutsam geworden sind, weil sie *Zeugnis* von jenem Ereignis ablegen, da zum erstenmal der Bann des Mythos und der Wiederholung durchbrochen wurde'). It is possible, however, to imagine a clause in which the bare noun follows a noun block, not a pronoun, and is in fact a dependent genitive instead of a direct object, e.g.

'Unter solchen Umständen besänftigt ein Trunk *Limonade*.'

The difficulty is increased if a noun like '*Glas*' is used, this being followed by an apposition instead of the genitive expected according to English usage, with the result that masculine and neuter nouns appear clearly as non-genitive (e.g. '*ein Glas Wasser*')—much to the machine's surprise. The solution, however, is simple enough, requiring only the formation of all nouns capable of being the first element in one of these constructions into a special class, membership being denoted by a symbol entered in the dictionary alongside the noun concerned. This will indicate to the machine that when one of these nouns is followed by a bare noun, the latter is to be translated as a genitive in English regardless of its form in the German text. This may be all right for a clause with a verb other than '*sein*' and its relations, '*werden*', '*bleiben*', etc., but trouble will arise with a sentence like:

'Er sagt, daß dieses Glas Material für ein Fenster ist.'*

What is the solution to this? Presumably to form not only all nouns capable of being the first element, but also all those capable of being the second element in the construction mentioned into a special class, so that one from each would have to occur together before the machine would interpret the second as a dependent genitive. If this were not sufficient, the rule would have to be made more precise and the occurrence of a particular noun of the first class with a particular noun or nouns of the second class specified.

One of the direct objects in a subordinate clause provided a good illustration of the pitfall created for a machine by a bare noun being adjacent to a syntactical unit with which—considered on form alone—it appears to form one whole. The instance in question occurred with a relative pronoun, but it could equally well crop up with the article at the beginning of a participial construction:

'In die Erinnerung Jaakobs spielt in entscheidender Weise der Gestalt Abrahams hinein, und zwar als des Menschen, *der Gott* im eigentlichen Sinn entdeckt habe.'

Another type occurs after adverbial phrases, e.g.

'Da diese Vermittlung *im besonderen Joseph* aufgegeben ist, stehen nicht Abraham und Jaakob, sondern er im Mittelpunkt des weit gespannten Romanzyklus.'

A solution seems to be attainable in all cases from a consideration of either the nature of the apparent 'noun block' or the syntactical requirements of the type of clause in which it stands, or both. In the first example, for instance, apart from the fact that the transitive verb requires an object and this can be found only in '*Gott*', '*der*' is denoted as the relative pronoun and not the definite article by the reversed positions of the two parts of the verb. In the second the fact that the verb is of the type often constructed with an indirect object is combined with the recognition of '*im besonderem*' as a regular adverbial expression in any case inapplicable to a proper noun.

The four bare nouns so far unaccounted for were all predicatives,

* NOTE: The addition of the definite article to '*Material*' would change the sense.

the three in a main clause being nominative, that in a subordinate clause accusative. The function of the form could be recognized by reason of the fact that a nominative or possible nominative unit consisting of either a pronoun or a noun block already existed in the clause, that the verb was of a type usually requiring a predicative, and that they were the only possible predicative unit in the clause, e.g.

'Vertreter dieser Ordnung sind in dem ersten Roman der alte Johann Buddenbrook und Lebrecht Kröger und im „Zauberberg" der Großvater des Helden.'

The function of the predicative accusative was recognized by the fact that a nominative unit and an accusative unit existed in the clause, that the verb was of the type requiring a predicative accusative, and that the bare noun in question stood within quotation marks, i.e.

'Für alle die diese Ordnung vertreten, ist noch das entscheidend, was eben die Existenz der vorbürgerlichen Gesellschaft strukturell auszeichnet: 1. Das ausschließliche Geformtsein durch die „Umwelt" und der mangelnde Bezug zu dem, was man im besonderen „Welt" nennt.'

Lastly there were the three bare nouns in an infinitive clause, two of which performed the function of direct object and the other that of predicative nominative. There is no need to discuss these, however, since the manner of recognition was the same as that described in the preceding paragraphs, but even easier due to the nouns concerned being the only ones in their respective clauses, e.g.

'In welchem Maße der Tod den Charakter der Zweideutigkeit annimmt, das ist in dem Roman so sorgfältig entfaltet, daß es sich erübrigt, Belege zu geben.'

As regards ambiguity of number, this was to be found in the forms of only four of the thirty instances, i.e. besides that quoted above (*Vertreter dieser Ordnung . . . usw.*').

1. 'Wie fremde die Vorstellung des Todes für die in autonomer Zwecksetzung befangene bürgerliche Welt ist, das haben *Historiker* und *Deuter* dieser Gesellschaft gezeigt.'

2. 'Wobei dem Gefährdeten im Verlaufe des Geschehens *Menschen* zur Seite treten, die ihm helfen können, die wahre Rangordnung des Seins zu erkennen.'

3. 'Und der Ernst, dessen sich Hans Castorp als so charakteristisch für den Alten erinnert, ist wiederum Zeichen für die Gebundenheit.'

All four instances could be solved by considerations of congruence in one way or another. In 2 the distinction in number is made as soon as '*Menschen*' is identified as the subject, and therefore nominative case. On the other hand, 1 is not solved solely by congruence with the verb, since there are two co-ordinate subjects, but by the combination of this with the absence of the article, which would be required before a singular noun in the same position. In the other two cases, where the noun is predicative, the only criterion is congruence with the subject: singular subject—singular predicative, plural subject—plural predicative. Though it works here, however, it is not difficult to imagine a sentence where the subject is plural and the predicative singular, e.g.

'Diese Bretter sind *Material* für eine Kiste.'

There is no difficulty with this particular instance, because the noun 'Material' has a distinct plural form, but this might not always be so, and a method is required for dealing with such exceptions when they arise. The practical solution would again seem to be to make a special class of those nouns which are capable of standing as a singular predicative to a plural subject and are also identical in their singular and plural nominative forms. It would, moreover, be advisable to distinguish within this class those nouns which regularly stood in the singular in such a construction and those which could be either singular or plural. In the latter case the translation would be made to correspond to whichever number was found to be the more frequent, but a symbol also included after the translation to indicate that a mistake in number was possible. The same would apply to all nouns capable of having their number identified by congruence (e.g. when other than nominative case) or by other means.

The third and last type of nominal unit is the proper noun, under which we include names of persons, towns, titles of books, etc., which are not likely to be included in the machine's dictionary, and the gender of which therefore is unknown and cannot be used to define the noun's function when this is accompanied by a predeterminer*. In actual fact, however, only one of the 60 proper nouns which were found in the text investigated was accompanied by a predeterminer; the rest were formally identical with the 'bare nouns' just discussed. The difference between the 'bare' and the 'proper' noun lies in their function. For, whereas all the bare nouns in our text were either subjects or direct objects, the majority of proper nouns were dependent genitives, the actual figures being: subject—23, direct

* Note: Not all titles of books and so forth pose this problem, since those of some are composed of ordinary nouns which will occur in the dictionary, e.g. 'Thomas Manns *die „Königliche Hoheit"*.'

object—1, dependent genitive—33, indirect object—3. Since most proper nouns in the text were the names of persons, the reason for the different distribution is obvious enough.

The ways in which the proper nouns functioning as subject or direct object are so identified are exactly the same as those used for bare nouns, so that there is no need to repeat them. The functions of dependent genitive and indirect object, on the other hand, ought to be examined, as they were absent in the former case.

The function of the only proper noun out of the 60 with a predeterminer—i.e. the only plural form—was determined as dependent genitive by reason of the noun following a 'repetitive' definite article:

'In die Handlung der zwei ersten Romane, in die der „Buddenbrooks" und des „Zauberbergs", ragt in gewisser Weise noch die vorbürgerliche Welt hinein.'*

For the rest of the proper nouns the same basic assumption may be made as with ordinary noun blocks, that is, if they cannot possibly be nominative or accusative, it should be assumed that, unless definite indications exist pointing to the dative, they are genitive. The question is whether it is possible to show that they cannot be nominative or accusative. Of the thirty-three genitive proper nouns in our text only one caused any difficulty in this respect; the others could be accounted for in the following ways:

Main Clause—1. The proper noun occurs before the finite verb and is preceded by another noun block, e.g.

'In die Erinnerung *Jaakobs* spielt in entscheidender Weise die Gestalt Abrahams hinein.'

2. The proper noun occurs after the verb, which is intransitive or passive, and is separated from it by a nominative or possibly nominative unit (the noun in this unit not belonging to the class capable of expressing duration of time), e.g.

'Im übrigen waren im Laufe der Jahre die ehemaligen Feudalherren als Hofbeamte in die Dienste *Pharaos* getreten.'

3. The proper noun occurs after the verb, which is transitive and has on one side of it a nominative or possibly nominative unit (not

* Note: '*der Buddenbrooks*' is not obviously genitive plural to the machine for the reason mentioned before; namely the fact that '*Buddenbrooks*' will not be an entry in its dictionary. As far as the machine is concerned it might be any of four cases—nominative singular (masculine), genitive or dative singular (feminine), or genitive plural.

belonging to the 'duration of time' noun class). The proper noun is separated from the verb by one of these, e.g.

'Besondere Gewichtigkeit hatte die Existenz *Abrahams* sowohl für den frühen Hegel wie für Kierkegaard.'

The same applies when the verb is '*sein*' or similar, except that the nominative and accusative are replaced by two nominatives, e.g.

'Das ist das Lebensproblem *Thomas Buddenbrooks*.'

4. The proper noun occurs after the verb (transitive), from which it is separated by a nominative or possibly nominative unit and followed by an accusative or possibly accusative unit (again not with a 'duration of time' noun), e.g.

'Von Anbeginn spielt das Land der Ägypter in den Mahnungen und Reden Jaakobs als das verfluchte Land des Geschlechtes, der Unzucht und des Todes ebenso eine Rolle, . . .'

The same applies here as under 3, when the verb is '*sein*', etc., e.g.

'So ist etwa das Sterben *Johann Buddenbrooks* ein anderes als das des Hans Lorenz Castorp.'

5. The proper noun occurs after the verb ('*sein*'), which is preceded by a predicative adjective and followed by a prepositional noun block, then the proper noun, and then a nominative/accusative form, e.g.

'Entscheidender dafür ist vielmehr auch in diesem Roman *Thomas Manns* die Tugend der Geduld.'

Since '*die Tugend*' is not the type of noun to express duration of time it can only be nominative, so that '*Thomas Manns*' is interpreted by the machine as genitive*.

Subordinate Clause—1. The proper noun occurs after a nominative or possibly nominative unit; the verb is intransitive or in the passive voice, e.g.

'So ist es kein Zufall, das auch bei ihm, nicht anders als bei Hegel, am Eingang die Gestalt Abrahams steht.'

* NOTE: It should be remarked that the mere fact that a noun belongs to the class capable of expressing duration of time is not to be taken to mean that a noun block containing such a noun will automatically be accusative. Naturally it depends on the other words in the noun block as well. For instance, though '*Zeit*' would certainly be denoted in the dictionary as belonging to this class, it would not be regarded as possibly expressing duration of time unless accompanied by some other word such as '*kurz*', '*lang*', etc., e.g.

'Er hatte nur eine kurze Zeit gewartet.'

2. A nominative or possibly nominative unit and an accusative or possibly accusative unit (not of duration of time) exist in the clause, and the proper noun is preceded by one or both, e.g.

'Und wie sich auf dem Berge die Gedanken Hans Castorps mit der Erinnerung an den Alten dem Tod zukehren, so auch dieser merkwürdigen Form der Zeiterfahrung.'

Infinitive Clause—The proper noun follows an accusative unit (not expressing duration of time), e.g.

'Der Versuch, von daher das Gesamtwerk *Thomas Manns* zu verstehen, müßte allein an dieser Tatsache scheitern.'*

All Clauses—Whatever the type of clause a proper noun preceding a bare noun may be interpreted as a dependent genitive, e.g.

'Wenn also *Thomas Manns Gedanken* von Anfang an um die Antinomie von Natur und Geist kreisen, dann hat er Gelegenheit, in den Geschichten der Genesis die Entstehung dieser Antinomie in der Wurzel zu verfolgen.'

provided that they occur in the same clause. This is a necessary precaution against such instances as

'Und so entwickelt sich aus dieser Voraussetzung die entscheidende Frage, auf die *Thomas Mann Antwort* zu geben bemüht ist.'

where '*Antwort*' belongs to the infinitive clause contained in the subordinate clause of which '*Thomas Mann*' is the subject.

The only instance out of the 33 genitives which caused any difficulty in identifying its function was the following in a subordinate clause;

'Als von den Erinnerungen *Hans Castorps* an den Großvater die Rede war, da wurde außer acht gelassen, daß schon in dieser Stunde des Rückblicks die Zeit für den Helden zum Problem zu werden sich anschickt.'

The difficulty lies in the fact that a clause with a verb like '*sein*' usually has two nominative units, either two nouns or a noun and a predicative adjective. Here there is only one, so the danger arises of the machine interpreting the proper noun '*Hans Castorps*' as the other, a danger which can, however, be avoided by indicating in the

* NOTE: Genitives like '*Thomas Manns*' could almost certainly be identified by the machine by their form, if so desired, even though not included in the dictionary, since the corresponding form without the suffix '-s' will usually be found in the same text.

machine's dictionary the existence of the construction '*die Rede ist von etwas*' where the prepositional phrase with '*von*' takes the place of a predicative.

The three proper nouns in our text which performed the function of indirect object all occurred in clauses with a passive verb and a possible nominative unit. They could, therefore, be only genitive or dative. In two the former case was rendered out of the question by reason of the proper noun standing after a syntactical unit incapable of having a genitive dependent on it and by the verb not being the type constructed with the genitive, e.g.

'Zusammengefaßt wird diese Erfahrung in jenem visionären Erlebnis, das *Hans Castorp* in der Schneelandschaft des Hochgebirges geschenkt wird.'

In the other a dependent genitive was not an impossibility, since the proper noun followed a noun block, but the form could have been identified as non-genitive in the way suggested above, that is, by comparison with similar forms in the text with a suffix '-s'.

'Welcher Aufgabe *Joseph* in diesem geschichtlichen Zusammenhang zugeordnet ist, das wird sehr schön am Anfang des ersten Teils offenbar.'

The verb in all three instances would be denoted in the machine's dictionary as of a type constructed with a dative.

SECTION II

VERB, RELATIVE PRONOUN, APPOSITION

The verb

The second syntactical unit which requires special attention is the verb. The difficulty here for the machine is twofold, caused partly by certain components of verbal blocks having a different translation according to the nature of the other words comprising the block, partly by different inflections having identical forms.

The latter problem presents seven types of ambiguity, i.e.

(*a*) The first and third person plural of the present indicative are identical in all verbs except '*sein*' to the infinitive.

(*b*) The first and third person plural present indicative of modal verbs are the same in form as the perfect participle when the latter has a dependent infinitive.

(*c*) The third person singular present indicative and the perfect participle of regular verbs with an inseparable prefix are identical.

(*d*) The first and third person plural imperfect indicative and/or subjunctive of some irregular verbs are identical to the past participle, e.g. '*betrügen*'–'*betrogen*'.

(*e*) The first and third person plural present indicative of one or two irregular verbs are the same as the perfect participle, e.g. '*empfangen*', '*vergessen*'.

(*f*) The third person singular present indicative of some compound verbs may be mistaken for the past participle of the corresponding simple verb, e.g. '*gebrauchen*'–'*gebraucht*' and the simple form '*brauchen*'.

(*g*) Many forms of the indicative and subjunctive moods are the same—which exactly depends on the type of verb. Considering only the first and third persons*, the verbs may be divided as follows:

1. Regular verbs—the first person singular and plural and the third person plural of the present, imperfect, future, perfect (unless the auxiliary is '*sein*'), and future perfect are the same in indicative and subjunctive.
2. Irregular verbs—the first person singular and the first and third person plural are the same in both moods in the present, future, perfect (unless '*sein*' is the auxiliary), and future perfect: also the first and third person plural imperfect of those verbs not modifying in the subjunctive of this tense.
3. Modal verbs—the same as for irregular verbs, except that there is no ambiguity in the first person singular of the present tense.
4. '*Werden*' and the passive voice constructed with '*werden*'—the first person singular and the first and third person plural of the present, future, and future perfect are the same in indicative and subjunctive.
5. '*Sein*' and the passive voice constructed with '*sein*'—the first person singular and the first and third person plural of the future and future perfect are the only forms identical in the two moods.

For (*a*), (*b*), and (*c*) the solution proposed by Oswald and Fletcher is satisfactory. It is as follows:

In any clause in which the only verb form present is an infinitive/plural form, this form is to be identified as a plural.

(3rd pl.)
'Die Elemente bilden eine Menge.'

* The second person is hardly likely to occur in the literature with which mechanical translation will be primarily concerned.

In any independent clause in which the only verb forms are two infinitive/plural forms, the first-occurring infinitive/plural form is to be identified as a plural, the second-occurring form is to be identified as an infinitive.

(3rd pl.) (inf.)
'Wir können die Menge aus diesen Elementen bilden.'

If two infinitive/plural forms occur in the same clause and a form of the verb '*werden*' also occurs, the first-occurring infinitive/plural form is to be identified as the dependent infinitive, the second-occurring infinitive/plural form is to be identified as the modal infinitive. The form of the verb '*werden*' is to be identified as the finite verb.

(finite) (dep. inf.) (modal inf.)
'Wir werden die Menge aus diesen Elementen bilden können.'

If two infinitive/plural forms occur in the same clause with some form of the verb '*haben*', the first-occurring infinitive/plural form is to be identified as the dependent infinitive, the second-occurring infinitive/plural form as the past participle. The form of the verb '*haben*' is to be identified as the finite verb.

(finite) (dep. inf.) (past. part.)
'Wir haben die Menge aus diesen Elementen bilden können.

In a dependent clause in which the only verb forms occurring are two infinitive/plural forms, the first-occurring infinitive/plural form is to be identified as a dependent infinitive, the second-occurring infinitive/plural form is to be identified as the plural form.

(inf.) (3rd pl.)
'. . .weil wir die Menge aus diesen Elementen bilden können . . .'

If a present/past participle verb form is the only verb form occurring in a clause, it is to be identified as a present singular.

(3rd sing.)
'Cantor definiert folgendermaßen den Begriff der Menge.'

In any clause in which a present/past participle form occurs with any form of the verb '*haben*' or '*sein*', the present/past participle form is to be identified as a past participle, the form of '*haben*' or '*sein*' is to be identified as the finite verb.

(past part.)
'Cantor hat den Begriff der Menge folgendermaßen definiert.'

(past part.)
'Er ist seit zwei Wochen verreist.'

The other four are not mentioned by Oswald and Fletcher, but (*d*) and (*f*) can be solved in the same way as (*c*), whilst (*e*) is almost identical to (*b*).

As for the subjunctive problem it turns out that there is hardly any such thing, since ambiguous forms are normally replaced by unambiguous forms (e.g. past for a present tense in indirect speech, periphrasis with 'mögen', etc.), or if they do occur, are signalled by another, unmistakable subjunctive form either in the same or the preceding sentence, e.g.

'Die Bildhauerei, sagen sie, *könne* keine Stoffe nachmachen; dicke Falten machten eine üble Wirkung (Lessing).'

There is a problem, to be sure, but it concerns the translation of the verb in general rather than the subjunctive mood alone, though it may be said that difficulties arise more frequently from constructions with this than from those with the indicative. Basically the problem arises out of the various ways in which a particular mood or tense in German has to be translated in English. This can be illustrated by the following uses of the subjunctive*:

1. English retains both tense and mood of the German, e.g.

'Die Prüfung sei leicht oder schwer, bestehen wirst du sie.'

'Whether the examination be easy or difficult, you will pass it.'

or 'Be the examination easy or difficult . . .'

likewise in final clauses, where 'might' is added, e.g.

'Die Glocke läutet, damit man wisse, daß jemand begraben werden soll.'

'The bell rings so that people might know that someone is to be buried.'

2. English retains the same tense, but changes the mood, e.g.

'Er bildet sich ein, die Finanzlage sei besser geworden.'

'He imagines the financial position has got better.'

3. English changes both tense and mood, e.g.

'Wir nahmen an, er sei aufrichtig.'

'We assumed he was honest.'

* NOTE: These are not by any means intended as a complete scheme.

4. Sometimes the construction has to be changed, e.g. from finite to participial as,

'Er antwortete, ohne daß ich ihn gefragt hätte.'

'He answered without my having asked him.'

or to infinitival,

'Er ist zu beschäftigt, als daß er mitspielen könnte.'

'He is too busy to be able to play with us.'

But, as we have said, these features are not peculiar to the translation of the subjunctive—similar changes are often necessary with the indicative, e.g. change of tense:

'Es sind schon viele Jahre, daß ich hier wohne.'

'It is for many years that I have lived here.'

Change from finite to participial construction:

'Dies führte dazu, daß ich zu einem anderen Regiment versetzt wurde.'

'This led to my getting transferred to another regiment.'

or from finite to infinitive construction:

'Es ist schön, wenn man wohlerzogene Kinder sieht.'

'It is good to see well brought up children.'

The question now arises of whether it is necessary for the machine to recognize the subjunctive mood as distinct from the indicative. Generally speaking, if the subjunctive occurs in a main clause it will require recognition and special translation (cf. 1 above). If it occurs in a subordinate clause, it will usually not require recognition, either because it is correctly rendered in English by the indicative (cf. 2 and 3 above), or because though there is a difference in sense between subjunctive and indicative in German, both must be translated by the indicative in English and the difference left to the context to bring out, e.g.

'Er verdient, daß man ihn lobt' . . . 'He deserves to be praised' (and he is)

'Er verdient, daß man ihn lobe' . . . 'He deserves to be praised' (but has not yet been.)

This is not universally true, however, because there are constructions where the distinction can be made in English too, e.g.

'Angenommen, sie kommt,' . . . 'Assuming she is coming,' . . . (reasonable certainty)

'Angenommen, sie komme,' . . . 'Assuming she comes,' . . . (some doubt)

For translating verbs, therefore, a system of classification on the lines of that for nouns is required. It will not be the verbs themselves, however, that will be classified, but the various types of constructions, since the way in which a verb is translated will depend on the construction in which it is found. As in the case of nouns the sole criterion in forming a class is the ability of all members of the class to be translated according to one and the same procedure irrespective of their form in the German. By way of illustration we may compare the instance given above,

'Er ist zu beschäftigt, als daß er mitspielen könnte.'

'He is too busy to be able to play with us.'

with the formally similar,

'Ich wäre eher dahin gefahren, als daß ich zu Hause geblieben wäre.'

'I would rather have gone there than remained at home.'

Though the constructions of the subordinate clauses are the same, the fact that the second is preceded by a verb instead of depending on a predicative adjective changes the mode of translation from infinitive to finite verb and therefore puts the two constructions in different classes.

In contrast, although the construction of

'Die Jungen begutachteten den Motor, als seien sie schon Techniker.'

'The youths appraised the motor as though they were engineers.'

is different from that of

'Wir nahmen an, er sei aufrichtig.'

'We assumed he was honest.'

the same mood and tense is used in translation for both, so that they may be placed together in one class.

The constructions might be conveniently divided in the first place into the four moods:

(*a*) Imperative.

(*b*) Infinitive—This would have to be subdivided into the type of construction which can be translated by the infinitive in English, this itself comprising various kinds, e.g.

'ich möchte *kommen*'	'I should like *to come*.'
'Ich bat ihn *zu kommen*'	'I asked him *to come*.'
'er hieß es *tun*'	'He ordered it to be done', etc.

and the type which requires a different construction, for instance, the participial, e.g.

'Sehen ist Glauben.'	'Seeing is believing.'
'Er blieb sitzen.'	'He remained sitting,' etc.

(*c*) Subjunctive—That is, only those constructions in which the subjunctives require a special translation in English.

(*d*) Indicative—That is, not only the constructions in which the indicative actually occurs, but also those in which the subjunctive does not require a different translation and can be regarded as indicative.

Within each of these four classes will be as many subdivisions as are necessary to account for every type of change that must be made in translating the constructions in that particular class, whether the change is merely one of tense or more fundamental. In some cases the construction which is the evidence for a particular change will be adequately defined in one clause (usually main), e.g. the expression of duration of time in

'Ich warte schon zehn Minuten.'

indicating the necessity of substituting a perfect (I have been waiting . . .) for the German present. In the majority, however, the construction will be a combination of a particular type of subordinate clause (e.g. that introduced by '*als daß*' above) with a characteristic of the governing clause (i.e. there the presence in the one of an ordinary verb, in the other of '*sein*' with a predicative adjective) or will consist simply of a comparison of the verb with that in the main clause. The latter is particularly so with the subjunctive used in indirect speech, e.g.

'Sie sagen, daß er das Gedicht lese.'	'They say that he reads (is reading) the poem.'
'Sie sagten, daß er das Gedicht lese.'	'They said that he read (was reading) the poem.'
'Sie sagen, daß er das Gedicht gelesen habe.'	'They say that he has read the poem.'
'Sie sagten, daß er das Gedicht gelesen habe.'	'They said that he had read the poem.'
'Sie sagen, daß er das Gedicht lesen werde.'	'They say that he will read the poem.'
'Sie sagten, daß er das Gedicht lesen werde.'	'They said that he would read the poem.'

'Sie sagen, daß er das Gedicht lesen würde.'	'They say that he would read the poem.'
'Sie sagten, daß er das Gedicht lesen würde.'	'They said that he would read the poem.'

For this it will be enough to include in the programme an instruction to the effect that in indirect speech a present tense must be translated as a past definite (or past continuous), a perfect as a pluperfect, a future as a conditional, when the governing verb is historic.

The tenses of the German verb may be identified by the normal stem-ending routine. Regular verbs cause no difficulty, inasmuch as they have only one stem*.

Irregular verbs, on the other hand, vary somewhat in their manner of conjugation and may have from one to five stems. The different types can be classified as follows†:

1 stem‡

'müssen' stem '**muss-**'; PI '*muss-t*', '*muss*'; II '*muss-te*'; IS '*muss-teu*'; PP '*ge-muss-t*'.

2 stems

1. *'bleiben'* stems '**bleib-**'; PI '*bleib-st*', '*bleib-t*'.
'**blieb-**'; II '*blieb*'; IS '*blieb-e*'; PP '*ge-blieb-en*'.

'fliegen' stems '**flieg-**'; PI '*flieg-st*', '*flieg-t*'.
'**flog-**'; II '*flog*'; IS '*flog-eu*'; PP '*ge-flog-en*'.

1 (*a*)§. *'befleissen'* stems '**befleiss-**'; PI '*befleiss-t*', '*befleiss-t*'.
'**befliss-**'; II '*befliss*'; IS '*befliss-e*'; PP '*befliss-en*'.

'betrügen' stems '**betrug-**'; PI '*betrug-stu*', '*betrug-tu*'.
'**betrog-**'; II '*betrog*'; IS '*betrog-eu*'; PP '*betrog-en*'.

* NOTE: As with nouns an umlaut is reckoned as part of the ending, not the stem, so that a verb with an umlaut in some of its inflections and without in others may still have only one stem. Verbs with two umlauts, e.g. '*überführen*', will have one omitted in the dictionary entry and also in the input text, if the prefix does not occur separately, the rule for the person punching out the input tape being that no word shall have more than one umlaut. If, however, the prefix is separate, it will retain its umlaut in the input text in accordance with the same rule, but the machine will discard it on associating it with the main part of the verb, when this already has an umlaut, prior to searching the dictionary.

† NOTE: PI = Present indicative second and third persons singular, II = Imperfect indicative, IS = Imperfect subjunctive, PP = Past participle.

‡ NOTE: For the purposes of M.T. the German ß need not have a symbol of its own but can be equated with ss.

§ NOTE: 1(*a*) is the same as 1 except that the verbs have inseparable prefixes and therefore cannot take the '*ge-*' prefixes indicative of the past participle. Though this variant is given here only, it applies to the following types as well.

2. '*bringen*' stems '**bring-**'; PI '*bring-st*', '*bring-t*'.
'**brach-**'; II '*brach-te*'; IS '*brach-teu*'; PP '*ge-brach-t*'.

3. '*dürfen*' stems '**darf-**'; PI '*darf-st*', '*darf*'.
'**durf-**'; II '*durf-te*; IS '*durf-teu*'; PP '*ge-durf-t*'.

4. '*erlöschen*' stems '**erlisch-**'; PI '*erlisch-st*', '*erlisch-t*'.
'**erlosch-**'; II '*erlosch*'; IS '*erlosch-eu*'; PP '*erlosch-en*'.

5*. '*rufen*' stems '**ruf-**'; PI '*ruf-st*', '*ruf-t*'; PP '*ge-ruf-en*'.
'**rief-**'; II '*rief*'; IS '*rief-e*'.

'*fahren*' stems '**fahr-**'; PI '*fahr-stu*, ', '*fahr-tu*'; PP '*ge-fahr-en*'.
'**fuhr-**'; II '*fuhr*'; IS '*fuhr-eu*'.

6. '*stecken*' stems '**steck-**'; PI '*steck-st*', '*steck-t*'; PP '*ge-steck-t*'.
'**stak-**'; II '*stak*'; IS '*stak-eu*'.

7. '*brennen*' stems '**brenn-**'; PI '*brenn-st*', '*brenn-t*'; IS '*brenn-te*'.
'**brann-**'; II '*brann-te*'; PP '*ge-brann-t*'.

8. '*schwören*' stems '**schwor-**'; PI '*schwor-stu*', '*schwor-tu*'; II '*schwor*'; PP '*ge-schwor-en*'.
'**schwur-**'; II '*schwur*'; IS '*schwur-eu*'.

3 stems

1†. '*singen*' stems '**sing-**'; PI '*sing-st*', '*sing-t*'.
'**sang-**'; II '*sang*'; IS '*sang-eu*'.
'**gesungen**' = PP.

2. '*beginnen*' stems '**beginn-**'; '*beginn-st*', '*beginn-t*'.
'**begann-**'; II '*begann*'; IS '*begann-eu*'.
'**begonn-**'; IS '*begonn-eu*'; PP '*begonn-en*'.

3‡. '*geben*' stems '**geb-**'; PP '*ge-geb-en*'.
'**gib-**'; PI '*gibst*', '*gib-t*'.
'**gab-**'; II '*gab*'; IS '*gab-eu*'.

* NOTE: The (*a*) variant of this type produces a past participle identical in form to the infinitive e.g. '*empfangen*'–'*empfing*'–'*empfangen*'. A distinction between the two can be made in the same way as between the infinitive and the past participle of modal verbs when the latter have an infinitive dependent upon them, i.e. by the existence of the auxiliary '*haben*', '*sein*' or '*werden*' in the same clause when the ambiguous form is the past participle.

† NOTE: Here the past participle can be entered in the dictionary as it stands, since its true stem '*sung-*' is not shared by any other form of the verb.

‡ NOTE: This type also produces an ambiguous past participle form in its (*a*) variant, e.g. '*vergessen*'–'*vergass*'–*vergessen*'.

4. '*gebaren*' stems '**gebar-**'; II '*gebar*'; IS '*gebar-eu*'.
'**gebier-**'; PI '*gebier-st*', '*gebier-t*'.
'**geboren**' = PP.

5. '*fechten*' stems '**fecht-**' (forms of present indicative other than second and third person singular and of present subjunctive).
'**fich-**'; PI '*fich-st*', '*fich-t*'.
'**focht-**'; II '*focht*'; IS '*focht-eu*'; PP '*ge-focht-en*'.

4 stems

1. '*brechen*' stems '**brech-**' (present indicative and subjunctive).
'**brich-**'; PI '*brich-st*', '*brich-t*'.
'**brach-**'; II '*brach*'; IS '*brach-eu*'.
'**gebrochen**' = PP.

2. '*bersten*' stems '**berst-**' (present indicative and subjunctive).
'**birst**' = PI.
'**barst-**'; II '*barst*'; IS '*barst-eu*'.
'**borst-**'; IS '*borst-eu*'; PP '*ge-borst-en*'.

3. '*schelten*' stems '**schelt-**' (present indicative and subjunctive).
'**schilt-**'; PI '*schilt-st*', '*schilt*'.
'**schalt-**'; II '*schalt*'.
'**scholt-**'; IS '*scholt-eu*'; PP '*ge-scholt-en*'.

4. '*dreschen*' stems '**dresch-**' (present indicative and subjunctive).
'**drisch-**'; PI '*drisch-st*', '*drisch-t*'.
'**drasch-**'; II '*drasch*'; IS '*drasch-eu*'.
'**drosch-**'; II '*drosch*'; IS '*drosch-eu*'; PP '*ge-drosch-en*'.

5 stems

1. '*sterben*' stems '**sterb-**' (present indicative and subjunctive).
'**stirb-**'; PI '*stirb-st*', '*stirb-t*'.
'**starb-**'; II '*starb*'.
'**sturb-**'; IS '*sturb-eu*'.
'**gestorben**' = PP.

2. *'bergen'* stems '**berg-**' (present indicative and subjunctive).
'**birg-**'; PI '*birg-st*', '*birg-t*'.
'**barg-**'; II '*barg*'; IS '*barg-eu*'.
'**burg-**'; IS '*burg-eu*'.
'**geborgen**' = PP.

If we examine the above types without regard to the number of stems each has, we find that they can be divided into the following categories:

I. Verbs in which the imperfect subjunctive is distinguished from the indicative in all its forms by an umlaut. Here the past tenses are indicated as such by

(*a*) ending or ending and prefix '*ge-*', e.g.

'*dürfen*'—'*durf*-**te**', '*durf*-**teu**', '*gedurf*-**t**'.

(*b*) different stem, e.g.

'*fliegen*'—'**flog**', '**flog**-*eu*', '*ge***flogen**'.

or in the case of some past participles solely by the prefix '*ge-*', e.g.

'**ge-***fahren*'.

(*c*) absence of umlaut from ending (this applies only to the imperfect indicative and past participle, not the imperfect subjunctive. This is homonymous with the present subjunctive), e.g.

'*erlöschen*'—'**erlosch**', '*erlosch-eu*', '*erlosch*-**en**'.

II. Verbs in which the imperfect subjunctive does not have an umlaut and is therefore not distinct from the indicative in the first and third plural forms.

Past tenses indicated as such by a different stem, e.g.

'*bleiben*'—'**blieb**', '**blieb**-*e*', '*ge*-**blieb**-*en*'

or in some past participles solely by the prefix '*ge-*', e.g.

'*rufen*'—'**ge-***rufen*'.

III. Verbs in which the imperfect subjunctive does not have an umlaut, but is nevertheless distinct in all forms from the indicative, because the stems are different.

Past tenses indicated as such by ending or prefix '*ge-*' and ending, e.g.

'*brennen*'—'*brann*-**te**', '*brenn*-**te**', '**ge-***brann*-**t**'.

We are now in a position to set out the system of stems and endings in full. As the following table shows there are six classes in all (the five irregular types above plus the regular verb). It should be noted that for clarity, regardless of repetition, the endings for all persons are given, but as with French each different ending would not be entered more than once in the actual ending dictionary, inasmuch as the endings serve to distinguish mood, tense, and number, but not person.

The second and lesser problem concerning the verb block is, as was said at the beginning, that caused by certain components of verbal blocks having a different translation according to the nature of the other words in the same block. The reference is specifically to '*sein*' and '*werden*', with which the difference in translation is not dependent entirely on whether they are used as full verbs or as auxiliaries.

With '*sein*' all forms of the present and imperfect indicative show this difference, but the third person plural may be taken for illustration,

1. Full verb: '*sie* **sind**'—they *are*.
2. Auxiliary in passive voice: '*sie* **sind** *gelobt*'—they *are* praised.
3. Auxiliary in active voice: '*sie* **sind** *gekommen*'—they *have* come.

Similarly with the imperfect, '*waren*', which would be translated as 'they *were*', 'they *were* praised', 'they *had* come', respectively. The infinitive itself may also have two translations, according to whether it occurs in a future tense as a full verb, e.g.

'*sie werden* (*stark genug*) **sein**'—'they will *be* (strong enough)'

or in a future perfect, as an auxiliary, e.g.

'*sie werden gekommen* **sein**'—'they will *have* come'.

The same applies to '*werden*' as to '*sein*', except that there is a possibility of four translations instead of two with the form of the first and third person plural present, since it is the same as that of the infinitive. Hence we have

1. Full verb (finite): '*sie* **werden**'—'they *become*'.
2. Full verb (infinitive): '*sie werden* **werden**'—'they will *become*'.
3. Auxiliary in active voice: '*sie* **werden** *loben*'—'they *will* praise.
4. Auxiliary (finite) in passive voice:
5. Auxiliary (infinitive) in passive voice:

} '*Sie* **werden** *gelobt* **werden**'—they *will be* praised'.

	Type of verb	*Person*	*Endings denoting*					
			Present indicative	*Present subjunctive*	*Imperfect indicative and subjunctive*		*Present infinitive and participle*	*Past participle*
A	Regular verbs and the regular parts of irregular verbs, e.g. '*loben*', '*fahren*'. Stems: '**lob-**', '**fahr-**'.	1	e * eu	e eu	(e)te (e)teu			†
		2	{(e)st (e)stu / t tu}	est estu	(e)test (e)testu		(e)n	(e)t
		3	(e)t (e)tu	e eu	(e)te (e)teu		(e)nu	(e)tu
		1	(e)n (e)nu	(e)n (e)nu	(e)ten (e)tenu			en
		2	(e)t (e)tu	(e)t (e)tu	(e)tet (e)tetu		(e)nd	
		3	(e)n (e)nu	(e)n (e)nu	(e)ten (e)tenu		(e)ndu	
B	The modal verbs '*sollen*' and '*wollen*'. Stems: '**soll-**', '**woll-**', '**will-**'. Also the past tenses of Type II irregular verbs, e.g. '*bleiben*'. Stem: '**blieb-**'‡.	1	—	e	te			
		2	(e)st	est	test		en	en
		3	—	e	te			
		1	en	en	ten			
		2	(e)t	et	tet		end	t
		3	en	en	ten			
					Indicative	*Subjunctive*		
C	The other 4 modals, e.g. '*mögen*'. Stems: '**mog-**', '**mag-**', '**moch-**'. Also the past tenses of Type 1*a* verbs, e.g. '*bringen*', Stem: '**brach-**' and the past indicative tenses of Type III verbs, e.g. '*brennen*' Stem: '**brann-**'‖.	1	—	eu	te	teu		
		2	(s)t §	estu	test	testu	enu	
		3	—	eu	te	teu		
		1	enu	enu	ten	tenu		t
		2	tu	etu	tet	tetu	endu	
		3	enu	enu	ten	tenu		
D	Those parts of Type III verbs not included in Class *C*, e.g. '*brennen*'. Stem: '**brenn-**'.	1	e ¶	e		te		
		2	st	est		test	en	
		3	t	e		te		
		1	en	en		ten		
		2	t	et		tet	end	
		3	en	en		ten		
E	(*a*) Past tenses of Type I*b* verbs e.g. '*fliegen*'. Stem: '**flog-**' (*b*) Present subjunctive of '*sein*' and the imperfect indicative and subjunctive of '*sein*' and '*werden*'. Stems: '**sei-**', '**war-**', '**wurd-**' **.	1	— e	eu				
		2	(e)st	estu				
		3	— e	eu				
		1	en	enu				en
		2	(e)t	etu				§§
		3	en	enu				
F	Type I*c* verbs e.g. '*erlöschen*'. Stem: '**erlosch-**' ¶¶.	1	eu	eu	—	eu		
		2	stu	estu	st	estu	enu	
		3	tu	eu	—	eu		en
		1	enu	enu	en	enu		
		2	tu	etu	t	etu	endu	
		3	enu	enu	en	enu		

NOTES TO TABLE:

* The 'e' in parenthesis throughout the regular conjugation results from the following three causes:

(*a*) Verbs with a stem ending in '-d', '-t', 'm', or '-n' (but not double '-mm' or '-nn') have an 'e' inserted before a 't' or 'st' inflection, e.g.

'*ich bilde*', '*du bildest*', '*er bildet*'; imperfect—'*ich bildete*'; past participle—'*gebildet*'.

(*b*) Verbs with a stem ending in a sibilant (-s, -ss, z, -sch, etc.) may either have 'e' inserted before the '-st' inflection of the second person singular present indicative, e.g.

'*du reisest*', '*sitzest*', '*wäschest*'.

or omit the 's' from the '-st' inflection, e.g.

'*du reist*', '*sitzt*', '*wäscht*' (but also '*wäschst*').

(*c*) Verbs with an infinitive ending in '-eln' or '-ern' (e.g. '*schütteln, klettern*) drop the 'e' of the '-en' inflection in the first and third person plural of the present tense, e.g. '*sie schüttel-n*', '*kletter-n*'.

With regard to these verbs it should be noted that in the first person singular of the present tense the '-eln' type loses the 'e' before the 'l' and the '-ern' type may, but need not necessarily lose the 'e' before the 'r', e.g.

'*ich schüttle*' and '*ich klettre*' or '*klettere*'.

This means that two stems are necessary in such cases, i.e.

'**schuttel-**' and '**schuttl-**', '**kletter-**' and '**klettr-**'.

The variant endings on the right of each section are for those verbs with an umlaut (this being represented as with nouns by the letter 'u').

† The '-en' ending is included here, although not entirely regular, in order to account for the past participle of otherwise regular verbs (e.g. '*mahlen*'–'*mahlte*'–'*gemahlen*') as well as of irregulars like '*fahren*'.

Naturally, to avoid unnecessary confusion between the past participle and certain forms of the present indicative and subjunctive which have the same endings, there must also be a stipulation that the participial form should have the prefix '*ge-*' unless the verb is one with an inseparable prefix, in which case it will not be able to take the prefix '*ge-*' as well. The solution to the ambiguity of form resulting from this has already been discussed (cf. p. 184).

‡ It will be observed that the stems of Type II verbs representing past tenses are included in a class where the endings appropriate to them are found under the present tense. This does not mean, however, that the past tense of a Type II verb (e.g. '*blieb*') will be translated as a present. Though the traditional nomenclature of present indicative, imperfect indicative, etc. has been used for the sake of convenience, and the meaning of the tense inflections remains basically the same, their application differs.

The essential difference is that whereas in normal grammar the endings denote absolute tense, in the system set up above for mechanical translation they denote only relative tense. By the latter is meant tense relative to the tense of the stem, every stem entered in the dictionary being classed as either present or imperfect. Whichever it is, present or imperfect, whether it remains so depends on the ending. Should the ending be listed under what we have called the present indicative, the indication will be that the word concerned is to be translated in the tense of the stem (e.g. '**bleib-en**' = 'remain', '**blieb-en**' = 'remained', 'were remaining', etc., according to the context). If, on the other hand, the ending occurs under the 'imperfect indicative', the word will be translated in the appropriate past tense of the stem's English equivalent (e.g. '**lob-**' = praise, '**lob-***te*' = praised, was praising, etc., or '**wahl-**' = choose, '**wahl-***ten*' = chose, was choosing, etc.). (NOTE: Each English equivalent will be denoted as either a regular or irregular verb. If it is regular the correct form for the tense required will be constructed by the machine according to a prescribed formula; if it is irregular, the appropriate form will be selected from a dictionary of the principal parts of English irregular verbs also contained in the machine's memory.) When the ending occurs under the past participle and the prefix '*ge-*' is present, the word will be translated as a past definite or, accompanied by an auxiliary, as either past definite or perfect ('*hat gelobt*'–'praised' or 'has praised').

If a verb has several stems, their relationship must be indicated in the machine's dictionary, even though they may be contained in different classes. This is made necessary by the fact that (*a*) the most economical way of translating verbs is not by including the appropriate English equivalent alongside each of the several stems, but by giving only the English present form (alongside the German present) and letting the machine construct the required tense as suggested above according to the information supplied by the ending or the past stem and endings and (*b*) in the subjunctive mood the endings serve only to distinguish the mood itself and are not reliable guides to the tense required in translation. This, as we have pointed out, is usually to be deduced from the construction in which the verb occurs, so that here too the machine can produce it from a single English equivalent given with the German present stem.

Lastly an instruction must be included in the dictionary to the effect that past stems in class B cannot take the ending given as that of the present infinitive; otherwise there will be confusion between this and that of the first and third person plural of the finite verb.

§ The 's' has to be omitted from the 'st' ending for '*müssen*', stem '**muss-**' and second person singular '*muss-t*'.

‖ In this case the endings appropriate to the stems representing the past tenses of Types I*a* and III verbs are themselves indicative of the past. The stems (e.g. '**brach-**' and '**brann-**') must therefore be regarded as present stems, because if they were marked in the dictionary as imperfect and were followed by an ending indicative of the imperfect, the machine might get the idea that the word in question was doubly imperfect and turn out a translation like 'burn-ed-ed'.

In some instances it is possible for there to be a confusion between the stems of different verbs;

here, for example, between that of '*bringen*', '**brach-**', and the same form of '*brechen*', which would belong to Class E. When this happens the distinction between the two verbs must be made by the respective endings, since these do not coincide.

¶ The stems of these verbs, which are not many, all end in '-nn' and do not have an umlaut, so that the (**e**)'s and umlaut variants in the endings are not necessary here.

** '*Sein*' is an exception to the rule that mood is distinguished by endings, since its stem '**sei-**' takes endings characteristic of the indicative and must itself therefore be indicated specifically as a subjunctive stem.

§§ The past participle ending applies only to the (*a*) verbs, not '*sein*' and '*werden*'.

¶¶ The second and third person singular present indicative forms of '*erlöschen*' ('*erlischst*', '*erlischt*') are not included here under a stem '**erlisch-**', because this would require the endings '-st' and '-t' being entered under the present indicative. Since the former of these is also characteristic of the imperfect, however, it is preferable to avoid the confusion by putting '*erlischst*' and '*erlischt*' in the dictionary as complete forms. The endings '-stu' and '-tu' in the second and third person positions are for a verb not varying here, e.g. '*schwören*'.

Since where the translation of '*sein*' and '*werden*' varies, the other components of the verbal unit also vary, this fact can be made the basis of a solution. Each type of component will be given a code number and a dictionary of all the possible combinations of these that can occur included in the translation programme. Then any translation of a particular form of a word can be related to one or more of these combinations. This can be illustrated with the few examples quoted above by adopting the code:

f = finite forms of '*sein*'.
s = infinitive '*sein*'.
P = past participle of transitive verb.
w = the finite or infinitive forms of '*werden*'.
I = infinitive of verb other than '*sein*' or '*werden*'.
Q = past participle of intransitive verb.

from which the following combinations result:

'*sie sind/sie waren*'	f
'*sie sind gelobt/sie waren gelobt*'	fP
'*sie sind gekommen/sie waren gekommen*'	fQ
'*sie werden sein*'	ws
'*sie werden gekommen sein*'	wQs
'*sie werden*'	w
'*sie werden werden*'	ww
'*sie werden loben*'	wI
'*sie werden gelobt werden*'	wPw

It is now possible to instruct the machine to translate the doubtful quantities f, s, and w as follows*:

f 1. 'are' (present tense), 'were' (past tense).
2. 'have' when accompanied by a Q, component.

* NOTE: When two *ws* occur in a clause one is to be translated as 'will' or 'shall', the other either as 'become', (if no P is present) or as 'be' (if a P is present). Which is translated as which is unimportant, provided that the correct order for English is produced, i.e. 'will become', not 'become will', or 'will be' not 'be will'.

s 1. 'be', when a *w* is present.
2. 'have', when both a *w* and a *Q* occur.

w 1. 'become', when alone or with another *w*.
2. 'will' ('shall'), when with another *w* or an *I* or a *wP*.
3. 'be', when another *w* and a *P* are in the same clause.

The samê method may also be useful for distinguishing between various senses with other verbs, for instance the sense of 'ability' or 'possibility' expressed by '*können*', e.g.

'*Er kann es getan habe*' = 'he may have done it'.
'*Er hat es tun können*' = 'he has been able to do it'.

Representing the modal verb by *m* and '*haben*' by *h*, the combinations are again seen to be different (i.e. *mPh* and *mIh*) and therefore to provide a criterion for the appropriate translation.

The association of this with the stem-ending system for the principal parts of the verb enables the machine to deal with compound as well as simple tenses.

COMPOUND VERBS AND SEPARABLE PREFIXES

The fact that several prefixes correspond in form to prepositions does not lead to confusion, inasmuch as, if separated from the verb, they must stand at the end of the clause and will therefore always be followed immediately either by a punctuation mark or a co-ordinating conjunction. For the rare occasions when they do not stand at the end of the clause a consideration of the syntactic or sense requirements would provide the solution, but the amount of material that would have to be incorporated in the machine's memory to make this possible would almost certainly make it an uneconomical proposition.

How the machine can identify a compound verb will naturally depend on how the latter is entered in the dictionary. If it is entered as one word, then of course the machine can simply re-connect the prefix and carry out the normal search routine. This will be the procedure with those compounds, the translation of which is different from the translations of its components put together; e.g. '*Die Sache ist gut ausgelaufen*' = the matter has turned out well (not 'run out', which would probably result from '*aus*' + '*laufen*').

If, however, the combined translations of its components provides a satisfactory translation for the compound (e.g. '*aufwecken*'—'wake up'), it is more economical—though slower of course in access time—to omit the compound from the dictionary and incorporate instead an instruction to the machine to identify the simple verb and prefix separately, then combine their translations.

This, though easy enough where the prefix occurs separated, would necessitate the machine separating it where not, that is, in the majority of cases—which would not be easy. In the first place the machine would attempt to locate the incoming compound verb among its dictionary entries, and on being unsuccessful might assume that it was a proper noun (the majority of these not being included in the dictionary, as was explained on p. 178) and leave it in its original form in the translation. This can happen, however, only if the compound verb is acting as a noun and has its first letter capitalized*, e.g. '*das Hinauslehnen ist gefährlich*'. Because all infinitives functioning as nouns are neuter singular and are always preceded by the definite article, the possible confusion is limited to those proper nouns with the predeterminer '*das*', '*des*', or '*dem*', and only these would have needed to be subjected along with all unseparated compound verbs (whether functioning as verbs or nouns) to the routine for identifying the prefix, if one is present, but for the fact that nouns may be formed from the participles of a compound just as from a simple verb (e.g. '*die Umstehenden*'—the bystanders) and these are not limited to the neuter gender or to occurring only with a predeterminer. For this reason all words which cannot be located in the main dictionary must go through the routine for identifying compound verbs.

This routine is again a stem-ending one, the endings in this case being the corresponding simple verbs, the stems the following separable prefixes†:

'ab', 'an', 'auf', 'aus', 'bei', 'bevor', 'da', 'dafür', 'dagegen', 'daher', 'dahin', 'dahinter', 'daneben', 'danieder' ('darnieder'), 'daran' ('dran'), 'darauf' ('drauf'), 'darein' ('drein'), 'darüber', 'darunter', 'davon', 'dazu', 'dazwischen', 'durch', 'ein', 'empor', 'entgegen', 'entzwei', 'fort', 'gegen', 'heim', 'her', 'herab', 'heran', 'herauf', 'heraus', 'herbei', 'herein', 'herum', 'herunter', 'hervor', 'hin', 'hinab', 'hinan', 'hinauf', 'hinaus', 'hindurch', 'hinein', 'hinter', 'hinunter', 'hinweg', 'hinzu', 'los', 'mit', 'nach', 'nieder', 'ob', 'über', 'überein', 'um', 'unter', 'vor',

* NOTE: It cannot be capitalized when it is a verb by standing at the beginning of a sentence, since in this position it must be separated from its prefix.

† NOTE: These are the prepositional and adverbial prefixes, from which the majority of compound verbs are formed. Other types are with

(*a*) an adjective, e.g. '*tot*' ('*totmachen*'), '*frei*', ('*freisprechen*')
(*b*) a noun, e.g. '*Acht*' ('*achtgeben*'), '*Teil*' ('*teilnehmen*')
(*c*) a prepositional phrase, e.g. '*zustande*' ('*zustandekommen*'), '*zugrunde*' ('*zugrundelegen*').

'voran', 'voraus', 'vorbei', 'vorher', 'vorüber', 'vorwärts', 'weg', 'weiter', 'wider', 'wieder', 'zu', 'zurück', 'zusammen', 'zuvor', 'zuwider'.

The incoming word (e.g. '*nachfolgen*') is compared with these 'stems' in the usual way (i.e. starting at the middle of the list and continually halving it) to see whether any, and if so, which is the longest possible stem that coincides with its first letters. If one does coincide (i.e. '*nach*'), the word is a compound verb with a separable prefix, the latter being in fact the 'stem' concerned. The part of the word remaining (i.e. '*folgen*') is the corresponding simple verb, and will be found by the machine in the stem dictionary proper.

This is how it will work out in most cases, but in a few the fact that the machine must equate the longest possible 'stem' with the first part of the incoming word (otherwise simple would always be chosen before compound prefixes, e.g. '*zu*' before '*zuvor*', with the result that a word like '*zuvorkommen*' would be divided as '*zu-vorkommen*', and the latter part would still not be able to be found in the dictonary) means that impossible divisions will be made. For instance, '*vorherrschen*' would be divided as if compounded from '*vorher*' and '*rrschen*'. This can be remedied by an instruction to the machine that, if on identifying a separable prefix it cannot find the remainder of the word in the main dictionary, the mistake lies in the prefix, which should be a simple not a compound one. Before this decision is reached, it is first necessary for the machine to make sure that the reason why the remainder cannot be found is not that it still has a prefix of another type attached to it. Such prefixes are '*ge-*' with the perfect participle (e.g. '*Er ist schon angekommen*) and '*zu*' with the infinitive (e.g. '*Im folgenden bitten wir Nichtzutreffendes durchzustreichen*)*.

Some of the above prefixes are both separable and inseparable (e.g. '*durch*', '*hinter*', '*über*', '*um*', '*unter*', '*wieder*', '*wider*'), and certain words compounded with them have a different meaning according to which is true, e.g.

'*übersetzen*' (separable) = to transport across or to cross.
'*übersetzen*' (inseparable) = to translate.

They will be distinguishable formally only where the separable

* NOTE: 1. The possibility of '*ge-*' or '*zu*' intervening between the otherwise inseparable prefix '*miß-*' and its verb (e.g. '*mißgedeutet*', and '*mißzudeuten*') must be taken into account before trying to locate the compound in the dictionary. 2. The infinitive without '*zu*' of certain compounds with 'hinzu' (e.g. 'hinzukommen' 'hinzuziehen) is identical in form to the infinitive with 'zu' of similar compounds with 'hin'. The two can be distinguished, however, by consideration of the factor producing the different infinitive forms, i.e. the governing verb and/or the construction in which they occur.

prefix does in fact occur separated from its verb either spatially or by reason of the intervention of '*ge-*' or '*zu*'. Elsewhere they must be regarded as one word with two different senses and the correct one in each particular case determined on a syntactical or contextual basis.

If a word which the machine has not been able to locate in the main dictionary is then compared with the dictionary of prefixes, but none of these coincides, then it cannot be a compound verb and must be a proper noun or a compound of some other part of speech (e.g. a compound noun)*. If a similar routine for dealing with compound nouns is included in the programme, the unidentified word must go through this too before it can be concluded, if still unidentified, to be a proper noun.

Such a system as that outlined is optional as regards existing compounds, providing—as has been said—economy in storage space, though only with some sacrifice in access time. Since, however, there is in modern German a tendency to create new compounds, particularly with the adjectival prefix, it would seem advisable to have some means of enabling the machine to cope with them. This, the above system will do, provided that the meaning of the new compound is not radically different from the combined translations of its constituents, and usually it is not.

THE RELATIVE PRONOUN

In dealing with noun blocks the difficulty of determining the function of the relative pronoun was encountered. However, this is not the only difficulty arising, since before it can be determined it must be recognized. At that time it was assumed that it had in fact been distinguished by the machine from the homomorphous demonstrative pronoun and from the definite article, which differs only in the genitive (singular and plural) and dative (plural), but no account of how the distinction could be made was given.

The method proposed by Oswald and Fletcher, which aims at distinguishing only between the relative pronoun and definite article on the one hand and the interrogative (indirect only; in direct questions the question mark will make its function obvious) and relative use of '*welcher*' on the other, is based on their Table of Coded Syntactic Units (cf. p. 131). Taking as a cue the fact that a form of '*der*' or '*welcher*' used as a dative will always be separated

* NOTE: A system of reducing compound nouns to their basic components has already been proposed by E. Reifler—'Mechanical determination of the constituents of German substantive compounds', *Mechanical Translation*, Vol. 2, No. 1, July 1955.

from the preceding word by a comma, unless this word is a preposition, in which case it will be separated from the preceding word by a comma, they would have the machine scan forwards from the comma to see whether a 'predicated nominal unit' follows—that is to say, a combination of code numbers listed in their Combination Chart for Nominal Blocks (cf. p. 148). If no predicated nominal unit follows, then the form is to be identified as a relative pronoun. As an example they give,

'Eine Menge ist eine Zusammenfassung bestimmter wohlunterschiedener Objekte unserer Anschauung oder unseres Denkens—welcher (5) die (5) Elemente (23) der Menge genannt werden—zu einem Ganzen.'

The sequence of code numbers 5 – 5 – 23 does not occur as a predicated nominal sequence in Oswald and Fletcher's chart.

This procedure is less satisfactory for '*der*' than '*welcher*' in two respects,

(*a*) It takes no account of the other homomorph, the demonstrative pronoun, with the result that this would be translated as a relative whenever it occurred after a comma, e.g.

'Warum ihm aber gerade diese Vorstellung der Zeit immer stärker zum Anreiz wird, das ist aus dem bisher Gesagten einigermaßen schlüssig.'

(*b*) Its reliance on appearances alone would lead it to interpret a relative plus a bare noun of the same gender as a 'predicated nominal sequence', e.g. the previously quoted.

'In die Erinnerung Jaakobs spielt in entscheidender Weise die Gestalt Abrahams hinein, und zwar als des Menschen, *der Gott* im eigentlichen Sinn entdeckt habe.'

A better solution can be obtained by using the verb as a criterion whenever possible and Oswald and Fletcher's method where not. This will account successfully for all but a few exceptions which can be solved only by consideration of the syntactical requirements of the clause. A possible scheme for distinguishing the three functions of '*der*', etc. (but not '*welcher*') is as follows*:

1. The verb in the clause concerned should be examined to see whether more than one syntactical unit precedes it, and if so,

* Note: It is assumed that the form of '*der*' has been ascertained to stand at the head of the clause, i.e. that the comma preceding it does not simply serve as the boundary mark of an inserted phrase or clause, e.g.

'Die Interpreten können sich, indem sie besonders dieses Motivfeld in den Vordergrund rücken, *auf den* Dichter selbst berufen.'

whether this fact is recognisable (i.e. by the machine). If it is, the clause may then be taken as subordinate and the form of '*der*' as the relative pronoun*.

Again, if the verb is a compound one, that is to say, if it is accompanied by an auxiliary or modal verb, a reversed order of finite verb following participle or infinitive will also indicate that the clause is subordinate†.

2. If the preceding does not produce a solution the rest of the sentence should be examined to see whether it already contains a main clause. If it does not, the clause introduced by the form of '*der*' must be the main clause and this form itself the demonstrative pronoun (as in example (*a*)). If, on the other hand, as is more likely, the sentence does contain a main clause, the form of '*der*' may be taken as the relative pronoun introducing a subordinate clause, provided that the '*der*' clause is an inserted clause as in

'Die Kühle und Distanz, die in seinem Verhältnis zu Gerda von der ersten Stunde an unüberbrückbar aufgerichtet und nicht zu schließen ist, zeigt an, wie verwehrt ihm die andere Sphäre ist.'

or if not, that the order of the syntactic units in the '*der*' clause is different from that in the main clause. The latter proviso is necessary to ensure that in sentences containing two or more uncoordinated main clauses those after the first are not mistaken by the machine for relative clauses. This is made possible by the fact that with such a sentence the syntactic order of each of the clauses will be usually (but not always) similar, e.g.

'Die Formen der Isolierung und Entgegensetzung wechseln, die psychologischen Bedingungen sind variabel, das Interesse als solches bleibt bis zuletzt thematisch bestimmend.'

whereas, when a relative clause follows, the main clause almost always has an inverted order (cf. example (*b*)).

3. Employment of Oswald and Fletcher's code number sequences to distinguish between the relative or demonstrative pronoun and the definite article and between the relative and indirect interrogative uses of '*welcher*'.

Despite the above precautions confusion may still occur in the

* NOTE: This, as was observed before, would not suffice to solve the example quoted above, because '*Gott im eigentlichen Sinn*', though actually two units, could not be recognized formally as such because of the existence of noun blocks with dependent prepositional phrases.

† NOTE: There is an exception to this, of course, in the case of a compound tense of a modal verb with a dependent infinitive.

case of '*welcher*', if as a relative it precedes a bare noun of the same gender and number, and in the case of '*der*'

(*a*) between the definite article and demonstrative uses, if the latter precedes a bare noun of the same gender and number.

(*b*) between the definite article and the relative only if all the following conditions apply:

(i) the relative is followed by a bare noun of the same gender and number.

(ii) the verb is either simple or a compound tense of a modal verb with a dependent infinitive,

(iii) the verb is not recognizably postponed after more than one syntactical unit.

(iv) the relative clause is not inserted and has a similar syntactical sequence to the main clause.

The likelihood of confusion with '*welcher*' is reduced by the tendency to make an indirect question introduced by this word the first clause in the sentence, e.g.

'Welcher Aufgabe Joseph in diesem geschichtlichen Zusammenhang zugeordnet ist, das wird sehr schön am Anfang des ersten Teils offenbar.'

and that between the uses of '*der*' as definite article and demonstrative (to which may be added that between the qualificative and non-qualificative uses of all demonstratives) by the fact that the demonstrative in its function as a reference back, e.g.

'Wie *das* im einzeln zu verstehen ist, möge zunächst einmal durch einige Hinweise auf die beiden ersten Romane gezeigt werden.'

or a signpost forwards, e.g.

'So gewissenhaft und angestrengt er bemüht war, in die Spuren seiner Väter einzutreten, so wichtig es ihm war, die Zeit auszukaufen, zu keiner Stunde war ihm indessen *das*, was sich am Ende verlockend öffnet, fremd.'

occurs comparatively rarely before a noun block, and correspondingly more so before a bare noun, though the latter can easily arise from the omission of some form of the verb '*sein*', e.g.

'Auch *dieses* Zeichen dafür, wie die alte Generation des zweiten Romans nicht anders als die des ersten für die „Umwelt" gegen die „Welt" plädiert.'

Considering the number of conditions that must apply, the probability of confusion between the definite article and relative pronoun is small enough, and even if these conditions were satisfied the problem might still be solved, as it might in the above cases too, by the verb being of a type requiring an object and thus leading to identification of the bare noun as the only solution (cf. the example quoted—'*der Gott im eigentlichen Sinn* **entdeckt** *habe*'). If consideration of the likely syntactical requirements of the particular clause does not help, as for instance with a verb which may be either transitive or intransitive, e.g.

'Der Pastor lobt den Menschen nicht, der Gott **zürnt**.'

then recourse must be had to contextual criteria. If these too prove of no avail, the solution will have to be that of choosing one alternative for the translation and indicating the possibility of the other by a code symbol at the end of the clause concerned.

Since the next subject to be discussed will be apposition, and one of the ways of introducing this is by '*als*' and '*wie*', a little ought to be said on the means of distinguishing the appositive from the other uses of '*als*' and '*wie*'.

ALS—Strictly speaking the term 'apposition' should only be applied to those cases where the words introduced by '*als*' are not closely connected with the verb; compare, for instance,

'Das Interesse als solches bleibt bis zuletzt thematisch bestimmend.'

with 'Beide Gestalten sind jeweils als Symbole des Ursprungs zu verstehen'.

Since even the latter, however, can occur more or less detached from the main construction, e.g.

(i) 'Der Tod tritt an ihn nicht mehr in der begrenzt-persönlichen Erfahrung des „Zauberbergs", sondern als der allmächtige Herr der Zeit und der Welt.'

(ii) 'Im Zauberberg wird die Person in unabdingbarer Weise beansprucht, und zwar als die Instanz, die allein beifügt ist, die Zweideutigkeit von Tod und Element zu enthüllen.'

(iii) 'Von da aus also ist die Bedeutung des Todesmotivs zu verstehen: als Rückwendung des allein auf Fortschritt und Zukunft bezogenen Daseins zur Vergangenheit, als Unbehagen gegenüber der Gefahr der Verfestigung, usw.'

since, too, the varying degrees of detachment make it difficult to draw a boundary line anywhere, and the translation of '*als*' in the majority of cases remains the same, i.e. 'as' (for exceptions cf. '*als*' in the section on Multimeaning, p. 269), we have decided to consider all the varieties as one type, which we may call the 'equatative'—in contrast, to the comparative use.

The comparative '*als*' can be recognized by the occurrence before it of

(*a*) A comparative adverb, e.g.

'Indem ihm auf diesem Weg jener Philosoph zum Führer wird, in dessen Gedanken der Geist des Ostens *stärker* zum Ausdruck kommt als irgendwo sonst in der Geschichte des deutschen Denkens, wird für ihn, dem so Unterwiesenen, *anders* als für die Helden des „Zauberbergs", dieser Abstieg zur Tiefe ein Weg des Vergessens und der Aufgabe des Selbst.'

The negatived '*anders*', which is very frequent, is best translated by the simple, positive expression in English, the '*als*' thereby becoming equatative and the translation 'as' instead of 'than', e.g.

'An diesem Punkt aber wird, nicht anders als im „Zauberberg", die Frage der Vermittlung aufs neue akut.' (. . . 'in the same way as in the "Zauberberg"', . . .).

(*b*) A comparative adjective*, e.g.

'Wenn nun in diesem Sinn Begriffe wie Bürgertum und Bürgerlichkeit in die Deutung eingeführt werden, so sind sie in sehr viel umfassenderem Sinne zu verstehen als sie von Thomas Mann selbst in bezug auf die eigene Biographie benutzt wurden.'

The adjective '*ander*', when positive, can be translated similarly to the adverb, e.g.

'So ist etwa das Sterben Johann Buddenbrooks ein *anderes* als das des Hans Lorenz Castorp.' (' . . . is different than that of . . . ')

but when negative need not be altered to the positive as before, e.g.

'In all dem kommt *nichts anderes* zum Ausdruck als was oben die Komplexität und Gebundenheit genannt wurde.'

Likewise with the interrogative form, which is a virtual negative†:

'Denn *was* kommt darin wiederum *anderes* zum Ausdruck als der geheime Wunsch, Zugang zu finden zu dem, was ohne Anstrengung

* NOTE: Subordinate clauses after a comparative '*als*' form an exception to the rule that all except certain co-ordinate clauses are marked off by punctuation.

† NOTE: The comparative '*als*' after a simple negative, e.g.

'Ich wünsche mir nichts als Ruhe'

belongs more to the spoken than to the written language.

in der Teilnahme des Allgemeinen steht.' '... nothing/what else is expressed ... but ... ').

The following are less common than the two main uses of '*als*':

1. '*Als*' = when, e.g.

'Als 1933 der erste Band des Romans erschien, spürte man in den Rezensionen im allgemeinen ein Befremden angesichts der Stoffwahl.'

This type can be distinguished from the preceding by the fact that in it '*als*' will always be preceded by a comma, unless it stands, as here, at the head of the sentence*.

2. '*Als*' = (according) as, (inasmuch) as, e.g.

'In diesem Sinn wird für ihn, den „Sohn und Enkel" der Einblick in das Reich des Todes und der Vergangenheit ungleich wichtiger, als es dem Vater erlaubt war.'

which construction differs formally from the comparative by the punctuation before '*als*' and from 1. above by the presence in all cases of a comparative adjective or adverb in the preceding clause and in the majority of '*um so*'†, e.g.

'Leider fand der Großkampftag nicht den erwarteten Besuch, was um so bedauerlicher ist, als die sportliche Ausbeute allgemein zufriedenstellte.'

3. '*Als wenn/als ob*' = as if, e.g.

'Er sieht aus, als ob er tot wäre.'

The '*wenn*' or '*ob*' suffices to identify this construction, except when it is omitted, in which case, however, the word order is altered, the verb coming at the beginning of the clause and thereby supplying a substitute mark of recognition, i.e.

'Er sieht aus, als wäre er tot.'

4. '*Als daß.*'

(*a*) Preceded by a comparative is the same as the normal comparative type except that it is followed by a clause instead of a word or phrase; its translation is the same, e.g.

'Ich wäre eher gestorben, als daß ich das getan hätte.'

* NOTE: The rules for reconnecting two halves of a divided clause would ensure that '*als*' after a comma in such circumstances would not be confused with the above, e.g.

'Politisch stellt sich das Ägypten, dem Joseph begegnet, als ein zentralregiertes Staatswesen dar.'

† NOTE: There is, of course, the possibility of a comparative form occurring in the clause preceding an '*als*' of Type 1 which is not connected with this '*als*', but it could not be anything but rare, and if desired might be taken care of by further instructions to the machine.

(*b*) Preceded by '*zu*'+adjective or adverb. The translation is by the infinitive in English, if the subject is the same as that of the governing clause, e.g.

'Sie ist zu artig, als daß sie das getan hätte.' (' . . . too well-behaved to have done. . . .)

and by 'for'+accusative and infinitive, if it is not the same, e.g.

'Die Fixsterne sind zu weit von uns entfernt, als daß wir von ihrer Natur etwas Genaueres wissen können.' (. . . 'too far distant for us to be able to know' . . . .)

5. Uses of '*als*' in conjunction with other words, e.g. '*insoweit als*', '*insofern als*' '*sowohl–als*', etc. can be identified by the presence in the clause or sentence of these words.

WIE—The commoner constructions are as follows:

(*a*) Direct questions—recognized by its position at the head of the sentence and the question mark at the end.

(*b*) Indirect questions—translation as with direct questions = 'how', e.g.

'Wir wollen uns darauf beschränken, zu zeigen, wie aus dieser Gleichung unter Verwendung von rechtwinkligen Koordinaten der Ausdruck für die Lorentz-Kraft folgt.'

(*c*) Explaining a preceding noun by giving examples—translation = 'such as', 'like',

(i) within the clause construction and therefore not separated by punctuation (cf. the example quoted under (*b*) of '*als*' above);

(ii) outside the clause construction and therefore preceded by a comma, e.g.

'Aus der Schweiz werden einzelne Produkte in bedeutender Menge ausgeführt, wie Vieh, Käse usw.'

This type can be distinguished from (*b*) by reason of the fact that the '*wie*' does not introduce a clause of its own.

(*d*) There is a large number of constructions expressing in some way or other equality or similarity, which—apart from those that are idiomatic—may be divided for the purposes of mechanical translation into two classes according to whether they require translating by 'as' or by 'like'. As illustrative may be quoted:

AS—(i) With an adjective, preceded by '*ebenso*', '*so*', etc.*, e.g.

'Er ist so groß wie ich.'

* Note: The '*ebenso*', '*so*', etc. may be omitted in some cases but the translation remains the same, since English permits a similar omission, e.g.

'Das Pferd war (so) weiß wie Schnee'—'The horse was (as) white as snow.'

(ii) With an adverb, preceded by '*ebenso*', '*so*' etc.*, e.g.

'Er spricht ebenso schlecht wie sie.'

(iii) With a noun or pronoun, preceded by '*gleich*', '*solch*', etc. both in the same clause, e.g.

'Im Falle (*a*) besteht in einer Meridianebene statt eines singulären Punktes eine singuläre Kurve, auf welcher das Potential den gleichen Wert hat wie auf der Blendenelektrode.'

and in a preceding, e.g.

'Die Analogie zwischen dem Verlauf der Lichtstrahlen und dem Verlauf der Elektronenbahnen in einander entsprechenden Medien läßt uns vermuten, daß es möglich sein wird, auch mit Elektronenstrahlen die gleiche Art von Abbildung zu erzielen, wie sie auf dem lichtoptischen Gebiete seit langem bekannt ist.'

(iv) With a noun or pronoun preceded by a preposition, no '*gleich*', '*solch*', etc.†, e.g.

'Er sprach zu dem Schüler wie zu seinem Sohn.'
'Die Elektronenbahn ist wie für E=0 eine Schraubenlinie auf einem Kreiszylinder parallel zur z-Achse.'

(v) With a verb; '*ebenso*', '*so*', etc. may or may not precede, e.g.

'Er muß leben, wie es ihm der Arzt vorschreibt.'

(vi) Connecting and comparing two clauses without reference to any particular part of speech, e.g.

'Die Sphäre des Privaten entzieht sich ebenso der der Repräsentation, wie das Leben sich vor der Macht und dem Anspruch des Todes zu sichern sucht.'

As regards ambiguity (i) and (ii) are satisfactorily characterized by their construction with an adjective and adverb respectively. (iii), which might be confused with (*c*), inasmuch as it is connected with nouns, is distinguished by being preceded by a word like '*gleich*', '*solch*', etc., whilst the distinguishing feature of (iv) is that, though no '*gleich*', '*solch*' etc., is present, the noun or pronoun following the '*wie*' is preceded by a preposition, and a preposition in

* Note: There too the '*ebenso*', '*so*', etc. may be omitted, but this entails a change in meaning from degree to manner and with it a change in translation from 'as' to 'like'.

† Note: This does not apply, if the preposition remains untranslated in English, e.g. 'He addressed the pupil *like* his son', not '. . . as his son.'

English must be preceded by 'as', not 'like'. (v) and (vi) may be distinguished from (*b*) either by the type of verb (for (*b*) it must be transitive and of a certain kind) or by the syntactical construction (there must be no direct object in the clause preceding the '*wie*'-clause, if the sentence belongs to (*b*), since here the '*wie*'-clause is itself the direct object of the preceding verb).

LIKE—(i) Corresponding to *AS* (iii), but without '*gleich*', '*solch*', etc.*, e.g.

'Das war ein Kampf, wie ihn keiner noch gesehen hat.'

(ii) Corresponding to *AS* (iv), but with a noun not preceded by a preposition, e.g.

'Ich ehre ihn wie meinen Vater.'

(iii) Closely connected with this, but differing inasmuch as the '*wie*' refers to the subject, is the type

'Er sprach zu dem Schüler wie ein Vater.'
'Der Junge benahm sich wie ein Erwachsener.'

(i) can be distinguished from (*c*) above by the fact that '*wie*' introduces a clause, but this distinction is unnecessary, since the translation in both cases is the same. (ii) and (iii) can be distinguished from the same by their having a noun with a predeterminer, whereas nouns after (*c*) '*wie*' are bare. If necessary, however, an identical translation (like) can be adopted for both types, leaving 'such as' for (i), which as we have said is readily distinguishable.

(*e*) The short interjected clause used to modify the sense of the main verb in some respect—translation = 'as', e.g.

'Das wird, wie es scheint, eine große Neuerung.'
'Er ist, wie wir hoffen, gesund.'

This can be distinguished from (*b*) in the same way as were the instances in (*d*) with the same translation (i.e. 'as') and from (*d*) *LIKE* (i) by referring to a verb, not a noun.

(*f*) '*Wie wenn*' = either 'as if' or 'as when', e.g.

'Wir werden deshalb den Einfluß der Raumladung vernachlässigen und zunächst so rechnen, wie wenn bei der Bewegung eines Elektrons nur dieses eine Elektron sich zwischen den Elektroden befindet.'

'Es zischt, wie wenn Wasser sich mit Feuer mischt.'

* Note: 'Such as' is, however, usually a better translation than 'like' with this kind of '*wie*'.

(*g*) '*Sowohl – wie*' = both – and, e.g.

'Er kannte sowohl Greichenland wie auch Italien genau.'

Both this and the preceding may be identified by their accompanying word, i.e. '*wenn*' and '*sowohl*'.

APPOSITION

1. *After* 'als' *and* 'wie'

We propose to discuss the words or phrases (not clauses) introduced by '*als*' and '*wie*' here, because although strictly speaking they are not appositions, they do present the same type of problem in identifying the part of speech to which the '*als*' or '*wie*' refers, discovering where the bit introduced by '*als*' or '*wie*' ends and the main construction of the clause is resumed, and finally putting it in the correct position in the English sentence.

As material for investigation we have 26 instances from the text previously used in none of which the noun introduced by '*als*' or '*wie*' has a unique case form. Ten are feminine or neuter nominative/accusative, one is feminine genitive or dative singular, and 15 are bare nouns. Naturally no definite conclusions can be reached from such limited material, but it is possible that some tentative solution may come to light.

As regards the identification of the end of the piece introduced by '*als*' and '*wie*', when this is inserted in the middle of the clause, since the piece must be a nominal unit, the machine need only look to see where the next syntactical unit begins, to discover where the former ends. Naturally this nominal unit may consist of more than one noun or noun block, if this has a dependent genitive or prepositional phrase attached to it, e.g.

'Von Anbeginn spielt das Land der Ägypter in den Mahnungen und Reden Jaakobs als das verfluchte Land des Geschlechtes, der Unzucht und des Todes ebenso eine Rolle.'

where the three genitives will all be accepted by the machine as part of the nominal unit, but not '*eine Rolle*', because it is not genitive, not a prepositional phrase, and not co-ordinate. Of course, there is the difficulty of attached and unattached prepositional phrases, but it is open to the same solutions as elsewhere (cf. pp. 140–143), and if these fail, the consequences in terms of odd word order in the English are usually less serious. This may be illustrated by the two instances in our text where a prepositional phrase follows the noun after '*wie*' or '*als*':

(i) 'Wenn nun in diesem Sinn Begriffe wie Bürgertum und Bürgerlichkeit in die Deutung eingeführt werden, . . .'

If the prepositional phrase is constructed with 'Bürgerlichkeit' instead of 'eingeführt', the result is

'If now in this sense ideas are introduced like *Bürgertum* and *Bürgerlichkeit* into the interpretation . . . '

instead of

'If now in this sense ideas like *Bürgertum* and *Bürgerlichkeit* are introduced into the interpretation . . .'

(ii) 'Im übrigen waren im Laufe der Jahren die ehemaligen Feudalherren als Hofbeamte in die Dienste Pharaos getreten.'

comes out as

'In general in the course of the years the former feudal lords had entered as court officials into Pharaoh's service'

instead of

'. . . had entered into Pharaoh's service as court officials'.

Identifying the part of speech to which the '*als*' or '*wie*' refers is not difficult, but it does not always help in obtaining the correct order in English. Compare, for instance, the second clause quoted above with

'Da ist wiederum die Zeit als Wiederholung, die mythische Zeit, in ihrer besonderen Gesetzlichkeit in dem Vorspiel „Höllenfahrt" dargestellt.'

In both the '*als*' follows the noun to which it refers immediately, but their positions in the English translations of the clauses are quite different, in the latter being retained immediately after the noun, in the former being separated from it by the verb. It is then superfluous to try and determine the case of the noun introduced by '*als*' or '*wie*', and as regards the position in English the best rule seems to be to place '*als*' and its phrase at the end of the clause, except when it is denoted as one unit by occurring with its noun *before* the verb in a main clause. Out of the 25 instances with '*als*' in our material (the other one is the '*wie*' example quoted above) this rule produces satisfactory results in every case except the one just mentioned, e.g.

(i) 'Und noch zur dieser Zeit trugen die Höflinge als Ehrenbezeichnung die Titel dieser ehemaligen Gaukönige.'

(ii) 'So ist des öfteren etwa von den Gaufürsten und Gaukönigen die Rede, die ehemals als die eigentlichen Herrscher die Städte und Länder Ägyptens regiert hatten.'

(iii) 'Beide Gestalten sind jeweils als Symbole des Ursprungs zu verstehen.' (cf. also the examples quoted above.)

For the exception—'*Da ist wiederum die Zeit als Wiederholung . .* '. etc. the subsidiary rule could be made that when the '*als*' phrase is followed by an apposition proper to the noun to which '*als*' itself refers, the '*als*' phrase is to be retained immediately after its noun in translation. This, however, is a very particular rule—whether it would be possible to find one for every exception, and whether if it were, it would be worthwhile entering them in the dictionary is open to doubt considering how rare such exceptions are likely to be. Further investigations, however, may reveal a complete solution for '*als*' and also for '*wie*', though instructions to the effect that the latter is to be retained in translation immediately after the part of speech after which it is found in the German would account satisfactorily for the majority of instances, and the exceptions due to the overall lower frequency would be even fewer than with '*als*'.

2. *Unpunctuated Apposition*

This proved to be the least common type of apposition, only seven instances of it occurring in our text, three of them being 'der Gegensatz Bürger-Künstler', e.g.

'Der Gegensatz Bürger-Künstler wird berührt in den „Buddenbrooks."

The others were:

(i) '. . . die sympathische Gestalt jenes Hofrats Behrens.'
(ii) '. . . die Entwicklung des Hauses Hagenström.'
(iii) '. . . in dem Vorspiel „Höllenfahrt".'
(iv) '. . . unter den Fürsten Wêses.'

The problem is simply this: How is such an apposition to be distinguished from a dependent genitive? The usual rule that if the proper noun ends in '-s', its genitive is indicated either by an apostrophe or by the addition of the definite article does not help because most proper nouns will not be included in the machine's dictionary: consequently it will have no means of telling whether the nominative form ends in '-s' or not. Thus the noun 'Wêses' above (iv) could be either the nominative of 'Wêses' or the genitive of 'Wêse', and as was said before, the only certain way in which the machine can find out which it is is by noting each occurrence of a proper noun as it goes through a text and comparing the different forms to see whether the '-s' is always present; if it is not, then the form with '-s' is the genitive. This, however, is only likely to work with nouns which occur several times in the text concerned. What of those that do not? Since these instances of a proper noun after another noun are rare in most texts, and one might even say practically non-existent in scientific literature, the most economical solution would simply be to indicate the alternatives in the translation by inserting (of), thus—in parenthesis, between the two nouns. On the other hand, if dictionary space is of no concern, many nouns can be classified in order to produce a solution. Thus '*Hofrat*' and '*Fürsten*' would be denoted as the type, a bare noun after which should always be translated as an apposition, since unlike '*Schwester*', for example, they are not likely to belong to anybody or anything—except a place, and this would be indicated by '*von*' rather than the genitive. '*Haus*', on the other hand, would belong with nouns like '*Universität*', '*Stadt*', etc., which, though followed by an apposition in German, always require a genitive in English. A proper noun in quotation marks immediately after another noun, like '*Vorspiel „Höllenfahrt"*' would be indicated as in apposition, and provision could no doubt also be made for hyphenated common nouns after a word like '*Gegensatz*', after which in fact a genitive would probably not occur except with some predeterminer.

3. *Punctuated Apposition*

Of this, the most frequent type, there were twenty-two instances in the text investigated. These can be divided into two types, the 'ordinary' and what one might call the 'repetitive'. In the latter a noun already occurring in the sentence is repeated in order to emphasize and describe it further by means of a following relative clause, e.g.

'Thomas Mann steht hier am Ende einer langen geistesgeschichtlichen Entwicklung, einer Entwicklung, die im Grunde alle entscheidenden Epochen des 18. und 19. Jahrhunderts einbegreift.'

Six of the instances belong to this type. Sometimes instead of the noun being repeated the demonstrative '*jener*' is used, but this need not concern us here, its treatment being the same.

For all 'ordinary' instances without exception the correct position of the apposition in English could be obtained simply by letting it follow the same word that it followed in the German, e.g.

(i) 'Denn beides, das Werk des Novalis und das Thomas Manns, darf als Ausdruck einer analogen geschichtlichen Situation verstanden werden.'

(ii) 'Und wenn Hanno Buddenbrook, die Geschichte der Familie abschließend, sich in die Musik verliert, einer Musik, die die Nähe Richard Wagners, des Gefährten Schopenhauers, nicht verleugnet, dann ist auch in diesem Motivzusammenhang das Erbe der Romantik nicht fern.'

Examination of the instance of 'repetitive' apposition in the latter sentence, however, will show that the same solution does not apply to this type; to let the translation of '*einer Musik*' follow that of '*verliert*' would produce an odd result! Yet there is no difficulty; all that is necessary is that the part of the sentence preceding the repeated noun should *all* be translated before it. This is the invariable rule.

It is perhaps worth noting in passing that it would be difficult to distinguish mechanically between a noun with a series of appositions, e.g.

'Wie mit der Unverläßlichkeit des Elementes alle spezifisch personalen Tugenden, Distanz, Entscheidung, Verantwortung, Fähigkeit der gestalthaften Einbegreifung angefordert sind, so geschieht es auch in dem Roman Thomas Manns.'

and a series of nouns, e.g.

'Denn Zeit in der einseitigen Deutung des Fortschrittes und der Zeitigung des Neuen bedeutet Gefährdung der Gebundenheit, Zerstörung der Substanz, Entfernung vom Ursprung.'

Fortunately, however, such a distinction is unnecessary, since both retain the same order in translation, and which is which becomes clear from the sense of the words themselves.

Determination of case of nouns in apposition—It is not necessary for the machine to distinguish the nominative and accusative cases, since whether the apposition belongs to the subject or object of the clause is obvious from its position in the case of the 'ordinary' type and from the actual repetition in the 'repetitive' type. Genitive and dative, however, must be distinguished, because the one requires the addition of 'of', the other that of 'to' in English. For distinguishing them where the forms are identical (e.g. in the singular of feminine nouns) the same procedure holds as was described with dealing with noun blocks (p. 169)*.

The word order of an apposition only rarely needs to be altered

* NOTE: It should be added that the case of any noun after a co-ordinating conjunction—provided this does not connect clauses—need not be determined, because the 'of' or 'to' characteristic of the genitive and dative are not used in this instance. Compare for example,

'Beide Ereignisse, die Entstehung dieses Romans und *die Entdeckung* der östlichen Dichtung, stehen darüber hinaus im Zusammenhang mit jener romantischen Renaissance, . . .' and

'Denn Zeit in der einseitigen Deutung des Fortschrittes und *der Zeitigung* des Neuen bedeutet Gefährdung der Gebundenheit, . .'

in English—for instance when a participle with verbal force instead of adjectival is found (cf. the instance quoted above, '*Und wenn Hanno Buddenbrook, die Geschichte der Familie abschließend*, . . .'), in which case it must be brought to the head of the apposition, if it does not already occupy this place.

4. *Extension*

By this name is meant to be denoted that type of apposition which follows a clause, be it main, subordinate, or infinitival, and is marked off from it either by a colon or less commonly a semi-colon, e.g.

'Dafür spricht das eine: die Bedeutung des Eros für seine Existenz.'

To the 16 such instances in our text the same remarks apply as regards the determination of cases and alteration of word-order as were made in connection with unpunctuated apposition. At the same time it may be noted that the position of this type of apposition after instead of within the clause allows it to be much longer, which explains why those constructions which do require an alteration to their word order in translation are more frequent here, e.g. those with a participle,

(i) 'Unverschränkt und unfruchtbar stehen sich die Gegensätze in Settembrini und Naphta gegenüber: hier der Optimismus der sich selbst bewahrenden und sich selbst genügenden Ration, dort die zynische Abdankung des Menschen—des verantwortlichen schöpferischen Menschen wohlgemerkt—angesichts der chaotischen Übermächtigkeit des Todes.'

(ii) 'Wenn gefragt wird, wo zum erstenmal in der deutschen Geistesgeschichte der Neuzeit die Einsicht in die Zweideutigkeit des Ursprungs entwickelt wird, dann ist sowohl auf das Alterswerk Goethes wie auch auf bestimmte Erfahrungen der Spätromantik hinzuweisen: beispielhaft gestaltet in den „Wahlverwandtschaften" und etwa in dem „Marmorbild" Eichendorffs, darüber hinaus von Goethe im Begriff des Dämonischen zusammengefaßt und in allen Möglichkeiten durchgedacht.'

Despite this, however, the word order of the German may be retained in the majority of the instances of 'extension', e.g.

'Zwei Formen des Zeitverständnisses spielten schon in den „Zauberberg" hinein: die Deutung der Zeit als Kreislauf und Identität des Bleibens und Wechselns und im Gegensatz dazu eine Deutung der Zeit im Sinne der „Zeitigung des Neuen", als Sprengung des Kreislaufs und der Wiederholung.'

SECTION III

IDIOGLOSSARY, MULTIMEANING

Having said something about grammar and syntax, it still remains to discuss the problem of multimeaning. In this respect one of the earliest solutions, or at least partial solution, to be suggested was that of putting in the machine a dictionary of only those words required to translate the subject in hand, i.e. an idioglossary. The assumption on which this was based, namely that each subject has a fairly restricted vocabulary, and in addition that most of the words in this vocabulary have only one meaning, is probably correct in so far as it refers to subjects within the field of science, for which mechanical translation was primarily intended. In order to give some illustration of by what extent an idioglossary might be expected to reduce the problem of multimeaning, the results will be given of an analysis of a piece of text (about 7000 words) from a work on electron optics (A. Rusterholz, '*Elektronenoptik*'). This is of course a smaller amount of text than is desirable, but the material yielded has been reproduced here in accordance with the popular law that anything is better than nothing.

The aim in assigning an English equivalent or equivalents to each German word was a dictionary which, assuming the grammatical and syntactical resources of the machine to be adequate, would produce not merely an intelligible, but a correct translation in good English. An expression striking the scientific reader as not quite usual would happen only in those cases where the appropriate phraseology could be arrived at only by a complete alteration of the original sentence structure. Though there was nothing to prevent this being done, it would have required a more specialized and more complex syntactical scheme than that already outlined, which the present dictionary was intended to complement. Therefore whilst the continual endeavour, in order to keep the dictionary as small as possible, was to find an English equivalent which would cover all the meanings of the German word (where the latter had more than one), this was never done at the expense of the English.

In the text concerned no count was made of the occurrences of the following words either because their translation was not expected to vary or, if they did vary, the conditions governing their variation were already known.

1. The definite article. (Although this may be either translated by the English definite or indefinite article or simply omitted, it

was not included in the analysis as requiring an investigation to itself.)

2. The indefinite article.
3. Demonstrative pronouns: '*dieser*', '*der*', '*derselber*', '*derjeniger*.'
4. Relative pronouns: '*der*', '*welcher*'.
5. Interrogative pronouns: '*welcher*', '*was*'.
6. Personal pronouns: '*es*', '*wir*', '*uns*', '*sie*', '*ihnen*'.
7. Indefinite pronouns: '*man*', '*nichts*'.
8. Possessive pronouns: '*unser*', '*sein*', '*ihr*'.
9. Reflexive pronoun: '*sich*'.
10. Reflexive adjective: '*selber*'.
11. The co-ordinating conjunctions: '*und*', '*sondern*', '*nicht nur—sondern auch*', '*oder*', '*sowohl—als*', '*entweder—oder*', '*weder—noch*', '*aber*' (when translatable as '*however*').
12. Subordinating conjunctions: '*daß*', '*sobald*', ('*daß*' translated as 'that' except after '*im Falle*' in which case it was rendered by 'where', this having the advantage of word for word translation as opposed to regarding '*im Falle daß . . .*' as an idiom and translating it by 'if', cf. 'Mit dieser Bezeichnungsweise, und demnach nur im Falle, daß ein Kräftepotential U existiert, lauten die drei Lagrangeschen Bewegungsgleichungen zweiter Art $(d/dt\ dL/dq_k) - (dL/dq_k) = 0)$.'
13. Negative: '*nicht*'.
14. Forms of '*sein*' and '*werden*': '*sein*', '*ist*', '*sind*', '*sei*', '*seien*', '*werden*', '*wird*', '*worden*'.
15. Cardinal numbers: '*zwei*', '*drei*'.
16. Ordinal numbers: '*erste*', '*zweite*'.
17. Numeral adverb: '*zweimal*'.
18. The prepositions '*um*' and '*zu*' before an infinitive.
19. '*So*' before an adjective or adverb or introducing the main clause when this is preceded in the sentence by a subordinate clause. In the former case the translation is 'so', in the latter it is omitted.
20. Abbreviations: '*z.B.*', '*vgl.*', '*d.h.*', '*bzw*'.

Apart from these the words which were found in the text are given below classified according to their part of speech and arranged in order of frequency:

NOUNS

	89		60
Feld	field	Potential	potential
	65		42
Elektron	electron	Wert	value

German	English
39	
Gleichung	equation
34	
Achse	axis
33	
Fall	case
Funktion	function
Geschwindigkeit	velocity
31	
Punkt	point
27	
Brechungsindex	refractive index
22	
Bahn	path
21	
Ebene	plane
20	
Feldstärke	field strength
19	
Größe	quantity
18	
Kathode	cathode
17	
Ausdruck	expression
Lochblende	aperture lens
Verteilung	distribution
16	
Elektrode	electrode
Lösung	solution
15	
Medium	medium
Zeit	time
14	
Form	form
Koordinate	co-ordinate
13	
Bewegung	motion
Einheit	unit
Komponente	component
Kraft	force
11	
Fläche	surface
Kurve	curve
Reihenentwicklung	series expansion
System	system
10	
Masse	mass
Verwendung	use
9	
Bewegungsgleichung	equation of motion
Ladung	charge
Potentialfeld	potential field
Potentialverteilung	potential distribution
Prinzip	principle
8	
Beziehung	relation
Energie	energy
Lichtoptik	optics
Niveaufläche	equipotential surface
Niveaulinie	equipotential line
Null	zero
Ort	position
Potenz	power
Richtung	direction
Symmetrieachse	axis of symmetry
Umgebung	neighbourhood
7	
Abstand	distance
Kreis	circle
Seite	side
Verlauf	distribution
Zylinderkoordinate	cylindrical co-ordinate
6	
Art	kind
Austrittsgeschwindigkeit	velocity of emission
Differentialgleichung	differential equation
Differentiation	differentiation
Elektronenoptik	electron optics
Elektronenstrahl	electron ray
Elektronenvolt	electron volt
Energiesatz	law of energy
Integral	integral
Leiter	conductor
Lichtgeschwindigkeit	velocity of light
Meridianebene	meridian plane
Öffnung	aperture
Radius	radius
Winkel	angle
Zusammenhang	connection

5

Bedingung	condition
Berechnung	calculation
Betrag	magnitude
Darstellung	representation
Elektrodenanordnung	electrode arrangement
Förmel	formula
Gebiet	region
Koordinatensystem	co-ordinate system
Lochblendenfeld	field of the aperture lens
Potentialdifferenz	potential difference
Potentialverlauf	potential distribution
Potentialwert	value of the potential
Randbedingung	boundary condition
Vakuum	vacuum
Variable	variable

4

Ableitung	derivative
Bedeutung	significance
Behandlung	treatment
Blendenöffnung	diaphragm aperture
Brechungsgesetz	law of refraction
Einschränkung	restriction
Elektronenbewegung	motion of electrons
Glied	term
Integration	integration
Kenntnis	knowledge
Koeffizient	coefficient
Methode	method
Mitte	centre
Ordnung	order
Raumladung	space charge
Reihe	series
Ruhemasse	rest mass
Sattelpunkt	saddle point
Spannung	voltage
Strahlrichtung	direction of the ray
Summe	sum
Tabelle	table
Überlagerung	superposition
Verhältnis	relation

3

Abbildung	image
Achsenpotential	axial potential
Anfangsbedingung	initial condition
Anordnung	apparatus
Arbeit	work
Beispiel	example
Bewegungsrichtung	direction of motion
Beweis	proof
Durchfallen	falling through
Einfluß	influence
Einsetzen	substitution
Elektronenbahn	path of electrons
Elektronenladung	electron charge
Entfernung	distance
Faktor	factor
Festlegung	determination
Grund	basis
Hyperbel	hyperbola
Induktion	induction
Integrationskonstante	constant of integration
Komponentendarstellung	componential representation
Kräftepotential	force potential
Kreisbewegung	circular motion
Krümmungsradius	radius of curvature
Lichtstrahl	light ray
Linienelement	line element
Mittelpunkt	centre
Nähe	vicinity
Oberfläche	upper surface
Problem	problem
Produkt	product
Raum	space
Rohrlinse	cylindrical lens
Scheitel	vertex
Schraubenlinie	helix
Stelle	place
Symmetriegrund	region of symmetry
Variationsproblem	variation problem
Vektor	vector
Verlauf	course
Voltgeschwindigkeit	velocity
Vorzeichen	sign
Weg	path

2

Abhängigkeit	dependency

GERMAN

Analogie	similarity
Änderung	change
Aufgabe	problem
Ausbreitungs-geschwindigkeit	velocity of propagation
Austritt	emission
Bahnkurve	trajectory
Beitrag	contribution
Beschleunigung	acceleration
Beschreibung	description
Bestimmung	determination
Betrachtung	consideration
Blendenelektrode	diaphragm electrode
Bogenlänge	curvilinear distance
Differenz	difference
Durchmesser	diameter
Eigenschaft	property
Einheitsvektor	unit vector
Elektronenlinse	electron lens
Frage	question
Gebrauch	use
Genauigkeit	accuracy
Index	index
Konstante	constant
Kreiszylinder	circular cylinder
Kristall	crystal
Krümmung	curvature
Lage	position
Lagekoordinate	position co-ordinate
Lehrbuch	text-book
Leiterelement	conductor element
Licht	light
Magnetfeld	magnetic field
Maßsystem	measuring system
Messung	measurement
Neigung	gradient
Parabel	parabola
Permeabilität	permeability
Rolle	rôle
Rotation	curl
Rotationsfläche	surface of rotation
Schlitzblende	slit lens
Strahl	ray
Strahlgleichung	ray equation
Theorie	theory
Übergang	transition
Übergangsgebiet	transition region
Unterschied	difference
Vektorpotential	vector potential
Vergleich	comparison
Vorschrift	precept
Wahl	choice
Weise	way
Wertbereich	range of values

1

Abhandlung	treatise
Abkürzung	abbreviation
Ablenkversuch	experiment on deviation
Achsenpunkt	point on the axis
Addition	addition
Allgemeinheit	generality
Anfang	beginning
Anfangsenergie	initial energy
Anfangsge-schwindigkeit	initial velocity
Anfangsvoltge-schwindigkeit	velocity at the initial potential
Anfangswert	initial value
Angabe	statement
Annäherung	approximation
Annahme	assumption
Anode	anode
Anschluß	connection
Anteil	contribution
Antwort	answer
Anwendung	application
Äquipotentiallinie	equipotential line
Argument	argument
Auffassung	interpretation
Aufpunkt	external point
Augenmerk	attention
Band	volume
Bereich	range
Berücksichtigung	consideration
Betrag	quality
Bewegungsart	kind of motion
Bewegungsgesetz	law of motion
Bezeichnung	expression
Bezeichnungs-weise	convention
Bezug	relation
Bildung	formation
Blendendurch-messer	diameter of the diaphragm
Blendenmitte	centre of the diaphragm
Blendenpotential	potential of the diaphragm

Brennweite	focal distance
Darstellungsart	kind of representation
Differenzieren	differentiation
Diskontinuität	discontinuity
Drehimpuls	angular momentum
Durchlaufen	traversing
Elektronengeschwindigkeit	electron velocity
Elektronenmikroskop	electron microscope
Elektronenradius	radius of electrons
Elimination	elimination
Emissionsart	kind of emission
Endliche (das)	finite space
Ergebnis	result
Ermittlung	determination
Extremwert	extreme value
Fahrstrahlvektor	position vector
Fehlen	absence
Feldrichtung	direction of the field
Figur	figure
Fluß	flux
Folge	set
Folgerung	conclusion
Fragestellung	question
Gang	working
Gebiet	field
Geradenstück	straight piece
Gesamtanordnung	total arrangement
Gesamtenergie	total energy
Gesamtzeit	total time
Geschwindigkeitskomponente	velocity component
Geschwindigkeitsvektor	velocity vector
Geschwindigkeitsverteilung	velocity distribution
Geschwindigkeitsverteilungsfunktion	velocity distribution function
Gesetz	law
Gestalt	form
Glaslinse	glass lens
Gleichungssystem	system of equations
Gradientenbildung	formation of the gradient
Größenordnung	order of magnitude
Grund	reason
Halbellipse	semi-ellipse
Hauptaufgabe	main problem
Hineingreifen	protrusion
Hinzunahme	inclusion
Hohlzylinder	hollow cylinder
Kegel	cone
Komponentenzerlegung	analysis of the components
Kreisradius	radius of the circle
Kreisumlauf	revolution
Linse	lens
Linsensystem	system of lenses
Literaturangaben (plur)	bibliography
Lochblenden-Immersionslinse	immersion lens
Massenveränderlichkeit	variability of mass
Mechanik	mechanics
Metall	metal
Metallelektrode	metal electrode
Mitberücksichtigung	additional consideration
Modell	model
Möglichkeit	possibility
Moment	moment
Näherungsverfahren	method of approximation
Natur	nature
Normal	norm
Nullpunkt	origin
Obengesagte (das)	what was said above
Öffnungsfehler	spherical aberration
Öffnungswinkel	vertex angle
Ort	locus
Ortsfunktion	position function
Physik	physics
Potentialsprung	jump of potential
Potenzreihe	power series
Projektion	projection
Publikation	publication
Punktladung	point charge
Radiusvektor	radius vector
Rechnung	account
Relativitätstheorie	theory of relativity
Resultat	result
Richtigkeit	correctness
Richtungsänderung	change of direction

Rohrelektrode	cylindrical electrode
Rotation	rotation
Rotationsellipsoid	ellipsoid of rotation
Rotationshyperboloid	hyperboloid of rotation
Rotationssymmetrie	axial symmetry
Schnitt	section
Schreibweise	convention
Schwierigkeit	difficulty
Sekundärelektron	secondary electron
Separation	separation
Spalt	gap
Spielraum	scope
Steigung	pitch
Stelle	point
Strahlvektor	ray vector
Strecke	distance
Strom	current
Stromstärke	current strength
Substitution	substitution
Tausendfache	thousandfold
Trog	trough
Umlauf	revolution
Umrechnung	conversion
Vektorprodukt	vector product
Veränderlichkeit	variability
Verfahren	method
Verfügung	disposal
Verhalten	behaviour
Verlassen	leaving
Veröffentlichung	publication
Versuch	experiment
Verwechslung	confusion
Voraussetzung	assumption
Vorzug	preference
Winkelgeschwindigkeit	angle of velocity
Winkelkoordinate	angle co-ordinate
Wirklichkeit	reality
Wirkungsfunktion	action function
Zusammenhang	context
Zusatzbedingung	additional condition
Zylinderelektrode	cylindrical electrode
Zylinderkoordinatensystem	cylindrical co-ordinate system

VERBS

	40
können	can
	39
haben	have
	30
erhalten	obtain
	28
müssen	must
	26
angeben	give
	23
folgen	follow
	20
gelten	be true
	18
geben	give
lassen (sich)	can be(perf. has been able to be)
	17
bestimmen	determine
schreiben	write
	12
lauten	read
	11
annehmen	assume
berechnen	calculate
einsetzen	substitute
liefern	yield
setzen	put
zeigen	show
	10
darstellen	represent
sollen	be to
	9
einführen	introduce
vorgeben	give
	8
wachsen	increase
wollen	let
	7
bedeuten	denote
bezeichnen	denote
bleiben	remain
ergeben (sich)	result
messen	measure
stehen	to be

vernachlässigen	ignore
wollen	shall
	6
abhängen	depend
beschränken	restrict
bestehen	consist
bezeichnen	call
übergehen	change
wählen	choose
	5
bedeuten	mean
berücksichtigen	consider
beschreiben	describe
bestehen	exist
durchlaufen	traverse
erfüllen	fulfil
	4
ableiten	derive
anordnen	arrange
anschreiben	write down
aussagen	state
behandeln	treat
besitzen	have
betrachten	consider
einschließen	include
entsprechen	correspond to
führen	lead
liegen	lie
stehen	stand
unterschieden	distinguish
verschwinden	disappear
verstehen	understand
verweisen	refer
	3
abweichen	differ
ändern (sich)	change
auffassen	regard
ausgehen	proceed
auslösen	release
enthalten	contain
ersetzen	replace
erzeugen	produce
genügen	satisfy
handeln (sich)	be a question
interessieren (sich)	be interested
legen	put
nehmen	take
sollen	need
untersuchen	investigate
zunehmen	increase
zurückkommen	come back
	2
abnehmen	decrease
auflösen	solve
austreten	be emitted
beachten	observe
beeinflußen	influence
benötigen	require
bewegen (sich)	move
bewirken	produce
beziehen (sich)	apply
brauchen	need
brechen	refract
bringen	bring
eliminieren	eliminate
erfolgen	occur
ergeben	give
erlauben	allow
ermitteln	ascertain
ersehen	perceive
erstrecken	extend
festlegen	state
fortschreiten	proceed
geben	to be
herausgreifen	choose
hinweisen	refer
kombinieren	combine
lassen	let
machen	make
rechnen	calculate
reduzieren (sich)	be reduced
ruhen	be stationary
schneiden	dissect
sehen	see
spielen	play
suchen	seek
tun	do
übereinstimmen	coincide
übertreffen	exceed
verallgemeinern	generalise
verbinden	connect
vergleichen	compare
verwenden	use
weglassen	omit
zukommen	belong
zusammenfallen	coincide
	1
abändern	change
abbrechen	terminate
abklingen	decrease
abschätzen	estimate
addieren	add
aneinanderstoßen	touch one another

annähern	approximate
annehmen	accept
annehmen	attain
anschließen	connect
ansprechen	speak of
antreffen	encounter
anwachsen	increase
aufdrücken	attribute
auferlegen	impose on
aufladen	charge
aufstellen	establish
auftragen	add
auftreten	arise
ausbreiten (sich)	propagate
ausdehnen	extend
ausdrücken	express
ausführen	perform
ausüben	exercise
auszählen	calculate
auszeichnen	distinguish
auszeichnen (sich)	be distinguished
bedingen	entail
befinden (sich)	to be
befürchten	fear
beibehalten	retain
beschleunigen	accelerate
besprechen	mention
betragen	amount to
betreiben	use
bewegen	move
bewerkstelligen	accomplish
definieren	define
denken (sich)	suppose
differenzieren	differentiate
durchfallen	fall through
durchführen	carry out
dürfen	may
einfallen	arrive
eintragen	introduce
eintreffen	arrive
entgegenrichten	oppose to
entnehmen	deduce from
entwickeln	expand
erinnern	refer
erleiden	undergo
erreichen	attain
erreichen	obtain
erstrecken (sich)	extend
erteilen	impart
erwähnen	mention
erweisen (sich)	prove
erzielen	obtain

existieren	exist
festhalten	retain
feststellen	establish
fließen	flow
fokussieren	focus
gelingen	be possible
genügen	be sufficient
greifen	adopt
herrschen	exist
hervorrufen	cause
integrieren	integrate
kennen	know
konvergieren	converge
krümmen	curve
lassen	allow
leisten	do
lösen	solve
mitnehmen	take
multiplizieren	multiply
nachbilden	reproduce
nennen	mention
ordnen	arrange
rationalisieren	rationalise
realisieren	realise
resultieren	result
richten	direct
schleifen	cut
schneiden (sich)	intersect
sicherstellen	prove
sinken	sink
sprechen	speak
springen	jump
stammen	originate
stellen	set
trachten	endeavour
tragen	take
treten	occur
übersehen	review
überzeugen (sich)	be convinced
unterscheiden (sich)	differ
vereinfachen (sich)	be simplified
vergrößern	increase
verhalten (sich)	behave
verlangen	require
verlassen	leave
verlaufen	travel
vermitteln	adjust
vermuten	conjecture
verschieben (sich)	travel
versuchen	attempt

vorgehen	proceed
vorkommen	happen
vorliegen	to be
vorliegen	there be
vorschreiben	prescribe
wirken	act
wissen	know
wünschen	wish
zeichnen	mark
ziehen	draw
zitieren	cite
zugrundelegen	take as a basis
zurückführen	reduce
zurückgehen	return
zurücklegen	cover
zusammensetzen	compose
zuschreiben	give

ADJECTIVES

25

magnetisch	magnetic

24

elektrisch	electric

22

beide	two

20

konstant	constant

19

all	all

18

elektronenoptisch	electronoptic

17

ander	other

14

Laplacesch	Laplace
rotationssymmetrisch	axially symmetric
verschieden	different

13

gleich	equal to
senkrecht	perpendicular

11

solch	such

10

gleich	same
homogen	homogeneous
rechtwinklig	rectangular

8

allgemein	general
parallel	parallel

7

bestimmt	particular
elektrisch-magnetisch	electromagnetic
unabhängig	independent

6

beliebig	arbitrary
elektromagnetisch	electromagnetic
elektrostatisch	electrostatic
kinetisch	kinetic
klein	small
Lagrangesch	Lagrange
lichtoptisch	optical

5

beide	both
bekannt	well-known
gleich	equal
größer	greater
klein	lower

4

axialsymmetrisch	axially symmetric
ein	one
gewöhnlich	normal
groß	high
groß	large
kein	no
möglich	possible
negativ	negative
numerisch	numerical
zylindrisch	cylindrical

3

abhängig	dependent
analytisch	analytical
anisotrop	anisotropic
bekannt	known
Besselsch	Bessel
Eulersch	Euler
ganz	entire
gewiß	certain
inhomogen	inhomogeneous
kleinst	least
nullte	zero
optisch	optical
singulär	singular
skalar	scalar

veränderlich	varying
viele	many
wichtig	important
zahlreich	numerous

2

analog	similar
bemerkenswert	noteworthy
diskret	discrete
einige	some
einzeln	various
ersichtlich	evident
extremal	extreme
fiktiv	imaginary
Gausch	Gaussian
geometrisch	geometric
gleichförmig	uniform
größer	some
gültig	valid
höher	higher
identisch	identical
isotrop	isotropic
jeder	each
kartesisch	cartesian
kontinuierlich	continuous
kürzest	shortest
link	left
Maxwellsch	Maxwell
Neumannsch	Neumann
potential	potential
schmal	narrow
speziell	special
spiegelbildlich	in the form of a mirror image
stationär	stationary
unwesentlich	immaterial
vektoriell	vector
zulässig	permissible
zweckmäßig	expedient

1

abbildend	image-forming
absolut	absolute
äußer	external
belanglos	unimportant
benachbart	adjacent
bequem	convenient
bequemer	more convenient
besonder	special
betreffend	concerned
brauchbar	applicable
charakteristisch	characteristic
dimensionslos	dimensionless
dreifach	treble
eben	plane
einheitlich	uniform
einzeln	individual
elektrolytisch	electrolytic
endlich	finite
entgegengesetzt	opposite
erforderlich	necessary
exakt	exact
fest	fixed
gebräuchlich	usual
geeignet	suitable
gegenseitig	mutual
gemeinsam	common
genügend	sufficient
gerad	even
gerad	right
gering	small
gesamt	entire
gesamt	total
gleichgerichtet	in the same direction
gleichgültig	irrelevant
gleichmäßig	uniform
gleichwertig	equivalent
graphisch	graphical
halb	semi-
häufiger	more frequent
hinreichend	sufficient
kleiner	smaller
koaxial	co-axial
kreisförmig	circular
krumm	curved
mathematisch	mathematical
meist	most
metallisch	metal
minimal	minimal
mühsam	laborious
nächst	next
neu	new
Newtonsch	Newtonian
nochmalig	further
nötig	necessary
ortsabhängig	dependent on position
positiv	positive
proportional	proportional
quasistatisch	quasi-static
räumlich	three-dimensional
rechnerisch	mathematical
relativistisch	relativistic

richtig	true
richtungsunabhängig	independent of direction
sämtlich	all
Snelliusch	Snell's
sogenannt	so-called
spezifisch	specific
stärker	stronger
statisch	static
stetig	continuous
stromführend	current carrying
überlagert	superimposed
unbestimmt	undetermined
unendlich	infinite
unmittelbar	direct
variabel	variable
vorteilhaft	advantageous
vorteilhafter	more advantageous
weitgehend	extensive
wenigste	very few
wesentlich	material
zeitabhängig	dependent on time
zeitraubend	time consuming
zugänglich	amenable
zweimalig	double

ADVERBS

	37
auch	also
	32
nur	only
	22
hier	here
	17
also	therefore
dann	then
	10
somit	therefore
wobei	where
	9
allerdings	of course
also	i.e.
hierfür	for this
	8
dabei	in this
weiter	further
zunächst	first of all
	7
daraus	from this
ebenfalls	likewise
wie	as
	6
demnach	consequently
so	in such way
	5
damit	hence
dazu	for this
deshalb	therefore
tatsächlich	actually
wie	how
	4
analytisch	analytically
andererseits	on the other hand
bis	up
jedoch	however
oben	above
so	thus
unendlich	infinitely
unmittelbar	directly
weiterhin	furthermore
zeitlich	temporally
	3
aber	but
also	and therefore
beliebig	arbitrarily
dementsprechend	correspondingly
gleichzeitig	at the same time
mehr	more
noch	also
schließlich	finally
später	later
stets	always
vollständig	completely
woraus	from which
	2
allgemein	generally
analog	similarly
ausdrücklich	explicitly
bekanntlich	obviously
bereits	already
darauf	to the fact
demgegenüber	in contrast
eindeutig	uniquely
fast	almost
folgendermaßen	as follows
hingegen	on the other hand
jeweils	in each instance
keineswegs	by no means

koaxial	co-axially
langsam	gradually
nämlich	then
rein	purely
schon	already
sehr	very
somit	i.e.
speziell	in particular
thermisch	thermally
ursprünglich	initially

1

aber	and
allein	alone
analogerweise	similarly
anders	otherwise
ausnahmslos	without exception
bestenfalls	at best
beträchtlich	considerably
dadurch	by
dadurch	by the fact
dafür	for this
dafür	in
daher	therefore
daneben	in comparison
darauf	to this
darin	in the fact
darin	in
deswegen	therefore
direkt	directly
dort	there
durchwegs	throughout
ebenso	just
einerseits	on the one hand
einzeln	individually
entsprechend	appropriately
etwa	say
experimentell	experimentally
ferner	further
formal	formally
früher	earlier on
gewöhnlich	normally
gleichfalls	likewise
gut	well
heute	today
hingegen	but
insofern	in so far
ja	in fact
jedoch	but
lediglich	solely
lichtelektrisch	photo-electrically
manchmal	often
näher	more closely
näherungsweise	by approximation
numerisch	numerically
nunmehr	now
oft	often
praktisch	practically
rasch	quickly
rund	about
senkrecht	perpendicularly
sofort	immediately
soweit	in such a degree
sowie	as well as
ständig	permanently
stetig	continuously
stückweise	partially
überall	throughout
überhaupt	simply
unabhängig	independently
unbedingt	absolutely
unbedingt	necessarily
ungleich	incomparably
vektoriell	by vectors
vorwiegend	predominantly
weit	far
weniger	less
wie	such as
wirklich	really

RECIPROCAL PRONOUN

2

voneinander	from one another
voneinander	of one another

1

aneinander	to one another
aufeinander	to one another
hintereinander	in series
miteinander	with one another
zueinander	to one another

SUBORDINATING CONJUNCTIONS

21

da	since

8

indem	by

7

wenn	if

5

falls	if

Frequency	German	English
4	weil	because
	wenn	when
3	damit	in order that
	während	while
2	ob	whether
	sobald	as soon as
1	ab	if

CO-ORDINATING CONJUNCTIONS

Frequency	German	English
35	als	as
5	als	than
3	denn	inasmuch as
	denn	for

PREPOSITIONS

Frequency	German	English
156	in	in
115	für	for
94	von	of
64	durch	by
50	mit	with
41	aus	from
39	auf	to
31	im	in the
30	zwischen	between
24	von	from
17	zur	to the
16	auf	on
	nach	according to
13	auf	along
	in	at
12	bei	for
10	bei	with
	im	at the
	mit	by
9	zur	for the
8	im	in
	nach	with respect to
	statt	instead of
	von	on
7	an	at
	aus	of
	bei	with the
	längs	along
	nach	in
	zu	to
6	auf	in
	durch	through
	in	into
5	bei	in
	bis	to
	gegenüber	in comparison with
	von	by
4	an	in
	aus	for
	in	in the
	im	in a
	nach	after
	über	over
	um	by
	unter	by
	vom	of the

3

an	to
auf	on the
auf	at
für	of
gegenüber	from
in	as a
nach	to
um	about
vor	above
vom	on the

2

an	on
beim	in the
beim	on
bei	during
für	in
innerhalb	within
nach	for
neben	in comparison with
ohne	without
über	on
um	of
unter	at
zum	for
zum	to the
zur	on the
zur	at the

1

am	at the
auf	to within
bei	at
bei	in the
bei	with a
durch	by the
in	at a
in	on
in	to the
mittels	by means of
nach	of
nach	towards
über	across
unter	under
unter	on
unter	with
unter	below
vor	before
vor	from
während	during
zu	at
zur	at
zur	on
vom	from the
vom	on
vom	by the
von	by the
von	from the
zu	thus

Besides the above there were a certain number of words and phrases which were classed as idiomatic, either because they needed no translation in English or because, as a phrase, the translation required differed from that obtainable from the words making up the phrase. The former were as follows, their number of occurrences being given in parenthesis when more than one:

'aber', 'als', 'an', 'auch', 'auf', 'bestehen', 'dadurch', 'danach', 'dann' (4), 'darauf', 'darum', 'dauernd', 'dazu', 'einander', 'herrschen' (2), 'hindurch', 'je' (2), 'miteinander', 'schon' (2), 'so', 'somit', 'stammen', 'stehen' (3), 'und zwar' (3), 'vorhanden'.

The latter were:

aus längs	along
Bei Angabe von H . . .	If H is given . . .
jedes beliebige	any (2)
des weitern	for the rest
elektronenoptische Linsenfehler	errors in electron lenses
entgegensetzt-gerichtet	in opposite directions
Genauigkeits-anspruch stellen	demand a degree of accuracy
im wesentlichen	essentially
in Angriff nehmen	set about

für die Praxis interessant	of practical interest	seit langem	for a long time
für uns in Frage kommend	concerning us	und zwar	namely (3)
ins Auge fassen	consider (2)	unter Berücksichtigung	with (3)
um so (kleiner A), je (stärker B)	the (smaller A), the (stronger B)	unter Umständen	under certain circumstances (3)
zu liegen kommen	lie	sich unterwegs befinden	move
nach wie vor	in the same way as before	von (etwas) aus	with respect to (3)
Näheres däruber vgl.	see further	vorhanden sein	there be (2)
nicht mehr	no longer (4)	wählbar	which may be chosen
		zunächst einmal	above all

If the items under each part of speech are added up, the following totals are obtained: nouns 373, verbs 246, adjectives 178, adverbs 135, reciprocal pronouns 7, subordinating conjunctions 11, coordinating conjunctions 4, prepositions 102, idioms requiring no translation 25, idioms proper 26. These, plus the 50 or so different forms which were not included in the frequency count, make up a grand total of about 1166 items. That does not mean, however, that to translate the passage in question the machine's dictionary would have to contain 1166 German and corresponding 1166 English entries. This figure is reduced somewhat by various considerations, which may best be discussed with reference to the individual parts of speech.

NOUNS

1. The number of entries is reduced on the side of the German by the fact that in the above list seven nouns are entered twice, inasmuch as they each have two English equivalents and these fall in different frequency groups. In the actual dictionary the German noun would be entered once only.

2. This is more than made up for on the side of the English by a saving of 29 entries in the same way, the following 56 German nouns being accounted for by 27 English equivalents—it should be mentioned that the coincidences were not engineered:

Abstand, Entfernung, Strecke—distance
Annahme, Voraussetzung—assumption
Anschluß, Zusammenhang—connection
Anteil, Beitrag—contribution
Aufgabe, Problem—problem
Ausdruck, Bezeichnung—expression
Bahn, Weg—path
Bestimmung, Ermittlung, Festlegung—determination
Betrachtung, Berücksichtigung—consideration
Betrag, Größe—quantity
Bezeichnungsweise, Schreibweise—convention

bezug, Beziehung—relation
Differenz, Unterschied—difference
Differentiation, Differenzieren—differentiation
Einsetzen, Substitution—substitution
Ergebnis, Resultat—result
Feld, Gebiet—field
Form, Gestalt—form
Frage, Fragestellung—question
Gebrauch, Verwendung—use
Geschwindigkeit, Voltgeschwindigkeit velocity
Kreisumlauf, Umlauf—revolution
Methode, Verfahren—method
Mitte, Mittelpunkt—centre
Publikation, Veröffentlichung—publication
Punkt, Stelle—point
Verlauf, Verteilung—distribution

As was remarked previously, the English equivalent for each German word was chosen to provide the appropriate translation of the clause in which it occurred, and not with a view to reducing the number of different words required to translate the whole passage. If this had been done, a much greater number of 'coincidences' could no doubt have been produced.

3. A further reduction is made on the side of the English by the fact that some nouns have the same form in both languages, and need therefore be entered in the German half of the dictionary only, provided that the machine is instructed to substitute a small letter for the capital except at the beginning of a sentence. There are 18 such nouns in the above list, but four of them already appear under 2:

Addition, Anode, Argument, Differentiation, Elimination, Form, Index, Integral, Integration, Medium, Moment, Potential, Problem, Radius, Rotation, Separation, Substitution, System.

Another 13 (one of which appears under 2) can be added to this list, if the computer is instructed to replace a 'k' in the German by 'c' in English, i.e.

Elektrode, Elektron, Faktor, Funktion, Induktion, Kathode, Koordinate, Kurve, Produkt, Projektion, Publikation, Vakuum, Vektor.

In addition, if in a full-scale dictionary the words in question were frequent enough to make it worthwhile, slightly more complicated instructions could be included in the programme for producing English words out of such forms as:

Komponente—by changing the 'k' to 'c' and dropping the final 'e'.
Masse—simply by dropping the final 'e'.
Figur—by adding an 'e'.

Mechanik—by changing the 'k' to 'c' and adding 's'.
Differenz—by changing the final '-z' to '-ce'.
Zylinder—by changing the initial 'Z' to 'c'.
Metall—by dropping an 'l'.
Energie—by changing '-ie' to 'y', and so on.

Each type would be given a code symbol indicating the operation to be carried out to transform the form found in the dictionary into that required for the output.

4. The number of nouns to be entered in the dictionary can also be lowered by omitting all those compound forms, both components of which already occur in the dictionary as independent words, and including instead in the programme a routine for (*a*) separating the compound into its components, (*b*) putting together the equivalents given for these components in the correct way. The first part can be carried out simply enough by using the stem-ending method in a similar fashion to that suggested for compound verbs (cf. p. 197). The usual rule, that the incoming word shall be identified with the longest possible stem, applies. This prevents an incorrect division of the compound due to taking too small a portion, e.g. '*über*' in '*Übergangsgebiet*'—'transition region'. On the other hand, this could lead on very rare occasions to incorrect division due to taking too long a portion. For instance, '*Arbeiterinvasion*' would be identified in its first part according to the rule with '*Arbeiterin*'. The remainder '*-vasion*' would not be found in the ending dictionary, and instructions would direct the machine to identify this too with the longest possible item in the stem dictionary. It would fail, of course, and the subsequent instruction would be to identify the first part with the next longest entry, i.e. '*Arbeiter*', then try again with the remainder.

This particular difficulty could only arise if feminine forms of nouns were included in the stem dictionary. In actual fact they would not. The above compound was chosen only in lieu of a better one to illustrate a type of problem that *might* be encountered. The method would work equally well with three or more components in the compound, and the only instance where an error would be made would be that in which a letter or syllable could belong equally well to either one or other of the components, e.g.

'*Wacht-raum*'—'guard-room', '*Wach-traum*'—'waking dream'
(quoted by Reifler, op. cit.).

Here the machine would arrive only at the division '*Wacht-raum*'. Since such examples are extremely rare, however, they are easily solved by putting them in the dictionary as a whole with both translations, leaving these to be distinguished in the same way as simple nouns with more than one meaning (see below).

In many compounds, the components are not juxtaposed, but separated by the genitive inflexion of the first component, i.e. by '-s-', '-en-' (or '-n-', if the preceding component already ends in '-e'), '-ens-', '-es-', '-er-', or by '-in-'. The former can be ignored for translation purposes, the latter indicates that the gender of the preceding noun is feminine, e.g.

Geschwindigkeitsverteilung—velocity distribution,
Elektronenlinse—electron lens,
Senninindustrie—Alpine herdswoman's industry (also quoted by Reifler, op. cit.).

With all these the second component will not be able to be identified at the first attempt due to the prefix, i.e. '-sverteilung', '-enlinse', '-inindustrie'*.
Identification will follow, however, on the subtraction of the '-s-', '-(e)n-', or '-in-'.

The second problem, that of arranging the English equivalents of the components in the correct way, can be better appreciated if the compound nouns found in our list are divided in categories, as follows:

A. *No letter 's' intervening between the components*

1. Order of nouns same in English as in German:

Lagekoordinate	position co-ordinate	Potenzreihe	power series
Lichtstrahl	light ray	Punktladung	point charge
Metallelektrode	metal electrode	Radiusvektor	radius vector
Potentialdifferenz	potential difference	Raumladung	space charge
Potentialfeld	potential field	Strahlgleichung	ray equation
Potentialverlauf	potential distribution	Strahlvektor	ray vector
Potentialverteilung	potential distribution	Vektorpotential	vector potential
		Vektorprodukt	vector product
		Winkelkoordinate	angle co-ordinate

2. Order of nouns reversed in English and insertion of 'of' required:

Lichtgeschwindigkeit velocity of light.

* Note: An instruction must be included to prevent the machine identifying the '-in-' with the preposition of the same form in the stem dictionary.

3. Order of nouns reversed in English and 'of the' inserted:

Feldrichtung	direction of the field	Potentialwert	value of the potential
Kreisradius	radius of the circle	Strahlrichtung	direction of the ray

4. Order of nouns reversed, 'of' inserted, and number of first component changed to plural:

Wertbereich—range of values.

B. *Letter 's' intervening between the components*

1. Order of nouns retained in English:

Einheitsvektor	unit vector	Geschwindigkeitsverteilungsfunktion	velocity distribution function
Geschwindigkeitskomponente	velocity component	Ortsfunktion	position function
Geschwindigkeitsvektor	velocity vector	Übergangsgebiet	transition region
Geschwindigkeitsverteilung	velocity distribution	Wirkungsfunktion	action function

2. Order of nouns reversed, 'of' inserted:

Austrittsgeschwindigkeit	velocity of emission	Integrationskonstante	constant of integration
Bewegungsart	kind of motion	Krümmungsradius	radius of curvature
Bewegungsgesetz	law of motion	Richtungsänderung	change of direction
Bewegungsgleichung	equation of motion	Rotationsfläche	surface of rotation
Bewegungsrichtung	direction of motion		
Darstellungsart	kind of representation		

3. Order of nouns reversed, 'of' inserted, and number of first component changed to plural:

Gleichungssystem—system of equations.

C. *Letters '(e)n' intervening between the components*

1. Order of nouns retained in English:

Blendenöffnung	diaphragm aperture	Elektronenladung	electron charge
Blendenelektrode	diaphragm electrode	Elektronenlinse	electron lens
Koordinatensystem	co-ordinate system	Elektronenstrahl	electron ray

2. Order of nouns reversed, 'of' inserted:

Massenveränderlichkeit—variability of mass.

3. Order of nouns reversed, 'of the' inserted:

Blendendurchmesser	diameter of the diaphragm	Blendenpotential	potential of the diaphragm
Blendenmitte	centre of the diaphragm	Lochblendenfeld	field of the aperture lens

4. Order of nouns reversed, 'of' inserted, and number of first component changed to plural:

Elektronenbahn	path of electrons	Elektronenradius	radius of electrons
Elektronenbewegung	motion of electrons	Linsensystem	system of lenses
Elektronengeschwindigkeit	velocity of electrons		

The above compounds are all constructed solely from nouns, but there are also two constructed from an adjective and a noun, the order of these being retained in English, i.e.

Gesamtenergie—total energy. Gesamtzeit—total time.

The first thing that becomes clear is that the order of the components and the insertion or omission of 'of', etc., in English has no connection with whether the components are separated by a letter in the German or not. What, however, seems to be likely—though not the only possible solution—is outlined below, but first mention should be made of the type of solution that might be regarded as practical. Whereas, once a complete dictionary had been compiled of all words used in a particular subject (in our case electron optics), it would be reasonable to expect future authors to confine themselves to this dictionary and not use new words, unless this were absolutely unavoidable—reasonable because the aim of the scientific writer is, or should be, solely to convey his meaning and not indulge in any 'literary' propensities or aspirations to be at one and the same time a manufacturer of belles lettres—we feel that it would be asking too much of our German friends to require them to refrain from their favourite sport of constructing new compounds. Obviously a compromise is necessary, and this can be arrived at by permitting the formation of new compounds, provided that the words comprising them are taken from the existing dictionary. This means that the routine for rearranging the order of the components in English must be designed to deal with all the compounds that can possibly be formed from the words available, not merely those already existing.

The solution offered is illustrated on a small scale with the 50 or so compounds just classified, no attempt being made in this case, however, to fulfil the condition that it should cover all possible formations. Nor is the system itself necessarily the optimum one. This, as will be seen, could only have been discovered by permutation of the various steps, to have done which for these few compounds would have served no practical purpose.

To begin with, the 54 nouns used to form these compounds are divided into two classes. The smaller of these, containing 21 nouns, can be ignored, whilst the rest are redivided into the following ten types:

I. Occurs either only as first component or only as second component (i.e. within the limits of the compounds under consideration); the order in English of the components of the compound in which it occurs is unchanged, and no 'of' is added:

'Differenz', 'Elektrode', 'Funktion', 'Komponent', 'Ladung', 'Öffnung', 'Potenz', 'Übergang', 'Verlauf', 'Verteilung', and the adjectival form 'Gesamt'.

II. Occurs either only as first component or only as second component; the order of the components is reversed in English and 'of' is inserted:

'Änderung', 'Austritt', 'Darstellung', 'Integration', 'Krümmung', 'Masse', 'Rotation'.

III. Occurs either only as first component or only as second component; the order is reversed in English and 'of the' inserted:

'Durchmesser', 'Kreis', 'Lochblende', 'Mitte'.

IV. Occurs as both first and second component; in both cases the order of the components is reversed in English and 'of' inserted. When, however, this noun occurs as second component, the number of the first component is plural in English:

'Bewegung'.

V. Occurs as both first and second component; order of German retained in English in either case and no 'of' inserted:

'Vektor', 'Koordinate'.

VI. Occurs as both first and second component; order of German retained when it is the second (no 'of'), reversed when it is the first ('of' inserted), and in the latter case its number is changed to plural:

'Gleichung', 'Linse'.

VII. Occurs as both first and second component: order of German retained when it is second (no 'of'), reversed when it is first ('of the' inserted):

'Feld', 'Strahl'.

VIII. Occurs as both first and second component; order reversed and 'of the' inserted in both cases:

'Potential'.

IX. Reverse order of components and insert 'of':

'Licht'.

X. Reverse order of components, insert 'of', and change number of this component to plural in English:

'Elektron', 'Wert'.

Each of the 33 nouns above is accompanied in the dictionary by its type symbol, and to solve any of the compounds listed it is only necessary for the machine to be instructed that if both the components of a compound have a type symbol (e.g. 'Elektronenlinse'—X and VI, respectively), operations are to be carried out in accordance with the lower one (i.e. VI in this instance).

With a somewhat greater number of nouns than have been used for the purposes of this illustration it is conceivable that a complete solution could no longer be arrived at merely by specifying one component for any compound, and in this case it would be necessary to carry out operations according to a specification of particular combinations of types. If, for example, it were found that the compounds

Elektronenbahn	path of electrons	Elektronenstrahl	electron ray
Elektronenbewegung	motion of electrons	Elektronenladung	electron charge
Elektronenradius	radius of electrons	Elektronenlinse	electron lens

could not be solved exclusively by their second components, it would be necessary to denote those on the left by a different symbol from those on the right. Thus '*Bahn*', '*Bewegung*', and '*Radius*' might be Type B, '*Strahl*', '*Ladung*', and '*Linse*' Type C, '*Elektron*' Type A. Then the combination AB would indicate one order of words to be adopted in English, the combination AC another.

Returning now to the subject which led into this discussion of the arrangement of compound components in English, namely the reduction of the number of nouns to be entered into the dictionary, we can now say that the 59 compounds constructed from the 54 nouns just dealt with can be omitted, if the compound dividing and rearranging routine is included instead.

Of the 73 other compounds in our lists seven cannot be divided, because they are translated by one word, which is not directly equatable with either of the compounds. They are

Bezeichnungsweise	convention	Schreibweise	convention
Literaturangaben	bibliography	Schraubenlinie	helix
Mittelpunkt	centre	Spielraum	scope
Nullpunkt	origin		

As for the other 66 the majority cannot be divided economically because either one or both of their components do not occur separately in our dictionary list, and thus there would be no saving, e.g.

'Ausbreitungsgeschwindigkeit'—'Ausbreitung' = propagation is not found in the list except in this compound. In others both of the components are found separately, but one has a different translation when part of a compound, e.g.

'Kreisbewegung'—circular motion, the translation of '*Kreis*' alone being 'circle'.

A saving of one entry could be made on the side of the German by omitting the compound from the dictionary and including two translations for '*Kreis*', one for when it occurs independently and the other for when it occurs in a compound, but this would mean a corresponding increase of one on the English side and no overall gain would be made. This is possible only if more than one compound of the word occurs, as with '*Anfang*' in

'Anfangsbedingung', 'Anfangsenergie', 'Anfangsgeschwindigkeit', 'Anfangswert'.

where at the cost of one additional translation for 'Anfang' when in a compound, i.e. 'initial', a saving of four results on the side of the German.

A saving, but only on the side of the English, can be made by entering separately any components which have the same form in both languages, provided again that the other component occurs separately in the dictionary list, e.g.

'Rotations*ellipsoid*', 'Rotations*hyperboloid*', '*Differential*gleichung', '*Meridian*ebene'.

A further saving can be made where one of the components, though not occurring separately in the dictionary list, is nevertheless found in two or more compounds. In this case, it can be profitably entered separately, where the other component already occurs in the list, e.g.

'Feld*stärke*', 'Strom*stärke*'.

and even where it does not, provided it in turn occurs in another compound, e.g. of

Niveaufläche—equipotential surface
Niveaulinie—equipotential line
Äquipotentiallinie—equipotential line
Linienelement—line element
Leiterelement—conductor element

only '*Fläche*' and '*Leiter*' occur separately in our list, but by also entering '*Niveau*' and '*Äquipotential*' = equipotential, '*Linie*' = line, and '*Element*' without translation a reduction of one on the German side and three on the English is obtained. The same applies to '*Symmetrie*' in '*Symmetrieachse*', '*Symmetriegrund*', and '*Rotationssymmetrie*', to '*Zylinder*' in '*Zylinderelektrode*' and '*Zylinderkoordinate*', to '*Rohr*' in '*Rohrlinse*' and '*Rohrelektrode*'.

VERBS

In the same way as with nouns there has to be a reduction in the number of verbs actually entered in the dictionary, since some were quoted more than once in the frequency lists. '*Angeben*', '*bedeuten*', '*bestehen*', '*bezeichnen*', '*erreichen*', '*geben*', '*lassen*', '*sollen*', '*stehen*', '*vorliegen*', '*wollen*', all occurred twice and '*annehmen*' thrice, so that the total number of different verb forms becomes 233 instead of 246 on the German side.

Consideration of the reflexive verbs in the list shows that this figure can be reduced further. In seven out of the 20 instances the non-reflexive form of the verb is also present in the list, which means that only this need be entered in the actual dictionary together with a set of instructions regarding the procedure to be adopted if the incoming verb is accompanied by the reflexive pronoun. For one type of verb, to which '*ergeben*', '*lassen*', '*schneiden*', and '*unterscheiden*' in this instance belong, the instruction will indicate that a different translation altogether is called for, when the reflexive is present (i.e. 'result', 'can be', 'intersect', and 'differ' respectively in place of 'give', 'let' or 'allow', 'dissect', and 'distinguish'); for another, to which only '*auszeichnen*' in our list belongs, it will indicate that the passive form of the translation is required, i.e. 'be distinguished' instead of 'distinguish'; for a third type, to which '*bewegen*', and '*erstrecken*' belong, it will indicate that the presence of the reflexive makes no difference to the translation, which is, of course, not to say to the meaning. In the latter case there is also a saving on the side of the English.

A somewhat greater saving in this respect, however, results from one English word serving to translate two or more German words, though here too it should be stressed that these coincidences were purely accidental and could be made more numerous by design. They are as follows:

Add—addieren, auftragen
attain—annehmen, erreichen
arrive—einfallen, eintreffen
allow—erlauben, lassen
be—befinden (sich), geben, stehen, vorliegen
change—ändern (sich), übergehen
connect—anschließen, verbinden
calculate—auszählen, berechnen, rechnen
consider—berücksichtigen, betrachten
choose—herausgreifen, wählen
coincide—übereinstimmen, zusammenfallen
decrease—abklingen, abnehmen
differ—abweichen, unterscheiden (sich)
distinguish—auszeichnen, unterscheiden
denote—bedeuten, bezeichnen
do—leisten, tun
establish—aufstellen, feststellen
extend—ausdehnen, erstrecken
exist—bestehen, existieren, herrschen
give—angeben, ergeben, geben, vorgeben, zuschreiben
have—besitzen, haben
increase—anwachsen, vergrößern, wachsen, zunehmen
introduce—einführen, eintragen
know—kennen, wissen
let—lassen, wollen
mention—besprechen, erwähnen, nennen
need—brauchen, sollen
occur—erfolgen, treten
obtain—erhalten, erreichen, erzielen
proceed—ausgehen, fortschreiten, vorgehen
produce—bewirken, erzeugen
prove—erweisen (sich), sicherstellen
put—legen, setzen
retain—beibehalten, festhalten
require—benötigen, verlangen
result—ergeben (sich), resultieren
refer—erinnern, hinweisen, verweisen
solve—auflösen, lösen
state—aussagen, festlegen
taken—mitnehmen, nehmen, tragen
travel—verlaufen, verschieben (sich)
use—betreiben, verwenden

ADJECTIVES

The same applies to adjectives and adverbs, where the coincidences are:

Adjectives

all—all, sämtlich
axially symmetric—axialsymmetrisch, rotationssymmetrisch
continuous—kontinuierlich, stetig
electromagnetic—elektrisch-magnetisch, elektromagnetisch
entire—ganz, gesamt
mathematical—mathematisch, rechnerisch
necessary—erforderlich, nötig
optical—lichtoptisch, optisch
some—einige, größer
sufficient—genügend, hinreichend
small—gering, klein
special—besonder, speziell
uniform—einheitlich, gleichförmig, gleichmäßig

Adverbs

also—auch, noch
already—bereits, schon
but—aber, hingegen, jedoch
directly—direkt, unmittelbar
for this—dazu, dafür, hierfür
further—ferner, weiter
i.e.—also, somit
in—dafür, darin
likewise—ebenfalls, gleichfalls
on the other hand—andererseits, hingegen
often—manchmal, oft
similarly—analog, analogerweise
therefore—also, daher, deshalb, deswegen, somit
then—dann, nämlich
throughout—durchwegs, überall

There is a corresponding saving on the side of the German, where one word requires two, and in some cases three, English equivalents:

Adjectives

beide—both, two
bekannt—known, well-known
ein—a, one
einzeln—individual, various
gerad—right, even
gesamt—equal, equal to, same
groß—high, large
größer—greater, some
klein—low, small

Adverbs

aber—but, however
also—and therefore, i.e. therefore
dadurch—by, by the fact

dafür—for this, in
darauf—to the fact, to this
darin—in, in the fact
hingegen—but, on the other hand
so—in such a way, so, thus
somit—i.e. therefore
unbedingt—absolutely, necessarily
wie—as, how, such as

A further reduction is possible in those cases where the comparative or superlative form also occurs and the translation of this is not irregular with respect to that of the positive form. In the present instance this is true only of three adjectival forms,

vorteilhaft—advantageous	vorteilhafter—more advantageous
bequem—convenient	bequemer—more convenient
klein—small	kleiner—smaller

Where more comparative and superlative forms existed, it would be profitable to employ the stem-ending method for regular adjectives and adverbs on the side of the German. In this respect those words taking an umlaut in the comparative and superlative would not be regarded as irregular, since as with all other parts of speech the umlaut forms part of the ending. Thus both

bequem -er -st and *kurz -eru -estu* (u = umlaut)

would be regular, only a letter change as in the superlative of '*nah*', '*nächst*', constituting an irregularity.

In the same way as with verbs the most economical way on the side of the English would be to have only the positive form entered for regular words and allow the machine to construct the others either by adding the suffixes '-(e)r', '-(e)st' or the adverbs 'more', 'most'. Thus for '*bequem*' and '*kurz*' the only translations entered in the dictionary would be 'convenient' and 'short'; the comparatives 'more convenient' and 'shorter' would be produced automatically when the original stem was lengthened by '-er'. Similarly with the superlative. Irregular forms would clearly need to be entered as they stood in the language in which they occurred, but even here this would not mean a direct relation of comparative to comparative, superlative to superlative.

Lastly, as regards adjectives and adverbs, a reduction in the total number is possible because the two parts of speech sometimes have the same form, and when this is so, it is unnecessary to enter it twice. In the English the adverb can usually be formed from the adjective by adding '-ly' or by making a slight change to the end of the word and then adding '-ly'. In this case the reduction applies to both languages. It concerns thirteen words in our list, i.e.

allgemein—general
analog—similar
analytisch—analytical
beliebig—arbitrary (omit 'y', add -ily')
einzeln—individual
gewöhnlich—normal
koaxial—co-axial
numerical—numerical
senkrecht—perpendicular
stetig—continuous
unabhängig—independent
unendlich—infinite
unmittelbar—direct

With two others English requires a different word for the adverbial form, and with these the saving applies only to German, speziell—special (adverb—'in particular', 'especially') vektoriell—vector (adverb—'by vectors)'.

PREPOSITIONS

The only other part of speech where any considerable saving can be made is the preposition. Many of these are entered several times over in the frequency lists according to how many English equivalents they require. They are as follows:

8 *meanings*

bei: at, during, for, in, in the, with, with a, with the.
in: at, at a, as a, in, in the, into, on, to the.
nach: according to, after, for, in, of, to, towards, with respect to.

7 *meanings*

auf: along, at, in, on, on the, to, to within.

6 *meanings*

unter: at, below, by, on, under, with.
von: by, by the, from, from the, of, on.
zur: at, at the, for the, on, on the, to the.

5 *meanings*

vom: by the, from the, of the, on, on the.

4 *meanings*

an: at, in, on, to.
im: at the, in, in a, in the.

3 *meanings*

aus: for, from, of.
durch: by, by the, through.
für: for, in, of.
um: about, by, of.
über: across, on, over.
vor: above, before, from.
zu: in, thus, to.

2 *meanings*

beim: in the, on.
gegenüber: from, in comparison.
mit: by, with.
zum: for, to the.

On the side of the English one word is several times found as the equivalent of more than one German preposition. The actual figures are:

'on' with 9 prepositions in the German, 'in' with 8, 'at' with 6, 'by', 'for', 'of', 'to' with 5, 'from', 'in the' with 4, 'at the', 'by the', 'on the', 'with' with 3, and 'along' ,'during', 'for the', 'from the', 'in comparison with', 'to the', with 2.

This results in a saving of 56 items on the English side compared with 71 on the German.

If we now add together all the reductions which are necessary or can be made by the adoption of various simple routines (compound dividing, etc.), we get the following totals for the main parts of speech:

Nouns:	on the side of the German	72
Verbs:	" " " "	20
Adjectives:	" " " "	14
Adverbs:	" " " "	29
Prepositions:	" " " "	71
		206

Nouns:	on the side of the English	125
Verbs:	" " " "	58
Adjectives:	" " " "	17
Adverbs:	" " " "	33
Prepositions:	" " " "	56
		289

thus allowing us to amend the total number of words required to translate the text in question from 1166 for each language to 960 German and 877 English.

Though the use of an idioglossary reduces the amount of multi-meaning to be dealt with, it clearly does not eliminate it altogether. Is it then necessary for the machine to print out the alternative translations in every instance where ambiguity exists or can something further be done towards solving these ambiguities? Of course, a solution proper would result only from an analysis of all the existing literature on the subject in question (here electron optics), but as in the previous section we propose for the purposes merely of illustration to confine the analysis and any solution arising to the small amount of text investigated.

Let us start with the prepositions, which represent the acme in the problem of multimeaning, and examine those involved in turn to see what can be done. First of all, however, consider the following:

'auf dem Tisch', 'auf dem Tanz', 'auf dem Lande'.

If, as is likely, these will always be translated by '*on* the table', '*at* the dance', and '*in* the country' respectively, the easiest solution to multimeaning in the preposition is to number each of its meanings (e.g. '*auf*' = 1) on, 2) at, 3) in), then place the appropriate number after each noun in the dictionary capable of being constructed with this preposition *and only in this one sense*. Each noun would have as many numbers after it as the prepositions with which it could be constructed; thus '*Tanz*' 5. 2. 1. 4. would mean that the translation of 'an' required with '*Tanz*' would be the fifth one listed under this preposition, that of '*auf*' would be the second (i.e. 'at'), that of '*aus*' the first, that of '*bei*' the fourth, and so on. Often, however, the translation required depends not on the noun with which the preposition is constructed, but on the verb, e.g.

'Schreib' an die Tafel'	Write *on* the blackboard.
'Seh' an die Tafel'	Look *at* the blackboard.
'Geh' an die Tafel'	Go *to* the blackboard.

and in this case the code number must be placed after the relevant verb. If the translation depends on both the noun and the verb, as the first of the above obviously does, when we compare it with

'Schreib' an meine Eltern'—Write *to* my parents.

then the reference must also be to the two combined. Let us now see whether these apply to the prepositions in our text.

an—1. = to (+accusative)

The nouns governed ('*Lichtgeschwindigkeit*', '*Lichtoptik*', '*Glaslinse*'), though not found with any other sense of '*an*' in the text investigated, are not particularly characteristic of the sense 'to'. On the other hand the words governing the preposition are (i.e. 'Annäherung'—approximation to, 'Anschluß'—connection to, 'erinnern'—refer to), e.g.

'Mit der Festlegung des Ausdruckes für den elektronenoptischen Brechungsindex ist der Anschluß der Elektronenoptik an die Lichtoptik bewerkstelligt.'

2. =at (+dative)

This sense is characterized in the main by the nouns governed, i.e. '*Anode*', '*Elektrode*', '*Fläche*', '*Kathode*', '*Punkt*', '*Stelle*'. Two of these, however, are also common to other meanings of '*an*', namely '*Elektrode*' (to the meaning 'on') and '*Stelle*' (to the meaning 'in'). With the latter the meaning of the preposition depends on the meaning of '*Stelle*', i.e. whether it is 'place' or 'point'. For the distinction of these see under '*Stelle*', p. 282. With '*Elektrode*', on the other hand, the difference depends on the word governing '*an*': if it is '*Potential*' or a symbol representing this (e.g. v), then '*an*' must be translated by '*at*', e.g.

'Die Koeffizienten sind so zu wählen, daß v(z, r) an den Elektroden die vorgeschriebenen Werte annimmt.'

if it is '*Spannung*', the translation of '*an*' is 'on'.

'Weit häufiger als diese Fragestellung haben wir jedoch das entgegengesetzte Problem zu behandeln, für eine vorgegebene Elektrodenanordnung und für vorgegebene Spannungen an denselben das zwischen den Elektroden herrschende Feld zu berechnen.'

3. =on (+accusative and dative)

This sense applied only to four instances of '*an*' with '*Stelle*' (see 2).

auf—1. =along (+dative)

'*Auf*' in this sense occurs 13 times and is fairly well characterized both by the noun which it governs and the noun which governs it. The former is '*Achse*' or '*Symmetrieachse*' in all but one instance, this being '*welcher*' (referring to '*Kurve*'), whilst the latter is either '*Potential*', '*Verlauf*', '*Potentialverlauf*' or '*Potentialverteilung*), e.g.

'Im folgenden werden wir das Potential auf der Achse mit Φ(z) bezeichnen.'

2. =at (+accusative)

Occurs twice with '*Ebene*' and once with '*Potential*', but all three also crop up with '*auf*' in the sense of 'to'. With the latter, however, the verbs are different from here, being '*stehen*' and '*bringen*'—

'Wir können (56) so auffassen, als ob der Beitrag dH senkrecht auf der Ebene von ds steht.

'Wir brauchen nur noch beliebige Flächen konstanten Potentials herauszugreifen, sie in Metall nachzubilden und auf die ihnen zukommenden Potentiale zu bringen.'

instead of '*eintreffen*', '*einfallen*', and '*aufladen*'—

'V_1 sei die Geschwindigkeit, mit welcher ein Elektron auf die Ebene F_1 eintrifft.'

'In größerer Entfernung D von E aufladen wir zwei parallele Ebenen auf die Potentiale $V_1 = E_1D$ und $V_2 = E_2D$ gegenüber E.'

and can so be used as the criterion.

3. =in (+accusative and dative)

In this sense '*auf*' is found six times and always with a noun which is sufficient to distinguish it, i.e. '*Weise*', '*Parabel*', '*Kreis*', '*Gebiet*', e.g.

'Das Elektron führt eine gleichförmige Bewegung auf einem Kreis aus.'

4. =on (+accusative and dative)

The preposition governs the following words: '*Elektron*' (four times), '*Ebene*', '*Seite*' (three times), '*Bahnkurve*', '*Kreiszylinder*' (twice), '*Bahn*' (twice), '*Achse*' (twice), and '*Blendenelektrode*'. None of these occurs with '*auf*' in another sense except '*Ebene*', '*Seite*', '*Achse*', and '*Kurve*' (in '*Bahnkurve*). With the first it is distinguished from the senses 'at' and 'to' by depending on a noun instead of a verb, e.g.

'Die Projektion der Bahn auf die (x, y)-Ebene ist ein Kreis mit dem Radius R.'

With '*Seite*' the case is a sufficient criterion, since when it is dative the translation of '*auf*' is 'on', when accusative 'to'.

With '*Achse*' it is distinguished from the sense 'along' by depending in the one instance on the noun '*Punkt*' and in the other on the verb '*liegen*', and from the same sense with '*Kurve*' also by depending on the noun '*Punkt*'.

'Wir wollen nun auf der Bahnkurve eines Elektrons zwei beliebige Punkte P_1 und P_2 herausgreifen.'

'*Elektron*' occurs with '*auf*' only in this sense of 'on', because the latter depends in all four instances either on '*Wirkung*', '*wirken*', or '*ausüben*'; consequently either '*Elektron*' or these could be made the distinguishing criterion.

5. =on the

Always and only with the noun '*Grund*' (three times), e.g.

'Es läßt sich aus dem lichtoptischen Brechungsgesetz auf Grund der Analogie zwischen n und V auch unmittelbar anschreiben.'

6. =to (+accusative and dative)

The most frequent sense, being found almost as often as all the rest put together. The only words with which the preposition is not unique in this sense are '*Ebene*', '*Potential*', '*Seite*' and '*Achse*'. The first three have already been mentioned; '*Achse*', which was taken to be a fairly safe criterion of the sense 'along', though it was also seen to occur with that of 'on', is easily accounted for here inasmuch as it follows the phrase '*in bezug auf*', and the criterion to be used is therefore '*bezug*', and not '*Achse*'.

In general with this sense of '*auf*' it was the verb and not a noun which was the characterising criterion. The verbs concerned were:

'beschränken (sich)'—4 times, 'anwachsen', 'Antwort geben', 'Augenmerk richten', 'beschleunigen', 'beziehen (sich)'—2, 'bringen'—2, 'führen'—3, 'reduzieren (sich)'—2, 'springen', 'senkrecht stehen'—2, 'übergehen', 'verweisen'—5, 'zurückführen', 'zurückgehen', 'zurückkommen'—2.

and the nouns:

'Beschleunigung', 'Hineingreifen', 'Potentialsprung (von—auf)' and 'Übergang (von—auf)'.

In addition there was the adverbial '*in bezug*' and '*bis*—2', quite concrete criteria.

7. =to within

Occurs only once in this sense and recognizable by depending on the verb '*übereinstimmen*', or even more certainly the combination of this and the fact that it governs a figure:

'Für kleine Geschwindigkeiten liefert die Gleichung für ß Werte, welche auf 1% mit den aus der exakten Formel berechneten übereinstimmen.'

8. It will be remembered that '*auf*' was included among the idioms requiring no translation. This applied to its use after '*greifen*', translated as 'adopt':

'Falls die Funktion $\Phi(2)$ analytisch vorgegeben ist, ist es vorteilhafter, auf eine andere Darstellung von V zu greifen.'

aus—1. =for

In all its occurrences (4) either with '*Grund*' or '*Symmetriegründe*', e.g.

'Aus Symmetriegründen muß die Komponente E in einem rotationssymmetrischen Feld überall verschwinden.'

2. =from

By far the most frequent sense of '*aus*', it could be regarded—as could 'to' in the case of '*auf*'—as the basic meaning and the machine instructed to translate all occurrences of the preposition so, unless specific indications existed that another meaning was required. This would save entering characteristic criteria for this meaning in the dictionary, but these may be quoted for the sake of interest. Again they are mainly verbs:

'ableiten' (2), 'auftragen', 'austreten' (3), 'anschreiben', 'berechnen' (2), 'bestimmen' (2), 'ergeben sich' (2), 'erhalten' (5), 'ersehen', 'eliminieren', 'folgen' (7), 'hervorgehen', 'schleifen', 'sehen'.

The nouns are:

'Austrittsgeschwindigkeit' (5), 'Austritt' (2), 'Einsetzen'.
These are governing the preposition. Those governed by the preposition are also characteristic except with '*Einsetzen*', this being '*Gleichung*', since they are in all seven instances '*Kathode*'. Besides the verbs and nouns two adjectives, '*ersichtlich*' (2) and '*bekannt*', also serve as criteria, e.g.

'Aus dieser Gleichung ist sofort ersichtlich, daß diese Potenzreihe nur Glieder mit geraden Potenzen von *r* enthalten kann.'

3. =of

There are seven instances of the preposition in this sense, one of which is a type that could be confused with the preceding sense, since in both the preposition governs a symbol instead of a noun, i.e.

'Aus T und U berechnen wir die Lagrange-Funktion L.'
'In dieser Gleichung ist (A, v) das skalare Produkt aus A und v.'

The characterizing feature of each, of course, is the verb '*berechnen*' for the sense 'from' and the noun '*Produkt*' for the sense 'of'. The other criteria for the latter sense are the governing nouns; '*Summe*', '*Produkt*' (a second time), and '*System*' (2) and the verb '*bestehen*' (2).

The nouns governed are also unique, but this is without doubt due only to the small amount of text examined.

bei—1. =at

Occurs only once in a reference:

'Zur Bewegung der Elektronen bei großen Geschwindigkeiten vgl. auch . . .'

2. =for

In this sense '*bei*' occurs thrice with a symbol and an =sign (the latter distinguishing it from the symbol occurring in 6 below):

'Wir entnehmen dieser Tabelle, daß die Masse m bei $v = 1\cdot5.10^8$ cm sek^{-1}, d.h. bei $\beta = 0\cdot05$, die Ruhemasse m_0 um 1‰ übertrifft.'

thrice with '*Elektron*' or a compound of it, e.g.

'ε hat bei thermisch ausgelösten Elektronen die Größenordnung 0·1 V.'

and nine times with '*Geschwindigkeit*'* or its compounds, e.g.

'Der angebene Wert gilt allerdings nur bei kleinen Geschwindigkeiten.'

This sense of '*bei*' with '*Geschwindigkeit*' can be distinguished from that of 1 above by always being dependent on the verb, not on a noun (i.e. '*Bewegung*').

3. =in

The criterion for the preposition in this sense is the noun which it governs: '*Behandlung*' (2), '*Berechnung*', '*Wahl*' (2), e.g.

'Wir werden auf (876) später, bei der Berechnung des Feldes von Rohrlinsen, zurückkommen.

4. =in the

Once only in the sentence

'Bei Fehlen von Raumladungen ergibt sich das Potential als Lösung der Laplaceschen Gleichung.'

The noun governed is a sure criterion of the translation required.

5. =during

Occurs twice with the noun '*Bewegung*', e.g.

'Die Summe aus potentieller und kinetischer Energie des Elektrons bleibt bei dessen Bewegung in einem zeitlich konstanten elektrischen oder magnetischen Feld konstant.'

Here too the noun governed is the criterion.

6. =with

This, though not the most frequent in this analysis, may be taken as the basic meaning of '*bei*'. In common with the rest of its

* NOTE: For 'Elektron' and also some of the instances of 'Geschwindigkeit' 'with' is a possible translation.

meanings the preposition is characterized here too by the noun it governs, though the weakness of the characterization in some cases makes it doubly convenient to regard this sense of the preposition as the basic one. These nouns are:

'*Emissionsart*', '*Kristall*' (2), '*Lösung*', '*Medium*', '*System*', '*Verwendung*', '*400 KV*', e.g.

'Bei elektronenoptische Medien können solche Diskontinuitäten nicht oder nur unter besonderen Bedingungen realisiert werden.'

7. =with a

This meaning was found only once with the noun '*Abstand*',

'Bei zu geringem Abstand der Lochblenden läßt sich das gemeinsame Feld nicht mehr als Überlagerung zweier Lösungen von der Form (100) darstellen.' (With too small a distance between . . .)

Again the noun is a safe criterion.

8. = with the

In this sense '*bei*' is used once with '*Annäherung*' and six times with '*Verwendung*', e.g.

'Für ein axialsymmetrisches Feld nimmt die Laplacesche Gleichung bei Verwendung von Zylinderkoordinaten eine von (80) abweichende Form an.'

On the whole, however, the phrase '*bei Verwendung*' is better translated simply as 'using' and placed at the beginning of the clause irrespective of its position in the German.

The reason why '*Verwendung*' also appears under '*bei*' in the sense of "with" is that the definite article was present in that particular instance.

beim—1. =in the

Occurs twice in this sense with the nouns '*Fehlen*' and '*Übergang*', e.g.

'In der Umgebung der Blendenöffnung ist das Feld nicht homogen, weil beim Übergang durch die Öffnung von der einen Seite von E nach der anderen die Feldstärke stetig vom Werte E_1 auf den Wert E_2 übergehen muß.'

2. =on

Also occurs only twice—with the nouns '*Verlassen*' and '*Austritt*', e.g.

'Sei V die Geschwindigkeit, welche das Elektron beim Verlassen der Kathode besitzt.'

With '*beim*', as with '*bei*', the noun governed by the preposition is the best, if not the only criterion of the translation required.

durch—1. =by

The basic meaning—ten times more frequent than the other two together. It is characterized naturally enough to some extent by the noun governed, but to a far greater extent by the verb, as is shown by the fact that half of the instances have one of three verbs: '*geben*' and '*bestimmen*' (both fifteen times and always in the passive voice) and '*erhalten*' (six times). Since it is so preponderant, however, it can be treated in the same way as the sense 'to' was with '*auf*' and no characterizing criteria set up for it.

2. =by the

Only once in the sentence:

'Erst durch Hinzunahme dieser Randbedingungen ist das Potential vollständig und eindeutig bestimmt.'
The noun governed and the absence of the definite article is the criterion.

3. =through

The preposition occurred six times in this sense. In all except two instances the noun governed does not occur with another meaning of the preposition, the exceptions being '*Achse*' and '*Symmetrieachse*'. This latter also occurs with the meaning 'by':

'Dies bedeutet, daß die Feldstärke E im Punkte P ständig in der durch die Symmetrieachse z und den Punkt P bestimmten Ebene liegt.'

But this is clearly denoted by the participle '*bestimmten*', whereas with the meaning 'through' it is characterized in the one case by the verb '*zusammenfallen*' and in the other by the noun '*Ebene*' without any verb, i.e.

'Wir lassen eine beliebige Ebene durch die Symmetrieachse mit der x, z–Ebene zusammenfallen.'

'Es besteht dann in allen Meridianebenen (Ebenen durch die z-Achse des rotationssymmetrischen Feldes) die gleiche Potentialverteilung.'

The other four instances where '*durch*' has the meaning 'through' are characterized by the nouns governed, and by the nouns or verb governing, i.e.

'Bewegung durch das System,'
'Übergang durch die Öffnung,'
'Hineingreifen durch die Blendenöffnung,'
'Legen wir die z-Achse durch die Mitte der Öffnung.'

für—1. =for

This is the basic and almost only meaning of the preposition, since it occurs 115 times compared with the five times shared by the other two meanings. For this reason it is not worthwhile speaking of characterizing criteria; these can be left to the other meanings.

2. =in

This meaning is found only after the verb '*interessieren* (*sich*)'. In the two sentences in which it occurs the noun governed is '*Verlauf*', e.g.

'Wir interessieren uns vor allem für den Verlauf des Potentials in der Nähe der Symmetrieachse.'

3. =of

This meaning too is characterized by definite criteria in the form of '*als Beispiel*' (twice) and '*charakteristisch*'; the nouns governed are irrelevant.

'Als Beispiel für eine solche Darstellung zeigen wir in Fig. 8 das Feld zwischen zwei koaxialen hintereinander angeordneten Hohlzylindern verschiedener Durchmesser.'

gegenüber—1. =from

With this meaning the noun governed is not so useful a criterion as that governing, which in all three instances indicates difference, i.e. '*Potentialdifferenz*', '*Differenz*', '*Unterschied*', e.g.

'Die Geschwindigkeit des Elektrons an einem bestimmten Punkte seiner Bahn ist gleich der Differenz des Potentials in diesem Punkt gegenüber dem Potential der Kathode, vergrößert um die Austrittsgeschwindigkeit des Elektrons aus der Kathode.'

A better translation for 'gegenüber' in each case would be 'and', at the same time inserting 'between' between the word expressing difference and the first of the two objects compared (here '*des Potentials in diesem Punkt*').

2. =in comparison with

This may be taken as the basic meaning again, thereby avoiding the need for characterizing criteria. These, if they had to be found, would come from the governing verb or noun rather than the noun governed, i.e. in the present instances '*vernachlässigen*' (2), '*aufladen*', '*Einschränkung*' (+'*bedeuten*'—2), e.g.

'Wir werden später sehen, daß dies gewisse Einschränkungen gegenüber der Lichtoptik bedeutet.'

im—1. =at the

This meaning is immediately distinguished by the noun, which in nine cases is '*Punkt*', in the other one '*Scheitel*'. No other meaning of '*im*' is found in the text that could possibly be applied to these words.

2. =in

The nouns which the preposition in this sense governs are not characteristic of this sense in themselves but only in so far as they are followed by a figure or symbol in apposition, e.g. '*Gebiet*' *II*, '*Medium*' *I*, '*Band*' *II*, '*Falle*' *a*). Two exceptions are '*Raum*' and '*Endlichen*', which may in fact be taken as characteristic as they stand, e.g.

So hat *z.B.* PLASS nach (85) die Potentialverteilung im Raume berechnet für die beiden Potentialverteilungen auf der z-Achse . . .'

3. =in a

This meaning was found with two nouns only, '*Vakuum*' (three times) and '*Medium*'. The former may be taken as a criterion for this meaning, but not the latter, which is followed by a symbol in apposition as in 2 above. The sentences in which they occur are:

(i) 'C_1' Lichtgeschwindigkeit im Medium I; C_2' Lichtgeschwindigkeit im Medium II; C: Lichtgeschwindigkeit im Vakuum.'

(ii) 'Da der Brechungsindex n als Verhältnis der Ausbreitungsgeschwindigkeit des Lichtes im Vakuum c zu dessen Ausbreitungsgeschwindigkeit im Medium C′ definiert ist, so ist. . . .'

The difference between the two is that the former is a particular medium out of several mentioned, the latter any arbitrary medium, which we shall call C′. . . . Though the mere presence of a symbol is an unsatisfactory criterion, therefore, it may be that the nature of the symbol is not, though this means that to obtain a solution symbols must be classified according to whether their function is merely to serve as an abbreviation for an object (e.g. C′ above, Potential *V*, Punkt *P*) or to distinguish this object from another similar object (e.g. Medium I, Falle *a*, etc.). Naturally a symbol in the latter sense can be added to one in the former sense, e.g. C'_1 and C'_2 above.

4. =in the

The basic meaning of '*im*', occurring half as many times again as all the rest together. Although, therefore, it is unnecessary to establish any characterizing criteria for it, we may note that it is especially frequent with the noun '*Fall*', this making up about a third of the instances, whilst '*Feld*' and '*System*' constitute between them another third. The only point of concern, however, is the occurrence here as well as with meaning 2, above, of '*Fall*' and '*Raum*'. The former, which as we have noted is more frequent here than there, is distinguished by not being followed by an apposition, the latter by being qualified, which particularizes its sense:

'Aus der Reihenentwicklung (85) folgt, daß das Potential V(z, r) im ganzen Raume durch die Festlegung des Potentialverlaufes auf der Symmetrieachse allein schon vollständig bestimmt ist.

in—1. =as a

In this sense only with the noun '*Funktion*' (thrice), e.g.

'Ferner muß das Kräftepotential U in Funktion der qk vorgegeben sein.'

2. =at (+dative)

Occurs twice with '*Entfernung*', twice with '*Mitte*', four times with '*Punkt*', and five times with the relative pronouns '*der*' and '*welcher*', the noun referred to being in every case '*Punkt*' or '*Aufpunkt*', e.g.

'Im Falle *b* erreicht das Potential auf der Achse in einem Punkte S einen Extremwert;'

These nouns may be taken as characteristic criteria for the meaning 'at' with certain conditions which will be explained in 3.

3. =at a (+dative)

Only with the noun '*Abstand*' in the sentence

'So ist z.B. in Fig. 8 jede der beiden Zylinderelektroden durch je zwei in gleichem Abstand von der z-Achse verlaufende Geradenstücke dargestellt.'

The different translations required with '*Abstand*' and '*Entfernung*' in 2 are due to the different qualifying adjectives, whereas the former is 'at an equal distance', the latter is 'at some distance' in

'In größerer Entfernung von der Blendenöffnung sind E_1 und E_2 homogen.'

4. =in (+accusative and dative)

This is naturally the basic meaning and the most frequent by a long way (over 150 instances compared with about 30 for all the other meanings together). We may, therefore, dispense with a wearisome enumeration of its characterizing criteria.

5. =in the (+dative)

In this sense the preposition occurred four times with the nouns '*Richtung*' (twice), '*Form*' and '*Umgebung*'. These are not to be regarded, however, as characteristic of this meaning, because they also occur with that of 4 above; it is the fact that they are without the definite article which is the distinguishing feature, e.g.

'Wir legen die z-Achse in Richtung der magnetischen Feldstärke H.'

6. =into (+accusative)

The preposition in this sense is characterized not by the noun it governs, but by the verb or noun by which it is governed, that is in five cases '*übergehen*' and in the other one '*Umrechnung*', e.g.

'Für kleines V und v geht n in den in (64) angegeben Ausdruck über.

7. =on (+accusative)

For this meaning the noun governed, '*Symmetrieachse*', is a safe criterion:

'Wir legen dabei die z-Achse des neuen Koordinatensystems in die Symmetrieachse des Feldes.'

8. =to the

Here too the noun governed is a certain criterion:

'Wir werden die Hauptaufgabe in Angriff nehmen, die Größen, welche für die Elektronenlinsen in gleichem *Maße* wie in der Lichtoptik ihre Bedeutung haben, aus den Eigenschaften dieser Felder zu bestimmen.'

mit—1. =by

Always governing a symbol and itself governed in all ten instances either by the verb '*bezeichnen*' (nine times) or the verb '*multiplizieren*'. The latter must be regarded as the characterizing criteria, since symbols also occur with the preposition when it has its usual sense of 'with', e.g.

'Im folgenden werden wir das Potential auf der Achse mit $\Phi(z)$ bezeichnen.'

2. =with

The basic meaning, occurring five times more frequently than the other. When it governs a symbol the verbs characteristic of 1 are not present, and it is only in the case of symbols that the two meanings can be distinguished.

nach—1. =according to

This may be taken as the basic meaning. Though not overwhelmingly the most frequent, it is at least twice as frequent as any other meaning. In 11 of its 16 instances it governs an equation or number, in the other five—'*Beziehung*', '*Genauigkeitsansprüchen*', '*Obengesagten*', '*FOURIER*', and '*welcher*' (referring to '*Vorschrift*').

2. =after

Occurs thrice with the noun '*Durchfallen*', which may be taken as characteristic, and once with the name 'TAYLOR', which may not because a name is also found under 1. For these the distinguishing mark must be the governing verb, which for the sense 'according to' is '*folgen*' and for the sense 'after' '*schreiben*', i.e.

(i) 'Daraus folgt nach FOURIER für den Koeffizienten ak. . . .'

(ii) 'Wir können die Werte von $\Phi(z)$, $\Phi'(z)$, $\Phi''(z)$ durch die Werte dieser Funktionen im Punkte $z=z_0$ ausdrücken, indem wir nach TAYLOR schreiben. . . .'

3. =for

This meaning is characterized by the governing verb, which in both cases is '*auflösen*', e.g.

'Lösen wir (22) nach ß auf, so erhalten wir ß=. . . .'

4. =in

With this meaning '*nach*' governs the nouns '*Potenz*' and '*Richtung*' (each three times), which can be taken as safe characterizing criteria. This is not true of the seventh instance, in which the symbol *r* is the item governed. This, however, has a criterion which distinguishes the use of the preposition here from that with symbols in the preceding types in the form of the noun which governs it, '*Reihenentwicklung*',

'Wir erhalten auf diese Weise für das Potential in der Nähe des Achsenpunktes z_0 eine Reihenentwicklung nach r und Δz.'

5. =of

Occurs once only with a proper noun,

'Im rationalisierten MKS-System nach GIORGI lautet der Ausdruck für die Lorentz-Kraft. . . .'

Here the feature which distinguishes the use with a proper noun from that in 1 and 2 above is the dependence of the preposition on a noun ('*System*') instead of a verb. '*System*' can, therefore, be regarded as the characterizing criterion.

6. =to

The preposition is characterized in this sense more by the governing than the governed nouns. The former are '*Richtung*', '*Radiusvektor*', and '*Übergang*', e.g.

'Wir können so auffassen, als ob der Beitrag dH senkrecht auf der Ebene von ds und dem Radiusvektor von ds nach P steht.'

A supporting criterion is the fact that '*nach*' in this sense is preceded in all three instances by '*von*'. These considerations serve to distinguish the use of the preposition with a symbol here from that in 1, 2, 3, and 4, though this is not really necessary since P always stands for '*Punkt*' in the text in question, and '*Punkt*' would hardly be found with '*nach*' in other senses. In fact the application of each symbol seems to be fairly fixed, with the result that symbols are just as capable of serving as characterizing criteria as are nouns and verbs.

7. =towards

Only in the sentence

'Wir berechnen zunächst das Feld zwischen zwei Rohrelektroden, welche für $z=0$ aneinanderstoßen und sich nach der anderen Seite bis $z=+\infty$ bzw. $z=-\infty$ erstrecken.'

It is difficult to distinguish this from 6. It obviously cannot be done by making '*Seite*' the characterizing criterion, because '*nach*' may equally well mean 'to' with this word. Perhaps the verb '*erstrecken*' is the answer, but the difference between this and 6 is in any case slight.

8. =with respect to

Here the preposition occurs in each of the eight instances with a symbol, but no confusion can arise with the other meanings where '*nach*' governs symbols by reason of the distinctive governing nouns and, in one case, verb, i.e. '*Differentiation*' (5), '*Ableitung*' (2), and '*ableiten*', e.g.

'Da für die Niveaulinie v(z, r) $=\Phi_0$ das Potential konstant ist, folgt durch Differentiation von v nach z . . .' (equation follows)
Only with the sentence in which the verb 'ableiten' is the characterizing criterion does any difficulty arise:

'Indem wir die Reihenentwicklung (84) zweimal nach z und r ableiten, erhalten wir. . . .'

It is caused by the occurrence before '*nach*' of the noun '*Reihenentwicklung*', which was denoted in 4 above as characteristic of the meaning 'in'. Fortunately the intervention here of '*zweimal*' prevents the machine interpreting the '*nach*' as dependent on the noun instead of the verb, but even if this solution were not available, one could be provided for by indicating alongside the characterizing criteria which was to be regarded as valid in the case of two giving contrary evidence. Here, for example, '*ableiten*' would take preference over '*Reihenentwicklung*'.

über—1. =across

Only with '*welches*' (referring to '*Gebiet*') in the sentence

'Dies ist allerdings nur zulässig, wenn zwischen L_1 und L_2 ein Gebiet praktisch konstanter Feldstärke vorhanden ist, über welches wir die beiden Lochblendenfelder aneinander anschließen können.'
Either '*Gebiet*' or '*anschließen*', or better still both combined will serve as a characterizing criterion.

2. =on

This meaning occurs with the nouns '*Genauigkeit*' and '*Strahlgleichung*'. Both are satisfactory criteria so far as the text investigated is concerned, but a more universal feature is the fact that they both occur in references, this being denoted by the abbreviation *vgl.*, e.g.

'Über die Genauigkeit der angegebenen Werte vgl. . . .'

3. =over

As with 2 this sense is characterized for the limits of the text investigated by the nouns governed, i.e. '*Linienelemente*', '*Werte*', '*Wertbereich*', and '*k*', but better by the governing nouns '*Summe*' (twice), and '*Integration*' + the verb '*erstrecken*' (twice), e.g.

'Die allgemeine Lösung von (103) ist eine Summe der speziellen Lösungen $N_k(z)$ $M_k(z)$ über die verschiedenen Werte k.'

um—1. =about

In the three instances in which it occurs with this sense '*um*' governs '*Achse*' (twice) and '*Symmetrieachse*', e.g.

'. . . Rotationsflächen, welche um die Symmetrieachse koaxial angeordnet sind.'

2. =by

In this sense it was found four times and always governing a figure, '*Betrag*' plus a figure, or a symbol, e.g.

'Weiterhin ist zu beachten, daß das Potential von diesem Wert um den Betrag $1/\pi(E_1-E_2)r_0$ abweicht.'

The governing verbs, '*übertreffen*' (twice), '*abweichen*', and '*zunehmen*' are also characteristic for this meaning.

3. =of

Only in this sense with the verb '*handeln sich*' (twice), which is a sure criterion, e.g.

'Allerdings handelt es sich bei den Kristallen um homogene Medien.'

unter (+dative)—1. =at

Characterized in this sense by the noun which it governs '*Winkel*' (twice), e.g.

'Dieser Punkt, in welchem sich zwei Kurven gleichen Potentials unter dem durch (97) gegebenen Winkel schneiden, ist ein Sattelpunkt.'

2. =below

Occurs once only governing a figure, but is better characterized by the verb '*sinken*':

'Die Feldstärke klingt hier langsam ab, und zwar so, daß sie Punkte auf der Achse, deren Entfernung von der Blendenmitte größer ist als der Blendendurchmesser, unter 1% ihres in der Mitte der Blendenöffnung vorhandenen Wertes gesunken ist.'

3. =by

'*Unter*' in this case has as its characterizing criterion in all the four instances in which it occurs the verb '*verstehen*',

'Unter elektrischen Feldern werden wir dementsprechend elektrostatische Felder zu verstehen haben.'

4. =on

Once only, with the noun '*Voraussetzung*, this being a safe criterion:

'Unter diesen Voraussetzungen läßt sich auch schreiben . . .'

5. =under

Again once only, this time with the noun '*Bedingung*', also a safe criterion,

'Bei elektronenoptischen Medien können solche Diskontinuitäten nicht oder nur unter besonderen Bedingungen realisiert werden.'

6. =with

Yet a third single occurrence, in this case governing '*Verwendung*', likewise acceptable as a certain criterion for the meaning required in the English:

'Wir wollen uns darauf beschränken, zu zeigen, wie aus (57) unter Verwendung von rechtwinkligen Koordinaten der Ausdruck für die Lorentz-Kraft (4) folgt.'

vom—1. =by the

The noun governed is '*Leiterelement*', but the characterizing criterion is the governing verb, '*erzeugen*'

'Wir können so auffassen, als ob der vom Leiterelement ds am Ort P erzeugte Beitrag dH zum Magnetfeld senkrecht auf der Ebene von ds und dem Radiusvektor von ds nach P steht.'

2. =from the

This sense of the preposition too has the governing verb rather than the noun governed as its criterion:

'In der Umgebung der Blendenöffnung ist das Feld nicht homogen, weil die Feldstärke stetig vom Werte E_1 auf den Wert E_2 übergehen muß'.

and the following '*auf*' provides subsidiary evidence.

3. =of the

This meaning can be recognized by the presence before the '*vom*' of a noun expressing difference and after it of the preposition '*gegenüber*' (q.v.).

'V_2 sei die Potentialdifferenz vom Punkt P_2 gegenüber der Kathode.'

This criterion occurs, however, in only one of the four instances where '*vom*' is to be translated by 'of the'. For the other three the characterizing mark is the noun governing, i.e. '*Umrechnung*', '*Richtung*', and '*Gebrauch*', e.g.

'Zur Umrechnung vom elektromagnetischen CGS-System in das MKS-System beachte man, daß für die verschiedenen Einheiten folgende Beziehungen gelten.'

4. =on

In this sense the preposition is characterized (*a*) by depending on the adjective '*abhängig*', (*b*) by governing the noun '*Ort*' which is not qualified:

'Da V eine nur vom Ort abhängige Größe ist, . . .'

5. =on the

The same applies to this as to 4, except that the noun '*Ort*' is qualified and depends either on '*abhängig*' or the verb '*abhängen*', e.g.

'. . . welches zeitlich konstant und somit nur vom Ort x, y, z abhängig ist.'

von—1. =by

With this meaning the preposition occurred in the text only five times. In all these it was distinguished from the basic meaning 'of' by the fact that it never followed a substantive, and from the other usual meaning of '*von*', 'from', by depending either on the passive form of the verbs '*einschließen*', '*durchlaufen*', '*angeben*' (twice), or the adjective with passive sense '*wählbar*', e.g.

'Wir fassen diese Kurven als Bahnen auf, welche von fiktiven Elektronen in der gleichen Gesamtzeit $t_1 - t_0$ durchlaufen werden.'

2. =by the

Once only in the sentence

'Der Übergang von V_1 auf V_2 erfolgt innerhalb der von beiden Ebenen F_1 und F_2 eingeschlossenen Gebietes.'

The criterion is the same as in 1 except that the attribute '*beide*' requires the addition of the definite article in the translation.

3. =from

In general there is no difficulty in distinguishing the preposition with this meaning from that with the basic meaning. Though for the most part the nouns governed are not to be trusted as characterizing criteria, since these include several symbols which are common to the other meaning, half these instances can be distinguished in the same way as 1, that is by not following a substantive, and the other half by being dependent on nouns like '*Entfernung*' (thrice), '*Abstand*', '*Übergang*,', *Potentialsprung*', '*Radiusvektor*', '*Zeit*' (the latter four all followed immediately after '*von*' and its noun by a phrase with '*auf*', '*nach*', or '*bis*'), a verb like '*springen*' (also followed by an '*auf*' phrase) or the adjective '*verschieden*'.

In three sentences, however, it is not so easy to find a satisfactory criterion. They are:

(i) 'Die Austrittsgeschwindigkeiten der Elektronen aus der Kathode sind keineswegs einheitlich, sondern durch eine kontinuierliche Geschwindigkeitsverteilungsfunktion gegeben, welche im Falle thermisch ausgelöster Elektronen die Maxwellsche Geschwindigkeitsverteilung ist, bei anderen Emissionsarten von der Maxwellschen Verteilung aber abweichen kann.'

(ii) 'Zählen wir das Potential V von der Kathode aus und bedeutet ε die Geschwindigkeit, mit welcher das Elektron die Kathode verläßt, so ist. . . .'

(iii) 'In der Umgebung der Blendenöffnung ist das Feld nicht homogen, weil beim Übergang durch die Öffnung von der einen Seite von E nach der anderen die Feldstärke stetig vom Werte E_1 auf den Wert E_2 übergehen muß.'

The problem with the first is that '*Art*' (in '*Emissionsarten*') is the type of word that could be regarded as a characterizing criterion of '*von*' in the sense of 'of', while the noun governed would not be marked as characteristic of any particular sense and so would not help. The solution, as has been suggested before, is to make one criterion (here the verb '*abweichen*') valid over another when there is a clash, but this means that we must be sure that when such clashes occur one criterion *always* prevails, not occasionally one, occasionally the other. If the latter is the case, we must find another solution or instruct the machine to print the two alternatives without making a decision. For the text in question '*abweichen*' is a satisfactory criterion, inasmuch as it does not occur in any clause where '*von*' bears the meaning 'of'.

The second sentence is more or less the same except that '*auszählen*' takes the place of '*abweichen*', and the same remarks apply. The third is awkward only in so far as the governing noun—and what should be the characterizing criterion, '*Übergang*'—is separated from the '*von*' by a dependent prepositional phrase, so that the word which apparently governs the preposition is '*Öffnung*', definitely to be regarded as characteristic of the meaning 'of'. Fortunately the noun governed, '*Seite*', is one that can be marked as characteristic of '*von*' = from (especially when followed by '*nach der anderen*') with preference in the same way as '*abweichen*' and '*auszählen*'. At the same time that '*Seite*' is marked as characteristic of the meaning 'from' when it is the noun governed it must be marked as characteristic of the meaning 'of' when it is the governing noun, as here for the second '*von*'.

4. = from the

Once only with the noun '*Anfang*', this forming a sure criterion:

'Bewegt sich das Elektron von Anfang an in der x, y-Ebene, so behält z dauernd seinen Anfangswert bei.'

5. = of

The basic meaning forming about 70% of all instances of '*von*'.

6. = on

All eight instances have as their characterizing criterion the fact that the preposition depends either on the adjective '*abhängig*', the verb '*abhängen*' or the noun '*Abhängigkeit*' (cf. '*vom*' 4).

vor—1. = above.

In this sense '*vor*' was characterized by occurring in all three instances with '*allem*', e.g.

'*Vor* allem interessieren wir uns für den Verlauf des Potentials auf der z-Achse.'

2. =from

The preposition governs the noun '*Bahn*', but is characterized rather by the verb, '*auszeichnen*' (*sich*):

'(41) sagt nun aus, daß die zwischen P_0 und P_1 tatsächlich durchlaufene Bahn sich vor allen anderen (fiktiven) Bahnen dadurch auszeichnet, daß . . .'

zu—1. =at

The preposition required this translation in only one sentence, where it governed the noun '*Zeit*' in the plural and was itself governed by the verb '*durchlaufen*':

'Allerdings wird die Wirkung dieser Felder auf Elektronen, welche sie zu verschiedenen Zeiten durchlaufen, verschieden sein.' (cf '*zur*'=at).

2. =to

The basic meaning and therefore requiring no characterizing criteria, though these can be found in the governing verb ('*ausbreiten*', '*addieren*'), noun ('*Normal*', '*Verhältnis*'), or adjective ('*parallel*', '*proportional*', '*senkrecht*').

zum—1. =for

Adequately characterized by the noun it governs, '*Beispiel*', in the one instance and in the other by the governing verb, '*benötigen*', rather than the noun governed—

'Das Prinzip von Fermat sagt aus, daß die Zeit, welche es zum Durchlaufen des Weges benötigt, minimal ist.'

It should be said, however, that '*zum*' with nouns formed from the infinitives of verbs would be better left untranslated after verbs like '*benötigen*', the noun itself rendered as the infinitive with 'to', and any dependent genitive treated as the object, i.e. '. . . which it requires to traverse the path . . .'

2. =to the

The basic meaning. If required it may be characterized by the adjective '*senkrecht*', which occurs in both the instances.

zur—1. =at

Characterized by the noun it governs, '*Verfügung*':

'Demgegenüber ist der Spielraum, der uns bei der Wahl des Brechungsindex zur Verfügung steht, ein ungleich größerer.'

In such cases the dative personal pronoun must be changed in English into the possessive with '*Verfügung*', i.e. 'stands at our disposal.'

2. =at the

Also characterized by the noun governed, '*Zeit*' (two instances), e.g.

'Sind zur Zeit $t=0$ die Geschwindigkeitskomponenten gleich V_{x0}, V_{y0}, V_{z0}, so ist . . .'

3. =for the

In the nine instances where the preposition has this meaning the noun governed is again the characterizing criterion. The nouns are '*Bestimmung*' (2), '*Beschreibung*' (2), '*Bewegung*' (in a reference—indicated by '*vgl*'), '*Darstellung*', '*Festlegung*', '*Lösung*', '*Umrechnung*', e.g.

'Die zahlreichen Methoden zur Bestimmung der beiden Größen e und m sollen hier nicht besprochen werden.'

4. =on

For the instance of the preposition in this sense the criterion occurs at first sight to be the governing noun, '*Abhandlung*', i.e. 'treatise on':

'Da in zahlreichen Abhandlungen zur Elektronenoptik von elektromagnetischen CGS-Einheiten Gebrauch gemacht wird, werden wir der Schreibweise (4) den Vorzug geben.'

but the noun governed, '*Elektronenoptik*', is the true criterion, because it cannot occur with any other meaning of '*zur*', whereas '*Abhandlung*' could equally well be constructed with '*zur*' in the sense of 'on the', if the noun governed were of the type taking the definite article in English.

5. =on the

Of the two examples of '*zur*' with this meaning one is in a reference (indicated by '*vgl.*'), the other in the title of a work—'*Zur Theorie der elektronenoptischen Linsenfehler*' given in italic type in the footnotes. The reference example could equally well be translated by 'for the' (cf. '*Bewegung*' in 3 above); in fact, if the abbreviation '*vgl.*' is present and '*zur*' stands at the head of the clause or phrase it may be safely rendered either by 'on the' or 'for the', unless the noun is plural in English (e.g. 'electronoptics' for '*Elektronenoptik*'), in which case the 'the' must be dropped.

6. =to the

The basic meaning, which can be characterized, if desired, by more or less the same words as for the basic meanings of '*zu*' and '*zum*', i.e. the adjectives '*senkrecht*' (eight times), '*parallel*' (six times), and '*spiegelbildlich*', the particle '*bis*' (immediately preceding the preposition), and the noun '*Beitrag*'. The nouns governed are: '*Achse*' (eight times with all three adjectives), '*Bewegungsrichtung*' (with '*senkrecht*'), '*Richtung*' (twice—with '*parallel*' and '*senkrecht*'), '*Ebene*' (twice—likewise with '*parallel*' and '*senkrecht*'), '*Feldstärke* (with '*senkrecht*'), '*Oberfläche*' (with '*senkrecht*'), '*Potenz*' ('*bis zur 12 Potenz*'), and '*Theorie*' ('*Beiträge zur Theorie der geometrischen Elektronenoptik*').

This method of resolving multimeaning could be used for the other parts of speech besides prepositions. Some idea of for how many words it would be needed in a given amount of text and how it would work with each may be gained from the following, taken from the text investigated:

aber—1.

The usual translation 'however' would also serve for those occurrences of the word where it was used as a co-ordinating conjunction connecting two clauses, if these clauses were made into separate sentences in English. If, on the other hand, it is desired to retain the single sentence structure, the '*aber*' must in such cases be translated by 'but' and placed at the head of the clause, if it does not already occupy this place, c.f.

'Hier ist k eine unbestimmte Konstante, welche unter Umständen beliebige Werte annehmen kann, manchmal aber auf bestimmte diskrete Werte beschränkt ist.'

2. Occasionally '*aber*' is best translated by 'and'. In the only instance in our text this was indicated by its connection with '*weiterhin*':

'Wir werden durch Betrachtung dieser Bahnen zeigen, daß eine Abbildung mit Elektronenstrahlen tatsächlich möglich ist, weiterhin aber die Hauptaufgabe in Angriff nehmen, die Größen, welche für die abbildende Wirkung der Felder charakteristisch sind, aus den Eigenschaften dieser Felder zu bestimmen.'

3. Also occurring once was a context where '*aber*' required no translation, inasmuch as it followed the co-ordinating conjunction '*oder*':

'In einem solchen Fall wird man entweder danach trachten,

$\Phi''(z)$ aus den Formeln zu eliminieren, oder aber den Potentialverlauf nicht nur auf der Achse selber, sondern auch in der Umgebung der Achse zu bestimmen.'

als—Besides the senses of 'as' and 'than' (for their distinction, cf. p. 210) this was found to require no translation in some cases (cf. under '*bezeichnen*' below).

also— =therefore

This is the normal translation which would serve for all occurrences, if where the word was used as a co-ordinating conjunction the two clauses connected by it were turned into separate sentences in English. If the original sentence is to be retained, this sense must be limited to those instances in the first clause of a sentence (in the text examined these were always main clauses), and those instances which attach another clause translated as follows:

2. =i.e.

This meaning is used when the clause attached by '*also*' is the last in the sentence, e.g.

'Die Bewegung des Elektrons im Felde ist bekannt, sobald wir wissen, wie sich diese drei Lagekoordinaten im Laufe der Zeit ändern, sobald wir also die drei Funktionen $q_1(t)$, $q_2(t)$, $q_3(t)$ angeben können.'

3. =and therefore

Used when the clause attached by '*also*' is not the last clause in the sentence*, e.g.

'Besteht der Wertbereich von *k* nicht aus einzelnen diskreten Werten, kann also k in einem gewissen Bereich sämtliche Werte annehmen, so ist statt einer Summe über *k* ein Integral zu schreiben.'

an—This is not used strictly as a preposition and is not translated in the phrase '*von Anfang an*'. The phrase itself serves as the feature distinguishing it from the prepositional use.

annehmen—1. =assume

This is the basic sense, e.g.

'm_0 ist die sogenannte Ruhemasse, der Wert, den die Masse bei kleinen Geschwindigkeiten annimmt.'

from which must be distinguished the next word.

* NOTE: If '*und*' precedes '*also*', it is not translated in the case of either 2 or 3.

2. =accept

This sense is characterized by the construction of '*annehmen*' with '*als*', e.g.

'Wir können nun die mittels der Methoden der geometrischen Lichtoptik erhaltenen Ergebnisse auch für die Elektronenstrahlen, allerdings in entsprechend abgeänderter Form, als gültig annehmen.'

3. =attain

A meaning required and characterized by the construction with '*Geschwindigkeit*' as the object of the verb, e.g.

'Die Geschwindigkeit „1 Elektronenvolt" ist somit die Geschwindigkeit, welche das ursprünglich ruhende Elektron nach dem Durchfallen der Potentialdifferenz von 1 V annimmt.'

auch—In one instance in our text '*auch*' needed to be omitted from the translation, i.e.

'*Diese Analogie* läßt uns vermuten, daß es möglich sein wird, auch mit Elektronenstrahlen die gleiche Art von Abbildung zu erzielen, wie sie auf dem lichtoptischen Gebiete seit langem bekannt ist.'

The expression '*gleich—wie*' may presumably be regarded as responsible for this.

auszeichnen—On this and similar verbs where the difference in meaning is directly related to whether they are reflexive or not see p. 240.

bedeuten—The two meanings of this word found in the text, i.e. 'mean' and 'denote', were distinguishable by the type of subject each had, that of the former always being a noun or pronoun, e.g.

'Wir sehen aus (63), daß die Größe des Brechungsindex n auch von der Bewegungs- oder Strahlrichtung *s* abhängt. Das bedeutet, daß unser elektronenoptisches Medium anisotrop ist.'

that of the latter, a symbol, e.g.

'Hier bedeutet A das Vektorpotential, durch welches wir das magnetische Feld H bestimmen können.'

beide—Whether '*beide*' is to be translated by 'both' or 'two' depends solely on whether it has the definite article with it or not. If it has, 'two' is the equivalent, if it has not, 'both' is used.

bekannt—The two meanings of '*bekannt*' in our text, 'known' and 'well-known' could be distinguished according to whether the word was predicative or with the indefinite article on the one hand, or with the definite article on the other. In the former case the translation would be 'known', e.g.

'Da auf jeder dieser Bahnen L(qk, $\dot{q}$k) eine bekannte Funktion der Zeit ist, läßt sich für jede dieser Bahnen und für jede Bewegungsart auf dieser Bahn das Integral $\int_{to}^{ti}$ L dt berechnen.'

and in the latter 'well known', e.g.

'Es besteht zwischen ihnen eine Beziehung, welche z.B. bei Verwendung rechtwinkliger Koordinaten gegeben ist durch die bekannte Gleichung $(dx/ds)^2 + (dy/ds)^2 + (dz/ds)^2 = 1$.'

beliebig—Usually means 'arbitrary', e.g.

'Wir wollen nun auf der Bahnkurve eines Elektrons zwei beliebige Punkte P_1 und P_2 herausgreifen.'

but with '*jeder*' is best translated in combination with this as 'any', e.g.

'Während uns die Natur lichtoptische Medien liefert, deren Brechungsindizes im Verhältnis von etwa 1 zu 2, 5 zueinander stehen, können wir in der Elektronenoptik durch geeignete Wahl der Potentiale fast jedes beliebige Verhältnis erreichen.'

Berücksichtigung—Though normally translated by 'consideration', when preceded by '*unter*' it seems to be best rendered with this simply by 'with', e.g. in

'Wir haben schon weiter oben darauf hingewiesen, daß dieses Problem in der Lösung der Laplaceschen Gleichung unter Berücksichtigung der Randbedingungen besteht.'

bestehen—Had two meanings in the text investigated, 'consist' and 'exist', the former of which was always constructed with either '*aus*' or '*in*', the latter with either '*zwischen*' or '*in*'. The problem of distinguishing the two meanings arises, therefore, only with the latter construction in each case. This appears to be solvable only by specifying in the dictionary those nouns liable to be used as the subject of the verb in each of its meanings. Theoretically there is nothing to stop the same noun being used with the verb in both its senses, but this would hardly be likely in practice—at least judging from the text in question, where '*bestehen*' in the sense of 'exist' had a fairly stereotyped application. The subjects of the verb in the two cases where '*bestehen*' was constructed with '*in*' in the sense of 'exist' were '*Potentialverteilung*' and '*Kurve*', whilst with the same construction in the sense of 'consist' they were '*Verfahren*', '*Unterschied*', '*Einschränkung*', and '*Problem*'. Since the '*in*' construction is much more common when the verb means 'consist', it would be economical to specify only the nouns used as the subject of the verb in the sense 'exist'. Then if in any particular instance the machine did not find one of these as the subject, the verb would be translated as 'consist'.

It was also noted that the subject of the verb in the sense 'exist' had in both cases the indefinite article, whereas that in the four instances with the sense 'consist' had the definite article, but whether this could be relied upon as a distinguishing criterion is doubtful.

Sometimes '*bestehen*' would appear to be best left untranslated, e.g. in

'Die im Übergangsgebiet zwischen F_1 und F_2 bestehende Feldstärke $= -V_2 - V_1/d$ steht senkrecht auf F_1 und F_2.'

The characterizing feature for this is its function as a participle in a participial construction. The same was found to apply to the verbs '*herrschen*', '*stammen*', '*stehen*', and '*verlaufen*', when they were used in this way, e.g.

(i) 'H erhalten wir durch vektorielle Addition der von den verschiedenen Leiterelementen stammenden Anteile dH.'

(ii) 'Wir gehen dabei von der Komponentendarstellung der in (52) stehenden Größen aus.'

Betrag—meant 'magnitude' in all its occurrences except one, where the translation 'quantity' was required—

'Weiterhin ist zu beachten, daß in der Mitte der Blende das Potential keineswegs gleich dem Blendenpotential V_0 ist, sondern von diesem Wert um den Betrag $1/\pi(E_1 - E_2)r_0$ abweicht.'

For this meaning the verb '*abweichen*' and also the preposition '*um*' may be taken as characteristic criteria. As an example of the normal meaning may be quoted

'Der Betrag der (konstanten) Geschwindigkeit sei V_0.'

bezeichnen—Was translated either as 'call' or 'denote'. In the latter sense the verb was always constructed with '*mit*', e.g.

'Mit K bezeichnen wir die äußere Kraft und mit v den Geschwindigkeitsvektor.'

in the former with '*als*', this itself requiring no translation, though the definite article must be inserted in its place in English, e.g.

'An die Stelle des Brechungsindex n tritt im elektrischen Felde die Größe $\sqrt{v^*}$, welche wir dementsprechend als elektronenoptischen Brechungsindex des elektrischen Feldes V(x, y, z) bezeichnen wollen.'

bis—Translated by 'up' and distinguished from its prepositional use by occurring before a preposition like '*zu*' or '*auf*', e.g.

'—bis auf einen konstanten Faktor, dessen Größe für uns unwesentlich ist.'

dadurch— = by the fact

This meaning is required when a '*daß*' clause follows with a different subject from the governing clause, e.g.

'(41) sagt nun aus, daß die zwischen P_0 und P_1 tatsächlich durchlaufende Bahn sich vor allen anderen (fiktiven) Bahnen dadurch auszeichnet, daß für sie das Integral $\int_{t_0}^{t_1} L\,dt$ stationär ist.'

2. = by

The translation when the following '*daß*' clause has the same subject as the governing clause, e.g.

'Auf beiden Seiten der Ebene erzeugen wir die Felder E_1 bzw. E_2, und zwar dadurch, daß wir in größerer Entfernung D von E zwei parallele Ebenen auf die Potentiale $V_1 = E_1D$ und $V_2 = -E_2D$ gegenüber E aufladen.'

3. = no translation

'*dadurch*' is redundant when it refers backwards instead of forwards, i.e. when it is not followed by a clause introduced by '*daß*', e.g.

'Wir können auch jede beliebige Niveaufläche durch einen metallischen Leiter ersetzen, ohne daß das Feld sich dadurch ändert, wenn wir nur dabei diesen Leiter auf das der betreffenden Niveaufläche zukommende Potential bringen.'

dafür—The basic meaning is 'for this', but one instance in our text depended on the verb '*interessieren*' and therefore had to be translated by 'in':

'Falls wir uns nicht dafür interessieren, wie die Bahn zeitlich durchlaufen wird, sondern nur die Bahn selber zu kennen wünschen, so müssen wir die Zeit eliminieren.'

cp. 'Weiterhin können wir als unabhängige Variable statt s auch eines der qk selber wählen. In rotationssymmetrischen Feldern wird es vorteilhaft sein, dafür die z-Koordinate zu nehmen.'

In both uses, however, '*dafür*' can be left untranslated without any detriment to the sense.

damit—May be translated as 'hence' or 'in order that' according to whether it is functioning as an adverb or as a subordinating conjunction. The two meanings can, therefore, be distinguished by the type of clause in which they occur—the former in main, the latter in subordinate, e.g.

(i) 'Damit erhalten wir für R im Scheitel der Niveaulinie Φ (z_0)' (equation follows).

(ii) 'Damit $\delta\int nds = 0$ wird, müssen für die Elektronenbahn die Eulerschen Differentialgleichungen dieses Variationsproblems erfüllt sein.'

dann—Was found either to mean 'then' or to require no translation. The former was the usual sense, e.g.

'Gewöhnlich läßt sich aber ε gegenüber V vernachlässigen; dann hat $n(x, y, z) = \sqrt{V(x, y, z)}$ für alle Elektronen den gleichen Wert.'

whilst the latter applied only to those instances occurring before a clause introduced by '*wenn*', this being the author's method of distinguishing plainly between the 'if' and 'when' senses of the latter, e.g.

'Von einem rotationssymmetrischen Feld sprechen wir dann, wenn das Potential V unabhängig von der Winkelkoordinate Φ ist.'

darauf—1. =to the fact

The translation required when it refers to a following '*daß*' clause, e.g.

'Wir haben schon früher darauf hingewiesen, daß die Laplacesche Gleichung für die elektronenoptischen Felder gegenüber den lichtoptischen Medien eine Einschränkung bedeutet.'

2. =to this

With this meaning the word refers back to something already mentioned. It is characterized by the type of verb governing it together with the absence of a '*daß*' clause, e.g.

'Wir werden darauf in Kap. X zurückkommen.'

3. Requires no translation when the following clause is infinitival, e.g.

'Wir wollen uns darauf beschränken, zu zeigen, wie aus (57) unter Verwendung von rechtwinkligen Koordinaten der Ausdruck für die Lorentz-Kraft (4) folgt.'

dazu—In all except one instance this was translatable by 'for this', e.g.

'. . . erhalten wir eine ebenfalls mit wachsenden Potenz von r fortschreitende Reihe, deren Summe jedoch für alle Werte von r verschwinden muß. Dazu ist nötig, daß die Koeffizienten der verschiedenen Potenzen von r einzeln verschwinden.'

In the exception mentioned '*dazu*' pointed forward to an infinitive clause and required no translation:

'Dies führt uns dazu, für das Potential V (z, r) eine Reihenentwicklung zu suchen, welche nach wachsenden Potenzen von r geordnet ist.'

denn—Used as a 'continuative' adverb, i.e. attaching a sentence to the preceding one, it could be given its usual translation of 'for', e.g.

'In rasch veränderlichen Feldern gilt der Energiesatz (13) nicht. Denn in solchen Feldern ist $\partial V/\partial t$ nicht Null und $\mathrm{d}V/\mathrm{d}t$ nicht mehr durch (11a) gegeben.'

but used as a co-ordinating conjunction it required some such translation as 'inasmuch as', if the original single sentence was to be retained in English, e.g.

'Wir interessieren uns vor allem für den Verlauf des Potentials in der Nähe der Symmetrieachse, denn die Bewegung der Elektronen durch das System erfolgt in den für die Praxis interessanten Fällen vorwiegend in Richtung der Symmetrieachse.'

einzeln—Is translated as 'individual' or 'various' according to whether it is singular or plural.

erreichen—Of the two instances of this verb in the text investigated one had the sense 'attain', the other the sense of 'obtain':

(i) 'Im Falle b erreicht das Potential auf der Achse in einem Punkte S einen Extremwert.'

(ii) 'Während uns die Natur lichtoptische Medien liefert, deren Brechungsindizes im Verhältnis von etwa 1 zu 2, 5 zueinander stehen, können wir in der Elektronenoptik durch geeignete Wahl der Potentiale fast jedes beliebige Verhältnis erreichen.'

A distinction between the two senses can only be made by reference to the accompanying substantives, in this case either the subjects or the direct objects—or both. A potential is hardly likely to 'obtain' anything or an extreme value to 'be obtained': similarly in the second sentence, though '*wir*' can be used with '*erreichen*' in the sense of 'attain', '*Verhältnis*' is not the sort of thing to 'be attained'. Wherever there is any doubt, a combined reference to the subject and object (provided, of course, the verb is active) can be made.

geben—Meant either 'give' or 'be', the latter being distinguished by having '*es*' as its grammatical subject.

Gebiet—The basic sense of the word in electron optics is 'region', but in a reference to the subject of optics it required translating by 'field':

'Diese Analogie läßt uns vermuten, daß es möglich sein wird, auch mit Elektronenstrahlen die gleiche Art von Abbildung zu erzielen, wie sie auf dem lichtoptischen Gebiete seit langem bekannt ist.'

The adjective '*lichtoptisch*' would serve as a distinguishing criterion, and might itself be better translated here by 'of optics' instead of 'optical', in which case '*Gebiet*' would serve as its criterion in this sense.

genügen—Was found to mean either 'satisfy' or 'be sufficient', the former being characterized by the construction of the verb with the dative case of a substantive, e.g.

'Für ein elektrisch-magnetisches Feld läßt sich jedoch statt der Funktion L eine andere Größe $\bar{L}$ angeben, welche ebenfalls den Gleichungen (40) genügen muß.'

the latter by its construction with an infinitive clause, e.g.

'Die Kenntnis der Funktion Ψ (ζ) genügt nach dem Obensagten, um Φ (z) für den allgemeinen Fall anzugeben.'

gerad—Also had two meanings, 'right' and 'even'. These could be distinguished by the type of noun to which the adjective was applied in each case, the former being with 'cylinder', the latter with 'powers'—

(i) 'Die Bahn ist somit eine Schraubenlinie auf einem geraden Kreiszylinder parallel zur z-Achse.'

(ii) 'Aus (77) ist sofort ersichtlich, daß diese Potenzreihe nur Glieder mit geraden Potenzen von r enthalten kann.'

gesamt—The two meanings of this word were likewise to be distinguished through the noun qualified. With 'velocity' it was translated as 'total', with 'field' as 'entire':

(i) 'Unter v_0 ist nicht mehr die gesamte Geschwindigkeit des Elektrons zu verstehen, sondern nur ihre zur z-Achse senkrecht stehende Komponente.'

(ii) 'Da das gesamte Feld durch den Potentialverlauf Φ (z) auf der Achse bestimmt ist, kann man . . .'

gleich—1. =same

This sense of the word is characterized by the presence in every case of the definite article, e.g.

'Wir fassen diese Kurven als Bahnen auf, welche von fiktiven Elektronen in der gleichen Gesamtzeit $t_1 - t_0$ durchlaufen werden.'

2. =equal

This sense is distinguished from the first by the absence of any article, e.g.

'Zur Darstellung dieser Potentialverteilung zeichnen wir die Kurven gleichen Potentials (die Niveau- oder Äquipotentiallinien), indem wir jeweils einen bestimmten Potentialwert ins Auge fassen und alle Punkte, in denen dieses Potential herrscht, durch eine Kurve verbinden.'

3. =equal to

This sense too never has an article, is always predicative (and therefore uninflected) and distinguishable from a predicative-form of 2 by the fact that it is always followed either by a dative noun or a symbol, equation, etc., e.g.

'Die Geschwindigkeit des Elektrons an einem bestimmten Punkte seiner Bahn ist gleich der Differenz des Potentials in diesem Punkt gegenüber dem Potential der Kathode. 1 eV ist gleich $5{,}390.10^7$ cm sek^{-1}.'

groß—Was translated as 'high' when it qualified '*Geschwindigkeit*', and as 'large' when it qualified '*Masse*', '*Abstand*', and symbols, e.g.

'Da das Potential für große z endlich bleiben muß, darf die Lösung die Neumannsche Funktion No (welche für $r=0$ unendlich wird) nicht enthalten.'

größer—This was translated by 'greater', which serves equally well as a comparative for both 'high' and 'large', except in two instances where it was not intended to express comparison. These were both characterized by the noun qualified, '*Entfernung*' (cf. the sentence quoted under '*dadurch*' = 'by').

Grund—Had the two meanings of 'basis' and 'reason', the former characterized by the preposition '*auf*', the latter by the preposition '*aus*': e.g.

(i) 'Anders ist es, wenn der Verlauf von Φ (z) auf Grund von Messungen an Modellen ermittelt wird.'

(ii) 'Aus diesem Grunde müssen die Bewegungsgleichungen, von denen wir ausgehen wollen, in einer Form vorliegen, welche die unmittelbare Verwendung dieser „verallgemeinerten Koordinaten" erlaubt'.

hingegen—The basic translation was 'on the other hand', but this applied only when the word was functioning as a continuative adverb, e.g.

'Eine Abhängigkeit des Brechungsindex von der Strahlrichtung treffen wir in der Lichtoptik bei Kristallen an; unser allgemeines elektronenoptisches Medium hingegen zeigt eine Abhängigkeit des Brechungsindex von Ort *und* Strahlrichtung.'

Used as a co-ordinating conjunction it was translated by 'but';

'In einem rein elektrischen Feld ist dies der Fall, nicht hingegen in einem magnetischen Feld.'

je—Occurred three times. In one, where it was with a comparative answering '*um so*' with a comparative, it was translated by 'the':

'Der Radius des Kreises R ist also um so kleiner, je stärker das magnetische Feld H ist.'

In the other two it could be left untranslated, e.g.

'Dies verlangt aber, daß der Abstand D der beiden Lochblenden mehr oder weniger groß ist, je nach den Genauigkeitsansprüchen, welche wir für die Ermittlung des Feldes stellen.'

jedoch—Proved to be similar to '*hingegen*'. The two meanings were 'however' and 'but' and these were differentiated in exactly the same way as with the earlier word.

klein—Was translated as 'low' when it qualified '*Geschwindigkeit*' or '*Potential*', as 'small' when it qualified '*Abstand*', '*Wert*' or a symbol.

lassen—1. =can be

The most frequent meaning: distinguished from the others by the verb being reflexive, e.g.

'(22) läßt sich nun nach wachsenden Potenzen von β entwickeln.'

the infinitive with which it is constructed is to be translated in English as a past participle.

2. =let

The usual translation of the non-reflexive verb, e.g.

'Die Nullpunkte der beiden Koordinatensysteme lassen wir zusammenfallen.'

3. =allow

The translation preferred with an inanimate subject and an animate object (cf. the sentence quoted under '*Gebiet*' =field).

miteinander—Normal translation 'with one another', e.g.

'Vergleichen wir nur Bahnen miteinander, für welche die Gesamtenergie $W = T + U$ den gleichen Wert hat, so folgt . . .'

but it can be omitted without any detriment, and should be in some cases, e.g.

'Der Winkel, den die Richtungen der beiden Felder miteinander einschließen, soll beliebig sein.'

Whether it may be retained or not depends upon the verb, and it is these that must be used as the distinguishing criteria.

ob—Was translated by 'whether', e.g.

'Verwechslungen sind nicht zu befürchten, weil es jeweils aus dem Zusammenhang ersichtlich ist, ob unter Elektronenvolt Geschwindigkeit oder Energie verstanden wird.'

except when preceded by '*als*', in which case it was translated by 'if':

'Wir können (56) so auffassen, als ob der vom Leiterelement ds am Ort P erzeugte Beitrag dH zum Magnetfeld senkrecht auf der Ebene von ds und dem Radiusvektor von ds nach P steht.'

Ort—Had two meanings, 'position' and 'locus'. The former was the more frequent, occurring eight times to the latter's once in

'Diese Kurve ist eine Halbellipse, der Ort aller Punkte mit dem Potential V_0 demnach ein halbes Rotationsellipsoid.'

In this sense the word can be distinguished by its predicative, '*Rotationsellipsoid*', which would not be applied to '*Ort*' meaning 'position'.

Rotation—Likewise had two meanings, 'rotation', as in

'Das räumliche Potentialfeld erhalten wir durch Rotation der D Potentialverteilung in einer Meridianebene der stehenden Figur um D z-Achse.'

and 'curl' as in

'Das räumliche Potentialfeld H läßt sich bekanntlich als Rotation eines Vektors a(Ax, Ay, Az) darstellen, welcher als „Vektor-potential" von H bezeichnet wird.'

A distinction between the two meanings can be made mechanically only by reference to the accompanying words or the construction. With the former meaning the construction with '*um*' is one criterion, the dependent genitive '*Figur*' another; with the latter the dependent genitive '*Vektors*' is a sure criterion. Similarly in the other instance where 'rotation' meant 'curl',

'Aus (53) und (55) folgt durch Bildung der Rotation das Gesetz von BIOT und SAVART.'

the governing noun '*Bildung*' provides a certain criterion.

schon—Occurred in four instances, in two of which it was translated by 'already' and in two left untranslated. In actual fact it could have been either translated or omitted in all four cases, the latter being preferable. In the two instances where it was translated it was pleonastic, since '*früher*' or '*weiter oben*' accompanied it (cf. the sentence quoted under '*Berücksichtigung*' = with), whereas in the other two it stood alone, e.g.

'Aus der Reihenentwicklung (85) folgt, daß das Potential V(z, r) im ganzen Raume durch die Festlegung des Potentialverlaufes auf der Symmetrieachse allein schon vollständig bestimmt ist.'

so—1. = in such a way

Recognizable in this sense by the fact that it always precedes a '*daß*' clause, e.g.

'Hier geht man bei der Lösung der Laplaceschen Gleichung so vor, daß man die Lösung als Produkt aus zwei Funktionen M und N anschreibt, deren eine nur von r und deren andere nur von z abhängen soll.'

2. = thus

'*so*' in this sense can be recognized by the absence of a following '*daß*' clause, and also in the majority of cases by the fact that it introduces the sentence, e.g.

'So hat z.B. PLASS nach (85) die Potentialverteilung im Raume berechnet für die beiden Potentialverteilungen auf der z-Achse . . .' (equations follow).

3. =the

The translation required when preceded by '*um*' and followed by a comparative (cf. '*je*'='the').

4. '*so*' required no translation when referring forward to a clause introduced by '*wie wenn*'.

'In Kap. III bis IX werden wir deshalb den Einfluß der Raumladung vernachlässigen und zunächst so rechnen, wie wenn bei der Bewegung eines Elektrons nur dieses eine Elektron sich zwischen den Elektroden befindet.'

sollen—In the majority of cases 'sollen' *could* be translated by 'is to' or 'are to', which according to the tone in which they are expressed may indicate, like '*sollen*', either obligation or mere futurity, e.g.

'Dabei bedeutet ds das Linienelement des Leiters und r den Abstand zwischen dem Linienelement ds und dem Aufpunkt P, in welchem A bestimmt werden soll.'

(cf. also the sentences quoted under '*so*'='in such a way' and '*miteinander*'=no translation).

In three instances, however, it was necessary to translate '*sollen*' by 'need', i.e.

'Die Lagrangeschen Gleichungen sollen hier nicht abgeleitet werden.'

'Der Beweis für (52) und (57) soll hier nicht gegeben werden.'

'Die zahlreichen Methoden zur Bestimmung der beiden Größen e und m sollen hier nicht besprochen werden.'

The characterizing criterion for this latter meaning is clearly the words '*hier nicht*' followed by a passive verb.

somit—1. =therefore

The normal translation, applied to the word when used as a continuative adverb (cf. the sentence quoted under '*gerad*'=right).

2. =i.e.

This is used, as with '*also*' (q.v.), to enable the German sentence to be retained in one piece in English, since 'therefore' is not a co-ordinating conjunction in the latter as it is in the former language, e.g.

'Denn längs ihrer Oberfläche ist das Potential konstant, ihre Oberfläche muß somit ebenfalls eine Niveaufläche sein.'

3. '*somit*' required no translation in one sentence, where it acted as a continuative adverb between the main clause and a preceding subordinate clause instead of between two sentences:

'Da die potentielle Energie E pot = −eV ist, erhalten wir somit den Energiesatz in der Form E kin + E pot = const.'

stehen—The usual translation was 'stand', but though this could have been used with '*senkrecht*' as well, if the latter had been translated 'perpendicularly' instead of 'perpendicular', it was decided that better English was produced in the instances with this word, if '*stehen*' was given the meaning here of 'be', e.g.

'E steht stets senkrecht zu den Niveauflächen und speziell senkrecht zur Oberfläche der Elektroden.'

Stelle—Meant either 'place' or 'point', in both cases constructed with the preposition 'an' but distinguished by the absence of a predeterminer and dependence of either a genitive or '*von*' with the dative when equivalent to 'place', e.g.

(i) 'Des weitern ist in allen Formeln, welche sich aus (4) ergeben, B an Stelle von H zu schreiben.'
(ii) 'Wir wollen nun an dieser Stelle ausdrücklich festlegen, daß. . . .'

unbedingt—Occurred twice, once in the sense of 'necessarily' and once in the sense of 'absolutely':

(i) 'Zur Festlegung des Ortes eines Elektrons haben wir drei Größen anzugeben, welche wir mit q_1, q_2 und q_3 bezeichnen wollen und welche nicht unbedingt die drei Koordinaten in einem rechtwinkligen Koordinatensystem sein müssen'.
(ii) 'Da heute elektronenoptische Anordnungen (Elektronenmikroskope) mit Spannungen bis zu 400 kV betrieben werden, ist in vielen Fällen die Mitberücksichtigung der relativistischen Massenveränderlichkeit unbedingt erforderlich.'

As distinguishing criteria may be taken in the first case the verb 'müssen', in the second the adjective qualified by '*unbedingt*', which we translated by 'necessary'; it would be verbose to say 'necessarily necessary.'

und zwar—When preceding '*so*' in the sense of 'in such a way' this expression was best omitted from the translation, e.g.

'Die Feldstärke klingt hier langsam ab, und zwar so, daß sie für Punkte auf der Achse, deren Entfernung von der Blendenmitte größer ist als der Blendendurchmesser, unter 1% ihres in der Mitte der Blendenöffnung vorhandenen Wertes gesunken ist.'

Otherwise it was translated by 'namely', but even in these cases it could have been omitted without loss to the English (cf. the sentence quoted under '*dadurch*' = by).

vektoriell—The two translations 'vector' and 'by vectors' belong to the adjectival and adverbial form respectively.

Verlauf—Had two meanings in our text, 'course' and 'distribution' (or 'form'), the latter being the more frequent. With the meaning of 'course' '*Verlauf*' governed the nouns '*Lichtstrahl*' and '*Elektronenbahn*', e.g.

'Dieses Prinzip bezieht sich auf den Verlauf von Lichtstrahlen in optischen Medien.'

whereas with the meaning 'distribution' it either governed the nouns '*Potential*', '*Niveaulinie*', '*Brechungsindex*' and the symbol for '*Potentialverlauf*', Φ (z), or was governed by them, e.g.

'Die Reihenentwicklung (93) gibt uns auch die Antwort auf die Frage, welche Form die Elektroden haben müssen und welche Spannungen ihnen zu erteilen sind, damit längs der Achse das Potential einen vorgegebenen (stetigen) Verlauf Φ (z) annimmt.' (cf. also under '*Grund*' = basis.)

voneinander—Needed to be translated by 'from each other' when dependent on a word expressing separation, i.e. in this case '*Abstand*' and '*sich unterscheiden*', e.g.

'Der Abstand der Ebenen F_1 und F_2 voneinander sei d.'

by 'of each other' when dependent on '*unabhängig*', e.g.

'Dabei müssen wir allerdings berücksichtigen, daß die q'k nicht unäbhangig voneinander sind.'*

* NOTE: '*daß*' after the verb '*berücksichtigen*' is to be translated as 'the fact that' instead of simply 'that'.

vorliegen—Was translated as equivalent to the verb 'to be' when its subject had a predicate (cf. the sentence quoted under '*Grund*' = reason), as 'there' + 'be' when the subject had no predicate:

'Die Bewegung des Elektrons ist bestimmt, sobald uns diese drei Funktionen vorliegen.'

With this translation the 'dative of advantage', to use but one nomenclature, '*uns*' must be omitted in the English. In such cases, however, it would perhaps be better to change the impersonal into the personal construction and translate '*vorliegen*' by 'have'.

während = while—Is distinguished from the identical prepositional form by standing at the head of the clause (which does not of course distinguish it from *all* instances of the preposition) and by not governing a substantive in the genitive case.

wenn—Had the two meanings 'if' and 'when', the latter being clearly marked by having the word '*dann*' as a signpost in the preceding clause either at the end or, if this position was occupied by the verb or predicative adjective or both, immediately before these (cf. under '*dann*').

wie—Occurred with three meanings, 'how', 'as', and 'such as'. On how these may be distinguished cf. p. 208.

wollen—Though all the instances of '*wollen*' could have been translated by 'shall' without loss of meaning in the English, it was felt that in certain contexts the more affable 'let us' (all instances being with '*wir*') was a better translation. However, inasmuch, as there was no difference in construction in the German, finding a criterion or criteria to enable the machine to decide which translation was called for in any particular instance proved difficult—except for three occurrences of the word in subordinate clauses, where the translation 'shall' is obligatory. Out of the eight instances with the sense 'let us', '*nun*' was present in five (i.e. '*Wir wollen nun . . .*'), but this still left three others unaccounted for. In the end it seemed that reference to the verb governed by '*wollen*' provided the best criterion, since there are certain actions in which the author can invite the reader to share, for example, in 'investigating', in 'comparing' something, and others in which he cannot, for example, in 'showing' or 'giving', because in the latter case it is he that is showing or giving something to the reader, not in co-operation with the reader. Perhaps the distinction would not work out as logically as this, but it does seem likely that the English scientific writer uses 'let us' and 'we shall' in describing different actions and therefore with different verbs. Excluding the three instances in subordinate clauses, the verbs governed by '*wollen*' were as follows:

+shall: 'zeigen' (2), 'angeben' (2)
+let: 'untersuchen', 'bestimmen', 'vergleichen', 'schreiben', 'herausgreifen', 'zurückgehen', 'beschränken' (sich), and 'festlegen'.

the sense of 'wollen'='let' with the latter being not one of invitation to the reader but merely polite statement:

'Wir wollen nun an dieser Stelle ausdrücklich festlegen, daß . . .'

As illustrations of the two main senses may be quoted:

(i) 'Wir wollen hier den Gang der Berechnung nicht angeben, sondern verweisen auf die Veröffentlichungen von. . . .'
(ii) 'Statt V_1 und V_2 wollen wir im folgenden V und v schreiben.'

or with '*nun*':

'Wir wollen nun das Prinzip der kleinsten Wirkung mit dem aus der Lichtoptik bekannten Prinzip von FERMAT vergleichen.'

zu—Distinguished from the prepositional senses by occurring alone between two equations:

'Die Zeit, welche das Elektron für einen Umlauf benötigt, folgt aus der Bedingung

$$ST = 2\pi = T\frac{eH}{m}$$

zu

$$T = \frac{2m\pi}{eH}$$

The word is still a preposition, of course, and might have been translated by 'to', but it was thought that 'thus' would be more usual in such a position in the jargon of science.

Zusammenhang—Six of the seven occurrences of this word had the meaning 'connection' and all six were constructed with '*zwischen*', e.g.

'Der Zusammenhang zwischen v und m ist in Tabelle 1 angegeben.'

whilst the seventh, having the meaning 'context', was not constructed with '*zwischen*' or anything else (cf. the sentence quoted under '*ob*'=whether).

For the text investigated it can be seen, then, that it is possible to reduce multimeaning to such an extent as to make it almost non-existent, but this after all was to be expected when only actual occurrences and not all the possibilities as well were considered. In constructing a scheme for dealing with multimeaning in a translation programme proper, one of two procedures may be followed; it may either be based on all the existing literature in the field concerned on the assumption that this provides ample scope for the use of the words in all the senses in which they are likely to be used in this field—how far this was true would become evident only in translating subsequent literature—or it may be designed to deal with all the senses in which the words forming the vocabulary of this field or subject could possibly be used. The latter would be thankfully left by the authors to others with a higher degree of acquaintance with the German language.

10

RUSSIAN

THIS chapter will contain a short account of work at the 'Academy of Sciences of the U.S.S.R.' in Moscow on the mechanical translation of English into Russian. It is deliberately condensed because full details of the experiment carried out with the computer B.E.S.M. have been published in English[1].

The Russian programme uses a mechanical dictionary which selects the coded Russian equivalents of the input English words. This is accompanied by routines for constructing the inflections of the Russian words and for rearranging word-order to give correct Russian sentences.

The input text is presented to the computer on standard teletype tape and fed into the machine one sentence at a time. The dictionary mechanism is then brought into operation.

The dictionary itself is divided into sections, according to the number of storage locations occupied by the English words. The first part of the dictionary consists of English words which occupy one location only, the second part of English words occupying two locations, and so on. Within each section the words are arranged in numerical order of the coded English words. Comparison of English words with the dictionary therefore consists of a routine to determine the number of letters in the word, followed by a search of the relevant section of the dictionary by means of a bracketing procedure. The entry whose magnitude is identical with that of the input word is then the equivalent, and the search mechanism is thus conducted by means of tests for identity. Many English words are formed by means of endings, the most frequent of which are 'ed', 'er', 'est', 'ing', 's', ''s', etc. These affixes are few in number. The splitting into stem and ending is therefore performed by means of a subroutine which operates if the first comparison with the dictionary fails to give an exact entry. This routine tests for the above endings and, if they occur, subtracts them from the word and compares again with the dictionary. Some of the endings are accompanied by special code numbers to enable grammatical information from the ending to be used in conjunction with that found on locating the word in the dictionary.

Provided that the English word does not have an alternative meaning, the information extracted from the dictionary when an English word has been exactly located contains the address of the Russian equivalent, and also grammatical and other information to enable the correct inflexional ending to be given to the target language word. To decline a Russian noun, much information must be given: gender, declension, soft or hard stem, presence or absence of sibilants in the Russian stem, etc. Similarly information must be found for the determination of the inflected endings of verbs, adjectives, pronouns, and so on. An example is provided by the word 'problems'. The dictionary contains only the word 'problem' and so the input word is not detected on first comparison. The routine examining endings detects an 's', removes it, and thus a second comparison locates the word in the dictionary. The numbers 121000020001001000529, 3620 are extracted. 3620 defines the Russian equivalent 'задача'. The first number contains grammatical information which has been modified by the detection of the ending 's'. The significance of the digits of the first number are shown below:

1	noun
2	2nd declension
1	Russian stem (задач—) ends in sibilant or г, к, х
0	word has no flexion
0	plural
0	is not a predicate
0	case not determined (this is determined by a later routine)
2	feminine
0	word denotes animate object
0	word is not a proper noun
0	number indication of word not developed
1	English word has -s ending (this was determined by the routine for examining ending)
0	is not a verbal noun
0	is not a subject
1	word has soft stem (задач— is a soft stem)
0	person of word not determined
0	absence of 'omit' signal
0529	location of English word

These code numbers are then substituted for the English words. At this stage the occurrence of '0000' as the address of the Russian equivalent indicates that the exact equivalent of the English word has not yet been located. Sections of the programme following this initial extraction of code numbers examine the English sentence for the presence of words which determine the meaning. This is performed by means of a dictionary routine called the 'polysemantic dictionary'. Words which on initial comparison with the first dictionary yield code numbers indicating multiple meaning are afterwards referred to the polysemantic dictionary. Idioms can therefore be treated by including the key words of the idiom in the first dictionary marked as having multiple meaning.

Following this extraction of code numbers of Russian equivalents from the dictionary, the code numbers are processed by means of routines for grammatical analysis. These routines determine the presence or absence of certain characteristics in the word being scanned by means of a sequence of checking operations. Each test consists of a binary decision leading either to the next test of the sequence or to a final conclusion and to the substitution of grammatical digits in the code number of the word being examined. Each of the major types of word requires its own routine to scan the sentence. These routines are interconnected and cannot be operated one at a time. Thus the routine associated with verbs has to be performed before the routine dividing the sentence into clauses and before the routines for some other parts of speech, since these require some information derived from verbs for their operation. Having fully processed the prepositions, nouns and adjectives with the information derived from the partly processed verbs, the verbs are then reprocessed to render all the verb information fully explicit.

The mode of operation of these routines is illustrated by the following example: The Russian equivalent of the English word 'of' is found by examining one or two preceding or following English words. Code numbers indicating the case governed by the equivalent preposition and the exact equivalent are found by means of a subroutine operating the rules:

1. If the previous word is 'idea', 'discussion', 'account' extract the Russian preposition 'o' and the code number indicating that 'o' governs the prepositional case.
2. If the previous word is 'true', 'productive' then the equivalent is 'для' governing the genitive case.
3. If the previous words are 'fall short' or 'in place' then 'of' is untranslated but governs the genitive case.

4. If the following word is 'necessity' then 'по' governing the dative is the equivalent.

and so on.

When the correct coded equivalent has been found it is substituted for the code numbers initially found by the dictionary look-up. After this sequence of operations, a code number with the address '0000' of the Russian equivalent means that no output is given for this word. The corresponding English word is therefore not translated.

After the grammatical analysis routines, there follows a programme for the rearranging of the equivalents into Russian order, and then a series of routines to give the correct endings for the Russian words using the information contained in their code numbers which have been processed by the preceding routines. This section of the programme, unlike the preceding routines, proceeds without reference to the input text, and uses only the information contained in the Russian section of the dictionary and in the coded numbers. These routines are essential in a programme for translation into Russian since the information carried by the endings shows explicitly the grammatical functions of words. Furthermore, since pronunciation is directly related to spelling, there are a great number of endings varying with the hardness or softness of the stem, upon the consonant at the end of it and also upon case number. For instance, the Russian feminine word 'комнат/а = room' takes the hard ending -у in the accusative case (комнат/у), and -ы in the genitive (комнат/ы). These are hard endings. The word 'нян/я = nurse', having soft ending -я in the nominative singular, also takes soft endings for the accusative and genitive (няню, няни). If, however, a stem ends in г, к or х, there is a mixture of soft and hard endings. Thus:

Nominative singular 'книг/а = book' (hard ending)
Accusative singular 'книг/у' (hard ending)
Genitive singular 'книг/и' (soft ending)

The Russian section of the dictionary thus contains Russian words in a standard form—infinitives for verbs, nominative singular for nouns and so on. The code numbers processed by means of the preceding routines contain information concerning the hardness of stem, case, etc. Together, the Russian word and the code number are used to synthesize the Russian words containing the grammatical information explicitly in the inflected endings. The Russian words are finally printed.

Some aspects of translation from Russian into English are essentially different from the translation of English into Russian. Mechanical translation programmes for operation in either direction can make use of similar techniques for extracting information from dictionaries, investigating context, and changing word-order. The chief difference between the two problems lies in the fact that grammatical function in English is exhibited largely by word order; in Russian, function is represented explicitly by inflectional endings. Thus translation from Russian into English can make great use of the grammatical information explicit in the input text, probably most efficiently by means of stem-ending analysis. The translation of English into Russian, however, must include a stem-ending synthesis programme and must rely upon context search for a lot of grammatical information.

REFERENCES

1 Mukhin, I. S., *Proc. I.E.E.* 103, (B), (1956), 463–472

GENERAL BIBLIOGRAPHY

Kunetsov, P. S., Lyapunov, A. A. and Reformatskij, A. A. *Voprosy yazykoznaniya*, *V*(5) (Oct. 1956) 107.

Publications of the Georgetown University Institute of Languages and Linguistics (1957) :

Austin, W. M., MT–36, 53.
Belmore, D. A., MT–34, 47.
Brown, A. F. R., MT–18, 21, 55.
Fargo, N., and Rubin, J., MT–30, 31, 37, 40, 57.
Garvin, P. L., MT–41, 52, 60, 61, 62.
Glazer, D. A., MT–42.
Glazer, S., MT–26.
Lukjanow, A. W., MT–35.
Pacak, M., MT–15, 19, 20, 32, 54.
Pacak, M., and Pantzer, E., MT–50.
Pantzer, E., MT.–24, 25.
Pyne, J. A., MT–28, 38.
Sushko, M. M., MT–27.
Zarechnak, M. M., MT–29.
Zarechnak, M. M. and Pyne, J. A., MT–22, 48.

11

MULTI-LINGUAL TRANSLATION

APART from implications to the contrary, it has been assumed in the previous chapters of this book that translation is to be effected only from a single language into a single target language. Should machine translation ever become of practical importance, the problem will have to be considered of whether it is feasible to construct some universal means of effecting translation between any two languages from a selected field. This particular problem has been the subject of a great deal of philosophical discussion, which at one time appeared to be leading to the thought that what was required was a single intermediate language, sometimes called a meta-language, which should in some sense have the properties and attributes of the universal languages proposed in the past.

First, why should it be suggested that such an intermediate language would be advantageous? The original argument was as follows: Suppose that there exists a set of languages L_1, L_2, L_3, . . . L_N. Then, to effect translation between L_1 and all other languages, required, according to the early thinking on the subject, the construction of dictionaries and sets of machine grammatical procedures for the transitions L_1—L_2, L_1—L_3, . . . L_1—L_N. It will be seen that (N—1) dictionaries and grammatical procedures will be required, if all of the other languages in the group are to be handled. When multilingual translation is considered, the further proposition, that such translation must be possible for all other languages of the group, that is L_R to L_S, is also required. It is quite clear that, since the first language may be chosen in N ways, and each choice of a first language presupposes N—1 dictionaries and grammars, that the total number of dictionaries and grammars required for bilingual translation between all members in the group, is simply N(N—1), or if N is a sufficiently large number, the number of dictionaries is approximately N^2.

Now consider the effect of discovering some intermediate language, M. To effect multilingual translation using an intermediate language M, it is clear that N sets of dictionaries and grammars are required for translating each of the languages L_1 to L_N into M, and that N dictionaries are required for translating from M into any of the other languages. With this equipment 2N dictionaries is all that is required, and supposing that N is greater than 2, which of course it will be by the fundamental assumption made at the beginning that the group of languages is large, a very considerable saving will be effected by the use of the intermediate language M.

Unfortunately this approach, whilst it enabled interminable philosophical discussions to take place in an attempt to find a suitable intermediate language, is entirely fallacious. Its fallacy results from the superficial nature of the first analysis which purported to show that N(N—1) dictionaries and grammars were required for translations between all members of the group. For, suppose any language, L_1 say, is taken as the base, it is then necessary to construct N—1 sets of dictionaries and grammars for the translation of all other languages L_2 to L_N into L_1, and N—1 dictionaries and grammars for the translation of L_1 into all other languages L_2 to L_N. The total number of such procedures is thus 2N—2, which is less by two than the number of such aids required when the intermediate language M is used.

This, then, is a simple numerical demonstration that the case for an intermediate language is not a very strong one. The proponents of meta-language counter this argument with another, namely, that, by the use of a meta-language, it would be very much easier, in a technical sense, to effect the translation, the argument being that languages of dissimilar origins have structures which might be more easily related by an intermediate than by a direct communication between the two. This argument too is probably false. For, suppose that for communicating between a language L_R and another language L_S it was easier to proceed via the intermediate language M than directly, the best form for direct process between the two languages has not been discovered. Whether the transition L_R to L_S is called an intermediate language, or whether it is called a dictionary-grammar transition, is entirely immaterial. The rules of procedure will be chosen to minimize the effort required for the transition, and the construction of a completely artificial intermediate language cannot produce a positive saving. The most that it could do is to equal the work required without its formal presence.

Having said this, it is probably pointless to consider further the nature of a meta-language, if in fact it were to be used. Since, however, the above remarks are not likely to find a general acceptance by linguists, it is perhaps worth while saying a few things regarding the characteristics of any proposed meta-language. A number of possibilities have been suggested in the past ranging from the basic

English of Ogden and Richards through 'Tilp' and the model English of Stewart Dodd to Esperanto and some of the languages proposed by United Nations. The real objective of the proponents of meta-language is not to effect bi-lateral translation between all pairs of existing languages, but to force scientific and other readers to learn a single extra language instead of the range of languages at present required. In this way, a scientific paper could be translated into the intermediate language and the intermediate language could be read by any person who had been trained to understand it. Presumably it would be introduced in the schools as a replacement for the French, German, or Russian, which are taught at the present time. This proposal is of course quite unexceptionable. On a purely numerical plane, the use of such a universal language understood by all cultured people would require, in the above case, only the construction of N sets of grammars and dictionaries, since papers in the existing languages would be translated into the intermediate language, but the reverse process would never be carried out.

It is probable that no two linguists would agree on the characteristics required of the intermediate language. Certainly such a language should be constructed in such a way as to remove ambiguities both phonetic and structural, and in this sense it is probable that normal English would be unsuitable. It is equally probable that basic English and its variants are not suitable to become a universal intermediate language, both because of the paucity of their verbal content and because English, being an essentially positional language, lacks a certain precision of association between words which is present in languages which depend not on position but on inflexion for their precise interpretation.

On the other hand, if this project for the establishment of a universal language is not accepted (and in the opinion of the authors, such acceptance would be practically impossible to attain, especially when consideration is given to the extreme difficulty of getting agreement between experts even on trivial points, let alone the concepts of a universal language) there is a special case for the acceptance either of standard English or some modification of it as the language selected as the base of operations. The chief advantage of English lies in the fact that probably the majority of printed works in existence at the present time are already in English, and this would minimize the amount of translation needed in the future. This suggestion will of course be highly unpopular, both to the faddists, who seek to suggest their own particular artificial language, and those vast groups of people, the Russians and the Germans, of which the one is in the course of establishing a flourishing scientific and technical literature and the other has been noted in the past for the prolixity of its expression on even the simplest subject. Since work on machine translation is likely to go on whether a base language is accepted by international agreement or not, no great harm is likely to be done if any decision is postponed indefinitely. It is likely, in the present state of the art, that the Americans will devote enormous attention to translation from foreign languages in general and from Russian into English in particular, the Russians the same in reverse. In this case there will be available for study in years to come two bodies of information, and these may enable the matter to be re-examined on a more factual basis than is at present the case.

12

TECHNICAL DETAILS OF A PROPOSED TRANSLATING MACHINE

It seems appropriate to conclude the present book by giving some indication of the particular features which may find a place in a machine built specially for translation. No machine of this type is working at the present time, and all of the experiments which have been carried out have made use of ordinary automatic digital computers. This should have become clear to readers of the preceding text, but it is a remark which bears reiteration here. The reader who has been interested in the more technical aspects of the work described in this book will not have failed to realize that considerable improvement could be made both in speed and in simplicity of programmes if certain special machine instructions were available, and this leads naturally to an examination of the form which these instructions should take.

In the first place, consider the arithmetical operations which have been postulated for the computing machine used up to now. These include not only addition and subtraction but also multiplication, and it will have been seen that multiplication is not an operation which has been used. In view of this the translating machine of the future will quite clearly not possess a multiplier. Secondly it will have been noted that a single machine 'word' of the length common at the present is really insufficient either for a foreign language word or for the translation and grammatical notes which are required, and this suggests that a machine specially designed for translation should have a word length considerably greater than that which is available in contemporary machines. If word length is unduly extended, then as a corollary, it becomes undesirable to consider the performance of arithmetical operations in the so-called parallel mode, that is, the mode in which each digit of the accumulator and registers of the machine communicates with separate channels of storage on the drum or other medium. In particular, circuits for addition in the parallel mode are somewhat complicated, and, although they are capable of great speed, a properly balanced linguistic machine would not in fact require the operations of addition and subtraction to take place at such a speed as to make these refinements necessary. This leads, then, to the suggestion that the machine of the future might work in the serial mode.

Storage is, of course, a vitally important question. Machines of the past, designed primarily for calculation, have been possessed sometimes of one and sometimes of two storage organs, the first a fast, generally small-sized store, used for the actual performance of calculation, and the second a slow backing store, often on a magnetic drum. A magnetic drum has been mandatory in machines designed for calculation, because the data stored upon it is, generally speaking, changed from calculation to calculation, and during the course of calculations. For linguistic applications this is no longer true. The majority of linguistic data will be stored in a permanent form which it is highly desirable should not be erasable. Language is fairly static, dictionaries do not, by and large, alter or at least alter rapidly with time, and the same is true of sets of grammatical instructions. For this reason, it is entirely possible that the magnetic drums of the present machines may be replaced by some form of photographic storage in the machine of the future. Photographic storage has considerable attractions for linguistic use, most of which stem from the facts that it can be inspected visually, that it is permanent, and that its volumetric efficiency is even higher than that attainable on a magnetic drum. The speeds attainable are roughly the same. Some American experiments at Rome Air Force Base suggest that at the present time it is quite feasible to construct a photographic disc type store whose capacity could be several millions of words of real language. It is not vitally important whether this form of large-scale, relatively slow-speed storage is on a drum or on a photographed disc, but it is quite certain that the machine of the future will have one or other of these.

As far as high-speed storage is concerned, the processing of information will make a certain amount of this necessary even for a linguistic machine. It is too early to hazard a guess as to the exact size required, but there seems no reason to alter the current balance accepted in digital computing machines, which implies a storage of something like 1,000 words in the high-speed store. For the technical, this store will probably take the form either of a magnetic core matrix or of a ferro-electric matrix.

The arithmetic part of the machine will work in the serial mode as has already been stated. It will be devoid of a multiplier and, in order to avoid the complexity and wastage which would be involved in accepting a single word length for all of the operations of the machine, it will probably be satisfactory to have machine instructions which are capable of operating on words of different lengths. This can be attained simply enough, if the idea is accepted that several storage locations can be associated together in a block when required. This being the case, it is probably desirable that the machine should have a single unit, which may be called the 'adder and subtracter', and that this should be connected in circuit either with a single or with several registers of a serial type inside the machine. Here again, it is risky to predict in detail but certainly eight of these registers involving a total number of letters of the order of 50 would probably be adequate for most purposes.

The arithmetical operations required are simply those of addition and subtraction, but when discrimination is considered, the situation is more complex. In earlier chapters it has been shown how the ordinary branch instruction of a calculating machine can be used in conjunction with shift operations for the examination either of sets of letters in a word, or of single letters. On the other hand, it must have been clear that the normal jump instruction is not particularly suitable in this context. A better version would be a jump instruction which could operate on the N*th* digit of a given word. Since this is technically very easy to arrange, and since it includes the present operation as a sub-case, it will undoubtedly form a part of the future machine. Shifting instructions will be of the same type as heretofore, except that, since various registers of the machine may be connected together for the storage of different word lengths, it will be necessary to extend the number of different shift operations to include the cycling of data in various combinations of the registers. An operation which is not a part of the APEXC code, as given in this book, is the operation of collate. In this a word held in the machine registers is compared with a word derived from the storage organ and, when letters of the two are identical, zeros are written in the relevant binary positions available to the collate order, but when the letters become different, ones appear. This order enables a comparison of two words to be made in such a way that the common portions can be identified.

A more exotic instruction, whose need is clearly predicated in the previous work, is an operation which would enable information to be shifted by one place in the machine store at a single passage. This is of particular importance when the building up of concordances or dictionaries is considered. In Chapter 3 it was mentioned that the relatively inefficient method of interpolating a word into a given set of words would slow down the process of dictionary or of concordance-making considerably. What is required is the following: Suppose that a set of words is arranged in ascending alphabetical order in consecutive positions in the store, and a new word, not already contained in the dictionary, appears. This word must be inserted in its proper position. The simplest form of the process would be first to decide at what point in the array the new word is to be placed, then to proceed to the last word in the array and displace this by one position in the outward direction, then to the next to last and so on, this process continuing until the position for which room for interpolation is required, becomes free of data. The new word is then placed therein.

At the present, a number of instructions are required for each transposition of each word. A simple form of new instruction which would be useful is the following: displace the word in position X to the position X+1 leaving X vacant. A much more desirable form of the order, which would certainly be built into a future machine designed specifically for translation, would be: displace those words contained between position X and position X+N, so that they occupy positions X+1 to X+N+1 respectively. With a serial type of storage device this form of instruction is very simple to engineer. It involves only the insertion of a register whose length is equal to the length of a standard storage location between the input of data and its re-recording. Since the registers will in any case be available in the machine, there seems no valid reason why this instruction should not be provided. An even more useful form of the same instruction would be the following: compare the given word with each of the words in the store as these pass the reading station. As soon as the result of the comparison indicates the position of insertion of the new word, record it in that position and then proceed to read all following words via a single register delay, and re-insert them so that they are displaced by one position in the store. Here again, if a complete traverse of the store is required, the order is wholly admirable. It has the disadvantage, however, that because the hunting process is associated with the displacement process, it will in general be required to examine all of the data in the dictionary before any word can be placed. It is, therefore, far less efficient than the bracketing method with its associated logarithmic number of comparisons. On the other hand, the bracketing method is not, in its present form, suitable for displacing dictionary data; it enables the position of the new word in the scheme only to be located but not the word itself to be inserted, so that the new instruction should produce a net saving.

A conditional or jump instruction based on a group of digits instead of on one has been suggested as a useful addition to the instruction code. In fact, however, it is not required, since, as has already been shown in Chapter 3, the normal operation of partial substitution (that is, replace the first N digits of the word in position X by the first N digits of the word in the accumulator or register) already performs this function.

These then are a few of the arithmetical modifications which might be required in the new machine. Other alterations of current structure would be the provision of an input device which could read directly from the printed word and an output device of a speed which would make the use of the machine a practical proposition. Input character reading devices are already under development both for machine translation and for other purposes, and there seems no reason to doubt that they will be available in the next two or three years. On the output side various devices are possible. If it is not required to have immediate cognizance of the machine output, the most suitable way of producing this would be on a magnetic tape, which could be created at a very high speed. Magnetic tape produced by the machine could then be reproduced in typed form on a battery of electrical typewriters or even sent to those persons who commissioned the work, who might have their own electrical typewriter. In this way efficient use could be made of the machine's high speed. The alternative to this creation of an intermediate record is to produce machine output directly on a parallel printer. Printers of this type are already available to give speeds of up to 900 lines of 100 letters per minute, and this is probably sufficient for any machine which will be constructed in the next decade.

We conclude both the chapter and the book with the instruction code which we propose for a machine of this type. Though at the moment there seems to be little hope of obtaining financial support for the construction of this device, which would probably involve the expenditure of between £50,000 and £100,000, there is no doubt that the machine, once constructed, would cause a revolution in the availability of technical material to workers in countries distinct from those in which it originated. And furthermore the impetus which the physical presence of such a machine would give to linguists and to students of machine translation would be such as to produce a revolution in the quality of machine translations within a year or so of its availability.

*Proposed instruction code for linguistic machine**

Order	Symbol	Description
0	F	Stop.
1	I_n	Input n characters from tape. If n exceeds the number of characters contained in the word, input this number only.
2	P_n	Punch n characters from the register on to the output tape. If n exceeds the number of characters which precede the stop symbol, punch this number only.
3	$B^n(x)(y)$	If the nth digit in the computer word held in the accumulator is 1 go to (x) for the next instruction, if 0 go to (y).
4	l_n	Left shift contents of accumulator and register n places.
5	r_n	Right shift contents of accumulator and register n places.
6	D_s	Compare the word in the register with the stem dictionary, read the corresponding dictionary entry into the accumulator and shift up the register contents to bring any remainder into the leading positions.
7	D_e	As for D_s except that the reference is made to the ending dictionary.
8	$+c(x)$	Clear accumulator and add word in (x) to it.
9	$-c(x)$	Clear accumulator and subtract word in (x) from it.
10	$+(x)$	Add word in (x) into accumulator.
11	$-(x)$	Subtract word in (x) from accumulator.
12	T_x	Transfer contents of (x) to register.
13	$R_n(x)$	Record n digits of register contents in (x).
14	$A_n(x)$	Record n digits of accumulator contents in (x).
15	$E_{n4}(x)(y)$	Compare binary digits n to $n+4$ of the computer words held in the accumulator and the register. If they are identical go to (x) if not to (y).
16	S	Compare word held in the register with the contents of a dictionary. If it is not already present insert it in the appropriate place, displace all following entries and clear the register. If it is already present store its position in the register.

* NOTE: References to accumulator, register and storage involve a length parameter which is not written in the above code. This enables groups of 35 binary digits to be associated together.

SUBJECT INDEX

NAME INDEX